A Photographic Atlas

for the

Biology Laboratory

FIFTH EDITION

Kent M. Van De Graaff
Weber State University

John L. Crawley

Morton Publishing Company
925 W. Kenyon, Unit 12
Englewood, Colorado 80110

*To our teachers, colleagues, friends, and students
who share with us a mutual love for biology.*

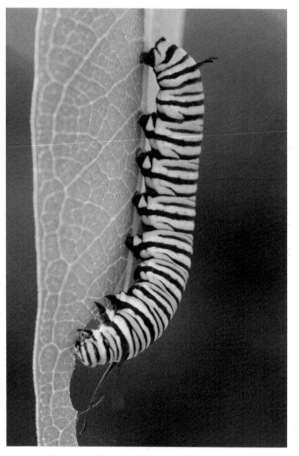

The caterpillar, larval stage, of the Monarch
butterfly, *Danaus plexippus*.

Copyright 1993, 1995, 1998, 2002, 2005 by Morton Publishing Company

ISBN: 0-89582-684-4

10 9 8 7 6 5 4 3 2 1

Printed in the United States of America

Preface to Fifth Edition

Biology is an exciting, dynamic, and challenging science. It is the study of life. You are fortunate to be living at a time when insights and discoveries in all aspects of biology are occurring at a very rapid pace. Much of the knowledge that you will learn in a biology course has application in improving humanity and the quality of life. An understanding of basic biology is essential for you to establish a secure foundation for more advanced courses in the life sciences or health sciences. The principles taught in a basic biology course are of immeasurable value in dealing with the ecological and bioethical problems currently facing us.

Biology is a visually oriented science. The fifth edition of *A Photographic Atlas for the Biology Laboratory* is designed to provide you with quality photographs of organisms, similar to those you may have the opportunity to observe in a biology laboratory. It is designed to accompany any biology text or laboratory manual you may be using in the classroom. In certain courses, this photographic atlas could serve as the laboratory manual.

An objective of this atlas is to provide you with a balanced visual representation of the kingdoms of biological organisms. Great care has been taken to construct completely labeled, informative figures that are depicted clearly and accurately. Many new photographs have been added to this edition of the biology atlas. The specimens depicted appear as you see them in the biology laboratory. The updated classification and terminology used in this atlas are the same as those found in the more commonly used college biology texts.

Numerous dissections of plants and invertebrate and vertebrate animals were completed and photographed in the preparation of this atlas. These images are included for those students who have the opportunity to do similar dissections as part of their laboratory requirement. In addition, photographs of a sheep heart dissection are included in this atlas.

Chapter 9 of this atlas is devoted to the biology of the human organism, which is emphasized in many biology textbooks and courses. In this chapter, you are provided with a complete set of photographs for each of the human body systems. Human cadavers have been carefully dissected and photographed to clearly depict each of the principal organs from each of the body systems. Selected radiographs (X-rays), CT scans, and MR images depict structures from living persons and thus provide an applied dimension to this portion of the atlas.

The success of the previous editions of *A Photographic Atlas for the Biology Laboratory* provided opportunities to make changes to enhance the value of this new edition in aiding students in learning about plants and animals. The total revision of this atlas presented in its fifth edition required an inordinate amount of planning, organization, and work. As authors we have the opportunity and obligation to listen to the critiques and suggestions from students and faculty who have used this atlas. This constructive input is appreciated and has resulted in a greatly improved atlas.

One objective in preparing this edition of the atlas was to create an inviting pedagogy. The page layout was improved by careful selection of updated, new and replacement photographs. Many illustrations were redrawn to be more appealing and accurate. Tables were redesigned to enhance access of information. Each image in this atlas was carefully evaluated for its quality, effectiveness, and accuracy. Quality photographs of detailed dissections were completed enhancing the value of this edition. The reformatting of the pedagogy, enabled more photographs, photomicrographs, enlarged images in certain chapters, and additional photographs of representative plants and animals.

Prelude

Scientists work to determine accuracy in understanding the relationship of organisms even when it requires changing established concepts. Development, structure, function, and the fossil record and geological dating are used to establish systematics and classify organisms. As new techniques become available, they too aid in our understanding of evolutionary relationships between groups of organisms and closely related species.

In 1758 Carolus Linnaeus, a Swedish naturalist, assigned all known kinds of organisms into two kingdoms–plants and animals. For over two centuries, this dichotomy of plants and animals served biologists well. In 1969, Robert H. Whittaker convincingly made a case for a five-kingdom system comprised of Monera, Protista, Fungi, Plantae, and Animalia. The five-kingdom basis of systematics prevailed for over twenty years, and is now being challenged with a new system that includes three domains (superkingdoms) and four kingdoms (see exhibit 1). This new system, which is used in this edition of *A Photographic Atlas for the Biology Laboratory*, is based on criteria used in the past and new techniques in molecular biology. It is important to note, however, that a classification scheme is a human construct subject to alteration as additional knowledge is obtained.

Exhibit I Domains, Kingdoms, and Representative Examples

Bacteria Domain– Cyanobacteria, gram-negative and gram-positive bacteria

Archaea Domain– Methanogens, halophiles, and thermophiles

Eukarota Domain– Eukaryotes, single-celled and multicelled organisms; fungi, protists, plants, and animals

Oscillatoria, a cyanobacterium that reproduces through fragmentation

Thiothrix, a thermophile that oxidizes H_2S for an energy source

| Kingdom Fungi | Kingdom Protista | Kingdom Plantae | Kingdom Animalia |

Aspergillus, a mold that reproduces asexually and sometimes sexually

Volvox, a motile green alga that reproduces asexually or sexually

Musa, the banana, is high in nutritional value and is one of the twelve most important human food plants.

Chamaeleo calyptratus, the veiled chameleon, is known for its ability to change colors according to its surroundings

Basic Characteristics of Domains

Domain	Characteristics
Bacteria Domain—Bacteria	Prokaryotic cell; single circular chromosome; cell wall containing peptidoglycan; chemosynthetic autotrophs, chlorophyll-based photosynthesis, photosynthetic autotrophs, and heterotrophs; gram-negative and gram-positive forms; lacking nuclear envelope; lacking organelles and cytoskeleton
Archaea Domain—Archaea	Prokaryotic cell; single circular chromosome; cell wall; membrane lipids, unique ribosomal RNA sequences; lacking nuclear envelope; some with chlorophyll-based photosynthesis; with organelles, and cytoskeleton
Eukarota Domain—Eukarya	Single-celled and multicelled organisms; nuclear envelop enclosing more than one linear chromosome; membrane-bound organelles in most; some with chlorophyll-based photosynthesis

Common Classification System of Selective Living Eukaryotes

Eukarota Domain– eukaryotes
    Kingdom Fungi– fungi
        Phylum Zygomycota– zygomycetes
        Phylum Ascomycota– ascomycetes
        Phylum Basidiomycota– basidiomycetes, teliomycetes,
          and ustomycetes
    Kingdom Protista– heterotrophic and photosynthetic
        protists
        Phylum Myxomycota– plasmodial slime molds
        Phylum Dictyosteliomycota (Acrasiomycota)– cellular
          slime molds
        Phylum Oomycota– water molds
        Phylum Euglenophyta– euglenoids
        Phylum Cryptophyta– cryptomonads
        Phylum Rhodophyta– red algae
        Phylum Dinophyta (Pyrrhophyta)– dinoflagellates
        Phylum Haptophyta– haptophtes
        Phylum Bacillariophyta– diatoms (diatoms are often
          placed in the phylum Chrysophyta)
        Phylum Chrysophyta– chrysophytes
        Phylum Phaeophyta– brown algae
        Phylum Chlorophyta– green algae
    Kingdom Plantae– bryophytes and vascular plants
        Phylum Hepatophyta– liverworts
        Phylum Anthocerophyta– hornworts
        Phylum Bryophyta– mosses

        Phylum Psilotophyta (Psilophyta)– psilotophytes
        Phylum Lycophyta (Lycopodiophyta)– lycophytes
        Phylum Sphenophyta (Equisetophyta)– horsetails
        Phylum Pterophyta (Polypodiophyta)– ferns
        Phylum Cycadophyta– cycads
        Phylum Ginkgophyta– Ginkgo
        Phylum Coniferophyta (Pinophyta)– gymnosperms
          (conifers)
        Phylum Gnetophyta– gnetophytes
        Phylum Anthophyta (Magniolophyta)– angiosperms
    Kingdom Animalia– invertebrate and vertebrate animals
        Phylum Porifera- sponges
        Phylum Cnidaria- coral, hydra, and jellyfish
        Phylum Ctenophora- comb jellies
        Phylum Platyhelminthes- flatworms
        Phylum Rotifera- rotifers
        Phylum Bryozoa
        Phylum Brachiopoda
        Phylum Phoronida
        Phylum Nemertea- proboscis worms
        Phylum Mollusca- clams, snails, and squids
        Phylum Annelida- segmented worms
        Phylum Nematoda- round worms
        Phylum Arthropoda- crustaceans, insects, and spiders
        Phylum Echinodermata- sea stars and sea urchines
        Phylum Chordata- lancelets, tunicates, and vertebrates

Acknowledgments

Many professionals have assisted in the preparation of *A Photographic Atlas for the Biology Laboratory,* fifth edition, and have shared our enthusiasm of its value for students of biology. We are especially appreciative of Drs. Wilford M. Hess, and William B. Winborn for their help in obtaining photographs and photomicrographs. Drs. Ronald A. Meyers, John F. Mull and Samuel I. Zeveloff of the Department of Zoology at Weber State University and Dr. Samuel R. Rushforth at Utah Valley State College were especially helpful and supportive of this project. The radiographs, CT scans, and MR images have been made possible through the generosity of Gary M. Watts, MD and the Department of Radiology at Utah Valley Regional Medical Center. Ryan L. Van De Graaff MD spent many hours in assisting us with dissections and labeling. Several other students were very helpful in performing dissections. We gratefully acknowledge the assistance of Nathan A. Jacobson, Scott R. Gunn, Sandra E. Sephton, Michelle Kidder, and Michael K. Visick. A special thanks is extended to Drs. Kent A. Vliet, University of Florida and Michelle Priest, at University of Southern California for proofing and reviewing the manuscript and many helpful suggestions. Thanks is extended to Christopher H. Creek and Jessica Ridd for the art throughout the book. We also appreciate Focus Design and its employees for the layout and organization of this atlas. We are indebted to Douglas Morton and the personnel at Morton Publishing Company for the opportunity, encouragement, and support to prepare this atlas.

Many of the photographs of living plants and animals were made possible because of the cooperation and generosity of the San Diego Zoo, San Diego Wild Animal Park, Sea World (San Diego, CA), Hogle Zoo (Salt Lake City, UT), and Aquatica (Orem, UT). We are especially appreciative to the professional biologists at these fine institutions.

Book Team

Publisher: Doug Morton
Biology Editor: David Ferguson
Typography and Design: Focus Design
Cover: Bob Schram, Bookends Publication Design
Illustrations: Jessica Ridd

Plumeria (Apocynaceae)
Flowers from frangipani, a group of common flowering trees
found in tropical regions.

Table of Contents

All organisms are comprised of one or more cells. *Cells* are the basic structural and functional units of organisms. A cell is a minute, membrane-enclosed, protoplasmic mass consisting of chromosomes surrounded by cytoplasm. Specific organelles are contained in the cytoplasm that function independently but in coordination with one another. Prokaryotic cells (fig. 1.1) and eukaryotic cells (figs. 1.3 and 1.18) are the two basic types.

Prokaryotic cells lack a membrane-bound nucleus, instead containing a single strand of *nucleic acid*. These cells contain few organelles. A rigid or semi-rigid cell wall provides shape to the cell outside the *cell (plasma) membrane*. Bacteria are examples of prokaryotic, single-celled organisms.

Eukaryotic cells contain a true *nucleus* with multiple chromosomes, have several types of specialized organelles, and have a differentially permeable cell membrane. Organisms comprised of eukaryotic cells include protozoa, fungi, algae, plants, and invertebrate and vertebrate animals.

Plant cells differ in some ways from other eukaryotic cells in that their cell walls contain *cellulose* for stiffness (fig. 1.3). Plant cells also contain vacuoles for water storage and membrane-bound *chloroplasts* with photosynthetic pigments for photosynthesis.

The *nucleus* is the large, spheroid body within the eukaryotic cell that contains the genetic material of the cell. The nucleus is enclosed by a double membrane called the *nuclear membrane*, or *nuclear envelope*. The *nucleolus* is a dense, nonmembranous body composed of protein and RNA molecules. The chromatin are fibers of protein and DNA molecules. Prior to cellular division, the chromatin shortens and coils into rod-shaped *chromosomes*. Chromosomes consist of DNA and structural proteins called *histones*.

The *cytoplasm* of the eukaryotic cell is the medium between the nuclear membrane and the cell membrane. *Organelles* are small membrane-bound structures within the cytoplasm. The cellular functions carried out by organelles are referred to as *metabolism*. The structure and function of the nucleus and principal organelles are listed in table 1.1. In order for cells to remain alive, metabolize, and maintain homeostasis, they must have access to nutrients and respiratory gases, be able to eliminate wastes, and be in a constant, protective environment.

The *cell membrane* is composed of phospholipid, protein, and carbohydrate molecules. The cell membrane gives form to a cell and controls the passage of material into and out of a cell. More specifically, the proteins in the cell membrane provide:

1. structural support;
2. a mechanism of molecule transport across the membrane;
3. enzymatic control of chemical reactions;
4. receptors for hormones and other regulatory molecules; and
5. cellular markers (antigens), which identify the blood and tissue type.

The carbohydrate molecules:
1. repel negative objects due to their negative charge;
2. act as receptors for hormones and other regulatory molecules;
3. form specific cell markers which enable like cells to attach and aggregate into tissues; and
4. enter into immune reactions.

Tissues are groups of similar cells that perform specific functions (see fig. 1.9). A flowering plant, for example, is composed of three tissue systems:
1. the *ground tissue system*, providing support, regeneration, respiration, photosynthesis, and storage;
2. the *vascular tissue system*, providing conduction passageways through the plant; and
3. the *dermal tissue system*, providing protection to the plant.

The tissues of the body of a multicellular animal are classified into four principal types (see fig. 1.36):
1. *epithelial tissue* covers body and organ surfaces, lines body cavities and lumina (hollow portions of body tubes), and forms various glands;
2. *connective tissue* binds, supports, and protects body parts;
3. *muscle tissue* contracts to produce movements; and
4. *nervous tissue* initiates and transmits nerve impulses.

Figure 1.1
Prokaryotic cell.
1. Cell wall
2. Cell (plasma) membrane
3. Ribosomes
4. Circular molecule of DNA
5. Thyakoid membranes

Table 1.1 Structure and Function of Cellular Components

Component	Structure	Function
Cell (plasma) membrane	Composed of protein and phospholipid molecules	Provides form to cell; controls passage of materials into and out of cell
Cell Wall	Cellulose fibrils	Provides structure and rigidity to plant cell
Cytoplasm	Fluid to jelly-like substance	Serves as suspending medium for organelles and dissolved molecules
Endoplasmic reticulum	Interconnecting membrane-lined channels	Enables cell transport and processing of metabolic chemicals
Ribosome	Granules of nucleic acid (RNA) and protein	Synthesizes protein
Mitochondrium	Double-membraned sac with cristae (chambers)	Assembles ATP (cellular respiration)
Golgi complex	Flattened membrane-lined chambers	Synthesize carbohydrates and packages molecules for secretion
Lysosome	Membrane-surrounded sac of enzymes	Digests foreign molecules and worn cells
Centrosome	Mass of protein that may contain rod-like centrioles	Organizes spindle fibers and assists mitosis and meiosis
Vacuole	Membranous sac	Stores and excretes substances within the cytoplasm, regulates cellular turgor pressure
Microfibril and microtubule	Protein strands and tubes	Forms cytoskeleton, supports cytoplasm and transports materials
Cilium and flagellum	Cytoplasmic extensions from cell; containing microtubules	Movements of particles along cell surface or cell movement
Nucleus	Nuclear envelope (membrane), nucleolus, and chromatin (DNA)	Contains genetic code that directs cell activity; forms ribosomes
Chloroplast	Inner (grana) membrane within outer membrane	Involved in photosynthesis

Photograph courtesy of Leica Inc.

Figure 1.2 (a) Compound monocular microscope, and (b) compound binocular microscope.
1. Eyepiece (ocular)
2. Body
3. Arm
4. Nosepiece
5. Objective
6. Stage clip
7. Focus adjustment knob
8. Stage
9. Condenser
10. Fine focus adjustment knob
11. Collector lens with field diaphragm
12. Illuminator (inside)
13. Base

Plant cell and tissues

Figure 1.3 Diagram of a typical plant cell.
1. Cell wall
2. Cell (plasma) membrane
3. Rough endoplasmic reticulum
4. Mitochondrion
5. Nuclear pore
6. Nucleus
7. Nuclear membrane (envelope)
8. Nucleolus
9. Smooth endoplasmic reticulum
10. Chloroplast
11. Vacuole
12. Plasmodesmata
13. Golgi complex

Cell

Tissue (leaf)
comprised of cells

Organ (leaf)
comprised of tissues

Organism (plant)
comprised of organs

Leaves

Stem

Roots

Figure 1.4 Structural levels of plant organization.

Figure 1.5 Live *Elodea* leaf cells (a) photographed at the center of the leaf and (b) at the edge of the leaf.

1. Cell wall	3. Nucleus	5. Spine-shaped cell on	6. Nucleus	8. Cell wall
2. Chloroplasts	4. Vacuoles	exposed edge of leaf	7. Chloroplasts	

Figure 1.6 (a) Cells of a potato, *Solanum tuberosum*, showing starch grains at a low magnification, and (b) at a high magnification. Food is stored as starch in potato cells, which is deposited in organelles called amyloplasts.

1. Cell wall   2. Cytoplasm   3. Starch grains   4. Nucleus

Photo courtesy of Wilford M. Hess

Figure 1.7 Electron micrograph of a portion of a sugar cane leaf cell.

1. Cell membrane	5. Grana
2. Cell wall	6. Stroma
3. Mitochondrion	7. Thylakoid membrane
4. Nucleus	8. Chloroplast envelope

Photo courtesy of Wilford M. Hess

Figure 1.8 Fractured barley smut spore.

1. Cell wall   2. Cell membrane

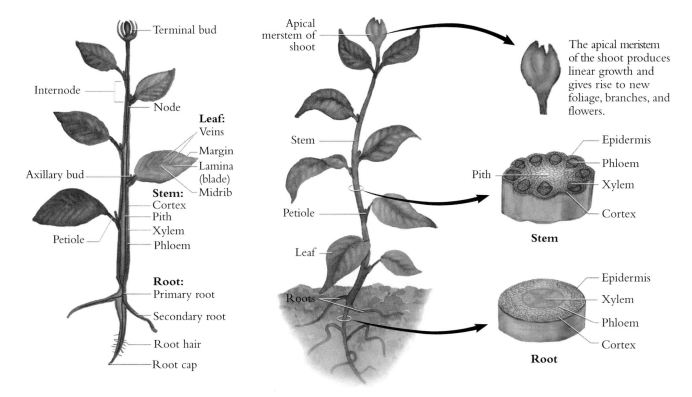

Terminal bud

Internode

Node

Leaf:
Veins

Margin

Lamina (blade)

Axillary bud

Midrib

Stem:
Cortex
Pith
Xylem

Petiole

Phloem

Root:
Primary root

Secondary root

Root hair

Root cap

Apical merstem of shoot

The apical meristem of the shoot produces linear growth and gives rise to new foliage, branches, and flowers.

Stem

Petiole

Leaf

Roots

Epidermis

Phloem

Pith

Xylem

Cortex

Stem

Epidermis

Xylem

Phloem

Cortex

Root

Figure 1.9 Diagram illustrating the anatomy and the principal organs and tissues of a typical dicot.

430X

Figure 1.10 Longitudinal section through the xylem of *Pinus,* showing tracheid cells with prominent bordered pits.

1. Bordered pits   3. Cell wall
2. Tracheid cell

160X

Figure 1.11 Longitudinal section through the xylem of a squash stem, *Cucurbita maxima.* The vessel elements shown here have several different patterns of wall thickenings.

1. Parenchyma   2. Vessel elements

Figure 1.12 Section through a leaf of the venus flytrap, *Dionaea muscipula*, showing epidermal cells with a digestive gland. The gland is comprised of secretory parenchyma cells.
1. Epidermis   2. Gland

Figure 1.13 Astrosclereid in the petiole of a pondlily, *Nuphar.*
1. Astrosclereid   3. Crystals in cell wall
2. Parenchyma cell

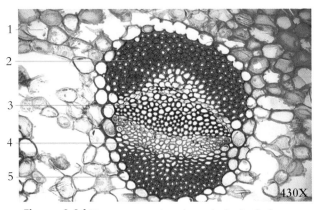

Figure 1.14 Transverse section through the leaf of a yucca, *Yucca brevifolia*, showing a vascular bundle (vein). Note the prominent sclerenchyma tissue forming caps on both sides of the bundle.
1. Leaf parenchyma   3. Xylem
2. Leaf sclerenchyma   4. Phloem
   (bundle cap)   5. Bundle cap

Figure 1.15 Section through the endosperm tissue of a persimmon, *Diospyros virginiana.* These thick-walled cells are actually parenchyma cells. Cytoplasmic connections, or plasmodesmata, are evident between cells.
1. Plasmodesmata   2. Cell lumen (interior space)

Figure 1.16 Transverse section through the stem of flax, *Linum.* Note the thick-walled fibers as compared to the thin-walled parenchyma cells.
1. Fibers   2. Parenchyma cell

Figure 1.17 Section through the stem of a wax plant, *Hoya carnosa.* Thick-walled sclereids (stone cells) are evident.
1. Parenchyma cell   2. Sclereid (stone cell)
   containing starch grains

Animal cell and tissues

Figure 1.18 Typical animal cell.

1. Smooth endoplasmic reticulum	7. Cell membrane
2. Nuclear membrane	8. Centrosomes
3. Nucleolus	9. Cytoplasm
4. Nucleoplasm	10. Lysosome
5. Mitochondrion	11. Vesicles
6. Rough endoplasmic reticulum	12. Ribosomes
	13. Golgi complex

Figure 1.19 Electron micrograph of a freeze fractured nuclear envelope showing the nuclar pores.
1. Nuclear pores

Figure 1.20 Electron micrograph of various organelles.

1. Nucleus	3. Mitochondrion
2. Centrioles	4. Golgi complex

2000X

Figure 1.21 Electron micrograph of centrioles. The centrioles are positioned at right angles to one another.
1. Centriole (shown in transverse section)
2. Centriole (shown in longitudinal section)

2000X

Figure 1.22 Electron micrograph of lysosomes.
1. Nucleus   2. Lysosomes

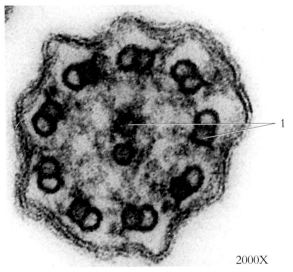

2000X

Figure 1.24 Electron micrograph of cilia (transverse section) showing the characteristic "9 + 2" arrangement of microtubules in the transverse sections.
1. Microtubules

2000X

Figure 1.23 Electron micrograph of a mitochondrion.
1. Outer membrane   3. Inner membranes
2. Crista

2000X

Figure 1.25 Electron micrograph showing the difference between a microvillus and a cilium.
1. Microvillus   2. Cilium

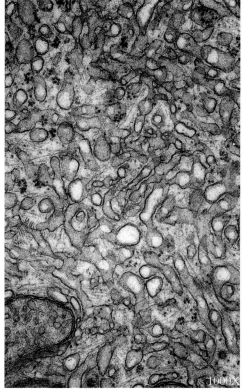

Figure 1.26 Electron micrograph of smooth endoplasmic reticulum from the testis.

Figure 1.27 Electron micrograph of rough endoplasmic reticulum.
1. Ribosomes
2. Cisternae

Figure 1.28 Rough endoplasmic reticulum secreting collagenous filaments to the outside of the cell.
1. Nucleus
2. Rough endoplasmic reticulum
3. Collagenous filaments
4. Cell membrane

Figure 1.29 Epithelial cell from a cheek scraping.
1. Nucleus
2. Cytoplasm
3. Cell membrane

Figure 1.30 Electron micrograph of an erythrocyte (red blood cell).

Photographs courtesy of Scott C. Miller

Figure 1.31 Types of leukocytes.

(a) Neutrophil   (d) Lymphocyte (1)
(b) Basophil   Monocyte (2)
(c) Eosinophil

Figure 1.32 Electron micrograph of a capillary containing an erythrocyte.

1. Lumen of capillary   3. Endothelial cell
2. Nucleus of endothelial cell   4. Erythrocyte

Figure 1.33 Electron micrograph of a skeletal muscle myofibril, showing the striations..

1. Mitochondria
2. Z line
3. A band
4. I band
5. T-tubule
6. Sarcoplasmic reticulum
7. H band
8. Sacromere

Figure 1.34 Electron micrograph of an osteocyte (bone cell) in cortical bone matrix.

1. Bone matrix   3. Lacuna
2. Canaliculi   4. Osteocyte

Figure 1.35 Neuron smear.

1. Nuclei of surrounding neuroglial cells
2. Nucleus of neuron
3. Nucleolus of neuron
4. Dendrites of neuron

Epithelial Tissue

Epithelial tissue covers the outside of the body and lines all organs. Its primary function is to provide protection.

Simple squamous epithelium

Nucleus

Cell membrane

Basement membrane (lamina)

Simple cuboidal epithelium

Goblet cell

Simple columnar epithelium

Connective Tissue

Connective tissue functions as a binding and supportive tissue for all other tissues in the organism.

Collagenous fibers

Fibroblasts

Dense regular connective tissue

Nucleus

Fat droplet

Adipose tissue

Osteocyte

Matrix

Bone tissue

Nervous Tissue

Nervous tissue functions to receive stimuli and transmits signals from one part of the organism to another.

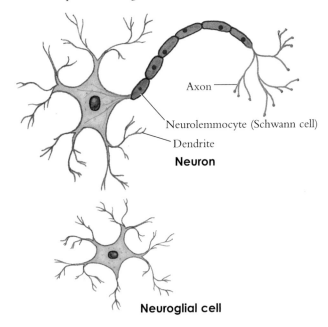

Axon

Neurolemmocyte (Schwann cell)

Dendrite

Neuron

Neuroglial cell

Muscle Tissue

Muscle tissue is adapted to contract. Muscles provide movement and functionality to the organism.

Nucleus

Striation

Skeletal muscle

Intercalated disc

Striation

Nucleus

Cardiac muscle

Nucleus

Smooth muscle

Figure 1.36 Examples of animal tissues.

Figure 1.37 Simple squamous epithelium.
1. Single layer of flattened cells

Figure 1.38 Simple cuboidal epithelium.
1. Single layer of cells with round nuclei

Figure 1.39 Simple columnar epithelium.
1. Single layer of cells with oval nuclei

Figure 1.40 Stratified squamous epithelium.
1. Multiple layers of cells, which are flattened at the upper layer

Figure 1.41 Stratified columnar epithelium.
1. Cells are balloon-like at surface

Figure 1.42 Pseudostratified columnar epithelium.
1. Cilia
2. Goblet cell
3. Pseudostratified columnar epithelium
4. Basement membrane

Figure 1.43 Adipose connective tissue.
1. Adipocytes (adipose cells)

Figure 1.44 Loose connective tissue stained for fibers.
1. Elastic fibers (black)
2. Collagen fibers (pink)

Figure 1.45 Dense regular connective tissue.
1. Nuclei of fibroblasts arranged in parallel rows

Figure 1.46 Dense irregular connective tissue.
1. Epidermis
2. Dense irregular connective tissue (reticular layer of dermis)

Figure 1.47 Electron micrograph of dense irregular connective tissue.
1. Collagenous fibers

Figure 1.48 Reticular connective tissue.
1. Reticular fibers

Figure 1.49 Hyaline cartilage.
1. Chondrocytes
2. Hyaline cartilage

Figure 1.50 Elastic cartilage.
1. Chondrocytes   3. Elastic fibers
2. Lacunae

Figure 1.51 Fibrocartilage.
1. Chondrocytes arranged in a row

Figure 1.52 Transverse section of two osteons.
1. Lacunae   3. Lamellae
2. Central (haversian) canals

Figure 1.53 Electron micrograph of bone tissue.
1. Interstitial lamellae   4. Lacunae
2. Lamellae   5. Osteon (haversian
3. Central canal   system)
   (haversian canal)

Figure 1.54 Electron micrograph of bone tissue formation.
1. Bone mineral (calcium salts stain black)
2. Collagenous filament (distinct banding pattern)
3. Collagen secreting osteoblasts

Figure 1.55 Osteoblasts.
1. Osteoblasts   3. Osteoid
2. Bone   4. Osteocytes

Figure 1.56 Osteoclast.
1. Osteocytes   4. Osteoclast in
2. Bone   Howship's lacuna
3. Howship's lacuna

Figure 1.57 Longitudinal section of skeletal muscle tissue.
1. Skeletal muscle cells, note striations
2. Multiple nuclei in periphery of cell

Figure 1.58 Transverse section of skeletal muscle tissue.
1. Perimysium (surrounds bundles of cells)
2. Skeletal muscle cells
3. Nuclei in periphery of cell
4. Endomysium (surrounds cells)

Figure 1.59 Attachment of skeletal muscle to tendon.
1. Skeletal muscle
2. Dense regular connective tissue (tendon)

Figure 1.60 Smooth muscle tissue.
1. Smooth muscle
2. Blood vessel

Figure 1.61 Cardiac muscle tissue.
1. Intercalated discs
2. Light-staining perinuclear sarcoplasm
3. Nucleus in center of cell

Figure 1.62 Transverse section of a nerve.
1. Endoneurium   3. Perineurium
2. Axons   4. Epineurium

Figure 1.63 Longitudinal section of axons.
1. Myelin sheath
2. Neurofibril nodes (nodes of Ranvier)

Figure 1.64 Neuromuscular junction.
1. Skeletal muscle   2. Motor nerve
   fiber   3. Motor end plates

Figure 1.65 Motor neurons from spinal cord.
1. Neuroglia cells
2. Dendrites
3. Nucleus

Figure 1.66 Purkinje neurons from the cerebellum.
1. Molecular layer of cerebellar cortex
2. Granular layer of cerebellar cortex
3. Dendrites of Purkinje cell
4. Purkinje cell body

The term *cell cycle* refers to how a multicellular organism develops, grows, and maintains and repairs body tissues. In the cell cycle, each new cell receives a complete copy of all genetic information in the parent cell, and the cytoplasmic substances and organelles to carry out hereditary instructions.

The animal cell cycle (see fig. 2.3 and 2.7) is divided into: 1) interphase, which includes G1, S, and G2 phases; and 2) mitosis, which includes prophase, metaphase, anaphase, and telophase. *Interphase* is the interval between successive cell divisions during which the cell is metabolizing and the chromosomes are directing RNA synthesis. The *G1 phase* is the first growth phase, the *S phase* is when DNA is replicated, and the *G2 phase* is the second growth phase. *Mitosis* (also known as karyokinesis) is the division of the nuclear parts of a cell to form two daughter nuclei with the same number of chromosomes as the original nucleus.

Like the animal cell cycle, the plant cell cycle consists of growth, synthesis, mitosis, and cytokinesis. *Growth* is the increase in cellular mass as the result of metabolism; *synthesis* is the production of DNA and RNA to regulate cellular activity; mitosis is the splitting of the nucleus and the equal separation of the chromatids; and cytokinesis is the division of the cytoplasm that accompanies mitosis.

Unlike animal cells, plant cells have a rigid cell wall that does not cleave during cytokinesis. Instead, a new cell wall is constructed between the daughter cells (see fig. 2.5 and 2.6). Furthermore, many land plants do not have centrioles for the attachment of spindles. The microtubules in these plants form a barrel-shaped anastral spindle at each pole. Mitosis and cytokinesis in plants occurs in basically the same sequence as these processes in animal cells.

Asexual reproduction is propagation without sex; that is, the production of new individuals by processes that do not involve *gametes* (sex cells). Asexual reproduction occurs in a variety of microorganisms, fungi, plants, and animals, wherein a single parent produces offspring with characteristics identical to itself. Asexual reproduction is not dependent on the presence of other individuals. No egg or sperm is required. In asexual reproduction, all the offspring are genetically identical (except for mutants). Types of asexual reproduction include:

1. *fission*—a single cell divides to form two separate cells (bacteria, protozoans, and other one-celled organisms);
2. *sporulation*—multiple fission, many cells are formed and join together in a cystlike structure (protozoans and fungi);
3. *budding*—buds develop organisms like the parent and then detach themselves (hydras, yeast, certain plants); and
4. *fragmentation*—organisms break into two or more parts, and each part is capable of becoming a complete organism (algae, flatworms, echinoderms).

Sexual reproduction is propagation of new organisms through the union of genetic material from two parents. Sexual reproduction usually involves the fusion of haploid gametes (such as sperm and egg cells) during fertilization to form a zygote.

The major biological difference between sexual and asexual reproduction is that sexual reproduction produces genetic variation in the offspring. The combining of genetic material from the gametes produces offspring that are different from either parent and contain new combinations of characteristics. This may increase the ability of the species to survive environmental changes or to reproduce in new habitats. The only genetic variation that can arise in asexual reproduction comes from mutations.

Figure 2.1 Sexual reproduction. A pair of California quail, *Callipepla californica*, in early spring.

Vegetative propagation

A plant produces external stems, or runners. Budding occurs in a number of flowing plants, such as strawberries.

Binary fission

A single cell divides forming two separate cells. Fission occurs in bacteria, protozoans, and other single-celled organisms.

Figure 2.2 Types of asexual reproduction.

Fragmentation

An organism breaks into two or more parts, each capable of becoming a complete organism. Fragmentation occurs in flatworms and echinoderms.

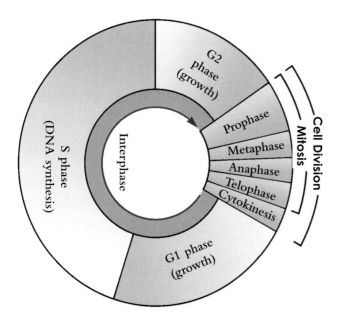

Figure 2.3 Animal cell cycle.

Figure 2.4 Each duplicated chromosome consists of two identical chromatids attached at the centrally located and constricted centromere.

Early prophase — Chromatin begins to condense to form chromosomes.

Late prophase — Nuclear envelope intact, and chromatin condensing into chromosomes.

Early metaphase — Duplicated chromosomes, each made up of two chromatids, at equatorial plane.

Late metaphase — Duplicated chromosomes, each made up of two chromatids, at equatorial plane.

Early anaphase — Sister chromatids beginning to separate into daughter chromosomes (unduplicated).

Late anaphase — Unduplicated daughter chromosomes nearing poles.

1

Telophase — Unduplicated daughter chromosomes at poles, cell plate forming.
   1. Cell plate

Interphase — Two daughter cells result from cytokinesis.

Figure 2.5 Stages of mitosis in *Hyacynth* root tip. (all 430X)

Prophase I—Each chromosome consists of two chromatids joined by a centromere.
1. Chromatids
2. Nucleolus

Metaphase I—Chromosome pairs align at the equator.
1. Chromosome pairs at equator
2. Spindle fibers

Anaphase I—No division at the centromeres occurs as the chromosomes separate, so one entire chromosome goes to each pole.
1. Chromosomes (two chromatids each)

Telophase I—Chromosomes shorten and become less distinct. The cell plate (in some plants) forms between forming cells.
1. Cell plate (new cell wall)
2. Chromosome

Prophase II—Chromosomes condense as in prophase I.
1. Chromosomes

Metaphase II—Chromosomes align on the equator and spindle fibers attach to the centromeres. This is similar to metaphase in mitosis.
1. Chromosomes

Anaphase II—Chromatids separate and each is pulled to an opposite pole.
1. Chromatids

Telophase II—Cell division is complete and cell walls of four haploid cells are formed.
1. Chromatids
2. New cell walls (cell plates)

Figure 2.6 Stages of meiosis in lily microsporocytes to form microspores. 1000X

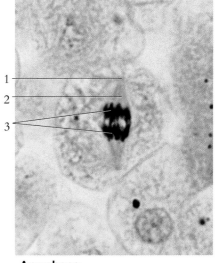

Prophase

Each chromosome consists of two chromatids jointed by a centromere. Spindle fibers extend from each centriole.

1. Aster around centriole
2. Chromosomes

Metaphase

The chromosomes are positioned at the equator. The spindle fibers from each centriole attach to the centromeres.

1. Aster around centriole
2. Spindle fibers
3. Chromosomes at equator

Anaphase

The centromeres split, and the sister chromatids separate as each is pulled to an opposite pole.

1. Aster around centriole
2. Spindle fibers
3. Separating chromosomes

Telophase

The chromosomes lengthen and become less distinct. The cell membrane forms between the forming daughter cells.

1. New cell membrane
2. Newly forming nucleus

Daughter cells

The single chromosomes (former chromatids—see anaphase) continue to lengthen as the nuclear membrane reforms. Cell division is complete and the newly formed cells grow and mature.

1. Daughter nuclei

Figure 2.7 Stages of animal cell mitosis followed by cytokinesis. Whitefish blastula. 500X

Spermatogonium (diploid)

Primary spermatocyte (diploid)

Secondary spermatocyte (haploid)

Spermatid (haploid)

Spermatozoan (haploid)

First meiotic division

Second meiotic division

Spermatogenesis

Spermiogenesis

Figure 2.8 Spermatogenesis is the production of male gametes, or spermatozoa, through the process of meiosis.

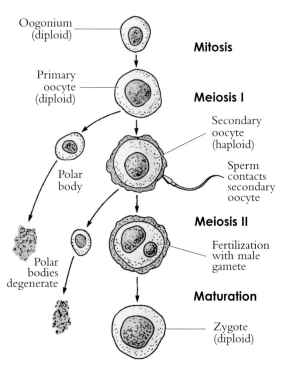

Oogonium (diploid)

Mitosis

Primary oocyte (diploid)

Meiosis I

Secondary oocyte (haploid)

Polar body

Sperm contacts secondary oocyte

Polar bodies degenerate

Meiosis II

Fertilization with male gamete

Maturation

Zygote (diploid)

Figure 2.9 Oogenesis is the production of female gametes, or ova, through the process of meiosis.

Figure 2.10 Frog testis.
1. Spermatocytes
2. Developing sperm

200X

Figure 2.11 Frog ovary.
1. Follicle cells
2. Geminal vesicle
3. Nucleoli

200X

(a)

(b)

Figure 2.12 (a) Intact chicken egg and (b) a portion of the shell is removed exposing the internal structures.

1. Shell
2. Vitelline membrane
3. Yolk
4. Shell membrane

5. Shell
6. Albumen (egg white)
7. Chalaza (dense albumen)
8. Air space

Unfertilized egg
1. Nuclear membrane
2. Nucleus
3. Nucleolus
4. Cell membrane

Fertilized egg
1. Fertilization membrane

2-cell stage

4-cell stage

8-cell stage

16-cell stage

32-cell stage

64-cell stage

Blastula
1. Blastocoel

Early gastrula
1. Blastocoel   3. Blastopore
2. Archenteron   4. Ectoderm
   (gastrocoel)   5. Endoderm

Late gastrula
1. Ectoderm   5. Archenteron
2. Mesenchyme cells   (gastrocoel)
3. Coelomic sac   6. Blastopore
4. Mesoderm

Bipinnaria larva
(lateral view)
1. Oral lobe
2. Mouth
3. Coelomic pouch
4. Stomach
5. Anus

Early brachiolaria larva
(anterior view)
1. Mouth
2. Stomach
3. Anus

Figure 2.13 Sea star development. 100X.

(n)
Young sea star

Fertilized egg

4-Cell stage

8-Cell stage

16-Cell stage

Fertilized egg

2-Cell stage

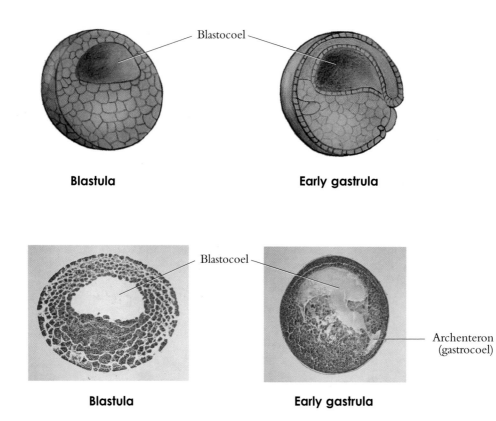

Blastocoel

Blastula   **Early gastrula**

Blastocoel

Archenteron
(gastrocoel)

Blastula   **Early gastrula**

Figure 2.14 Frog development from fertilized egg to early gastrula, shown in diagram and photomicrographs. 100X.

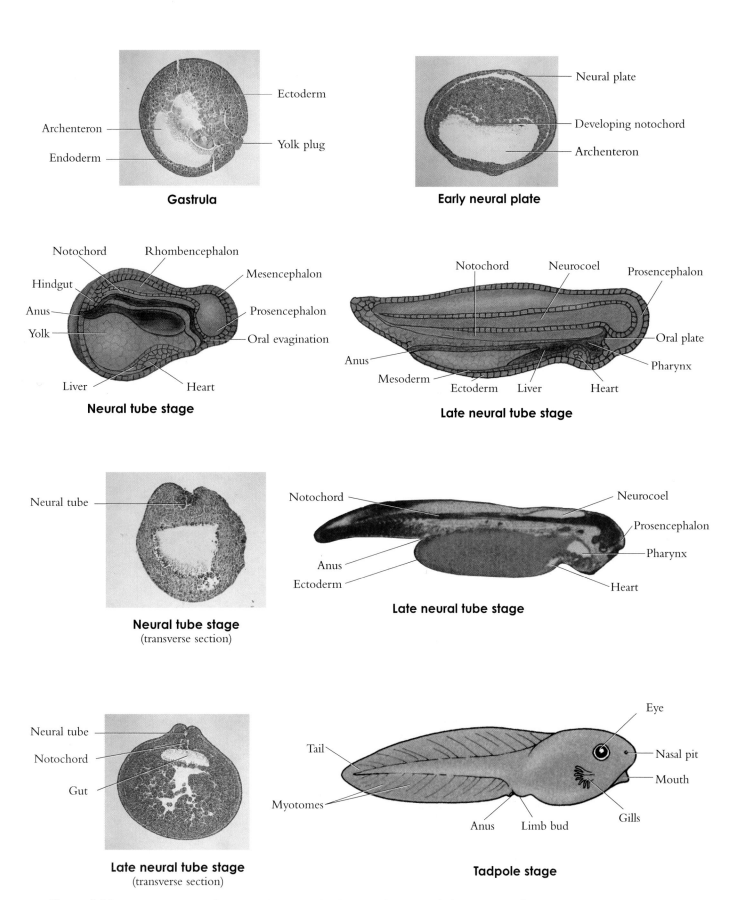

Figure 2.15 Frog development from gastrula to tadpole, shown in diagram and photomicrographs. 100X.

13 hour stage
1. Embryo main body formation

18 hour stage
1. Brain beginning to form
2. Main body

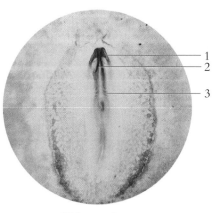

21 hour stage
1. Brain formation
2. Spinal cord beginning to form
3. Muscle plate

28 hour stage
1. Head fold and brain
2. Atery formation
3. Muscle plate
4. Blood vessel formation

38 hour stage
1. Brain with 5 regions
2. Heart

48 hour stage
1. Ear
2. Brain
3. Eye
4. Heart
5. Artery

56 hour stage
1. Ear
2. Brain
3. Eye
4. Heart
5. Artery

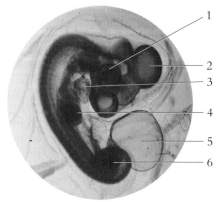

96 hour stage
1. Eye
2. Brain
3. Heart
4. Wing formation
5. Fecal sac
6. Leg formation

Figure 2.16 Stages of chick development. 20X

Bacteria range between 1 and 50 μm in width or diameter. The morphological appearance of bacteria may be spiral (spirillum), spherical (coccus), or rod-shaped (bacillus). Cocci and bacilli frequently form clusters or linear filaments, and may have bacterial flagellea. Relatively few species of bacteria cause infection. Hundreds of species of non-pathogenic bacteria live on the human body and within the gastrointestinal (GI) tract. Those in the GI tract constitute a person's gut flora, and are biologically critical to humans.

Photosynthetic bacteria contain chlorophyll and release oxygen during photosynthesis. Some bacteria are *obligate aerobes* (require O_2 for metabolism) and others are *facultative anaerobes* (indifferent to O_2 for metabolism). Some are *obligate anaerobes* (oxygen may poison them). Most bacteria are heterotrophic *saprophytes*, which secrete enzymes to break down surrounding organic molecules into absorbable compounds.

Archaea are adapted to a limited range of extreme conditions. The cell walls of Archaea lack peptidoglycan (characteristic of bacteria). Archaea have distinctive RNAs and RNA polymerase enzymes. They include methanogens, typically found in swamps and marshes, and thermoacidophiles, found in acid hot springs, acidic soil, and deep oceanic volcanic vents.

Methanogens exist in oxygen-free environments and subsist on simple compounds such as CO_2, acetate, or methanol. As their name implies, Methanobacteria produce methane gas as a byproduct of metabolism. These organisms are typically found in organic-rich mud and sludge that often contains fecal wastes.

Thermoacidophiles are resistant to hot temperatures and high acid concentrations. The cell membrane of these organisms contains high amounts of saturated fats, and their enzymes and other proteins are able to withstand extreme conditions without denaturation. These microscopic organisms thrive in most hot springs and hot, acid soils.

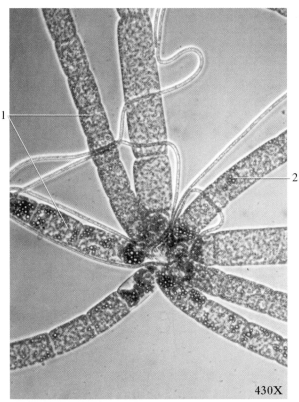

430X

Figure 3.1 *Thiothrix*, a genus of bacteria that forms sulfur granules in its cytoplasm. These organisms obtain energy from oxidation of H_2S.

1. Filaments
2. Sulfur granules

230X

Figure 3.2 *Thiothrix* filament with sulfur granules in its cytoplasm.

1. Filament
2. Sulfur granules

1200X

Figure 3.3 Magnified *Thiothrix* filament with sulfur granules in its cytoplasm.

1. Cytoplasm
2. Sulfur granules

1000X

Figure 3.4 *Bacillus megaterium.*
Bacillus is a bacterium capable of
producing endospores. This
species of *Bacillus* generally remains
in chains after it divides.

430X

Figure 3.5 Transverse section
through the root of a clover stem
showing intracellular nitrogen-fixing
bacteria.
1. Cell with bacteria
2. Epidermis

1000X

Figure 3.6 Spirochete, *Borella
recurrentis.* Spirochetes are flexable
rods twisted into helical shapes. This
species causes relapsing fever.
1. Red blood cells
2. Spirochete
3. White blood cell

1000X

Figure 3.7 *Treponema pallidum* is a
spirochete that causes syphilis.
1. *Treponema pallidum*
2. White blood cell

1000X

Figure 3.8 *Neisseria gonorrhoeae* is a
diplococcus that causes gonorrhea.

430X

Figure 3.9 *Anabaena* filament. This
organism is a nitrogen-fixing
cyanobacterium. Nitrogen fixation
takes place within the heterocyst cells.
1. Heterocyst   3. Vegetative
2. Spore (akinete)   cell

430X

Figure 3.10 *Anabaena* filament. This
is a nitrogen-fixing cyanobacterium.
Nitrogen fixation takes place within
the heterocyst cells.
1. Vegetative cell   3. Spore
2. Heterocyst

2500X

Figure 3.11 Flagellated bacterium,
Pseudomonas.
1. Flagellum

1700X

Figure 3.12 Conjugation of the
bacterium *Escherichia coli.* By this
process of conjugation, genetic
material is transferred through the
conjugation tube from one cell to the
other allowing genetic recombination.
1. Bacterium   2. Conjunction
tube

Table 3.1 Some Representatives of Bacteria and Archaea

Categories	Representative Genera
Bacteria	
Photosynthetic bacteria	
Cyanobacteria	*Anabaena, Oscillatoria, Spirulina, Nostoc*
Green bacteria	*Chlorobium*
Purple bacteria	*Rhodospirillum*
Gram-negative bacteria	*Proteus, Pseudomonas, Escherichia, Rhizobium, Neisseria*
Spirochetes	*Spirochaeta, Treponema*
Actinomycetes	*Streptomyces*
Rickettsias and Chlamydias	*Rickettsia, Chlamydia*
Mycoplasmas	*Mycoplasma*
Archaea	
Methanogens	*Halobacterium, Methanobacteria*
Thermoacidophiles	*Thermoplasma, Sulfolobus*

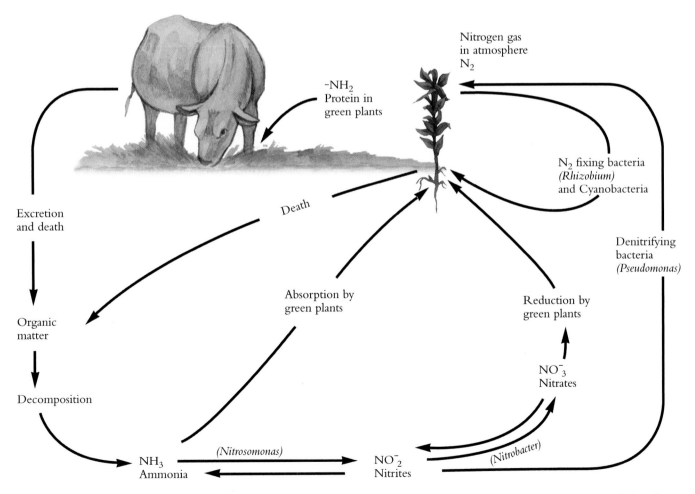

Figure 3.13 Few organisms have the ability to utilize atmospheric nitrogen. Nitrogen-fixing bacteria within the root nodules of legumes (and some free living bacteria), provide a usable source of nitrogen to plants.

Figure 3.14 Colonies of *Streptococcus pyogenes* cultured on a nutrient agar plate. *S. pyogenes* causes strep throat and rheumatic fever in humans. This agar plate is approximately 10 cm in diameter.

Figure 3.15 Cyanobacteria live in hot springs and hot streams, such as this 40 meter effluent from a geyser in Yellowstone National Park.

1. Mats of *Cyanophyta*

Figure 3.16 Closeup of cyanobacterial mats composed of several species.

Figure 3.17 *Nostoc* colony. Individual filaments secrete mucilage which forms a binding matrix binding filaments together. This compressed colony is unusual to most species of *Nostoc*.

1. Colony composed of tightly compressed filaments

Figure 3.18 *Merismopedia*, a genus of cyanobacterium, is characterized by flattened colonies of cells. The cells are in a single-layer usually aligned into groups of two or four.

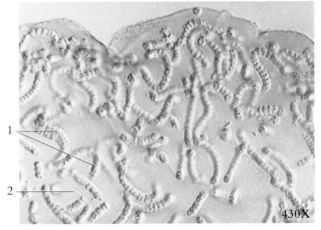

Figure 3.19 Colony of *Nostoc* filaments. Individual filaments secrete mucilage, which forms a gelatinous matrix around all filaments.
   1. Filaments   2. Gelatinous matrix

Figure 3.20 *Oscillatoria* filaments.The only way this cyanobacterium can reproduce is through fragmentation of a filament. Fragments are known as hormogonia.
   1. Hormogonium

Figure 3.21 Portion of a cylindrical filament of *Oscillatoria*. This cyanobacterium is common in most aquatic habitats.
   1. Filament segment   2. Separation disk
      (hormogonium)

Figure 3.22 *Scytonema*, a cyanobacterium, is common on moistened soil. Notice the falsely-branched filament typical of this genus.This species also demonstrates "winged" sheaths.
   1. False branching   2. "Winged" sheath

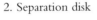

Figure 3.23 *Stigonema*, a cyanobacterium, has true-branched filaments caused from cell division in two separate planes.
   1. True branching

Figure 3.24 *Tolypothrix*, a cyanobacterium with a single false-branched filament.
   1. False branching   2. Heterocyst

Figure 3.25 *Glaucocystis* is a green alga with cyanobacteria as endosymbionts.
1. Cyanobacteria endosymbiont

Figure 3.26 *Microcoleus* is one of the most common cyanobacteria in and on soils throughout the world. It is characterized by several filaments in a common sheath

Figure 3.27 Satellite image of a large lake. The circular pattern in the water is comprised of dense growths of cyanobacteria.

Figure 3.28 *Arthrospira,* a common cyanobacterium.

Figure 3.29 *Aphanizomenon,* a cyanobacterium common in nutrient-rich (often polluted) waters around the world.
1. Spore (akinete)   2. Filament

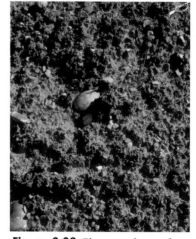

Figure 3.30 Spring seep in Zion National Park, Utah.
1. Mat of cyanobacteria.

Figure 3.31 Researcher examining cyanobacterial growths on soil in Canyonlands National Park, Utah.

Figure 3.32 Close up photo of cryptobiotic soil crust. These crusts are comprised of cyanobacteria, fungi, lichens, and other organisms.

Protists are eukaryotic organisms that range in size from microscopic unicellular organisms to giant multicellular kelp. Protists are all comprised of eukaryotic cells and therefore have a nucleus, mitochondria, endoplasmic reticulae, and Golgi complexes. Some contain chloroplasts. Most protists are capable of meiosis and sexual reproduction; these processes evolved a billion or more years ago and occur in nearly all complex plants and animals.

Protists are abundant in aquatic habitats, and are important constituents of plankton. Plankton are communities of organisms that drift passively or swim slowly in ponds, lakes, and oceans. Plankton are a major source of food for other aquatic organisms. Photosynthetic protists are the primary food producers in aquatic ecosystems.

The unicellular algal protists include microscopic aquatic organisms within the phyla Chrysophyta and Dinophyta. Chrysophyta are the yellow-green and golden-brown algae, and the diatoms. The cell wall of a diatom is composed largely of silica rather than cellulose. Some diatoms move in a slow, gliding way as cytoplasm glides through slits in the cell wall to propel the organism.

The Dinophyta are single-celled, algae-like organisms, the most important of which are the dinoflagellates. In most species of dinoflagellates, the cell wall is formed of armor-like plates of cellulose. Dinoflagellates are motile, having two flagella. Generally one encircles the organism in a transverse groove, and the other projects to the posterior.

Protozoa are also protists. They are small ($2\mu m - 100\mu m$), unicellular eukaryotic organisms that lack a cell wall. Movement of protozoa is due to flagella, cilia, or pseudopodia of various sorts. In feeding upon other organisms or organic particles, they use simple diffusion, pinocytosis, active transport, or phagocytosis. Although most protozoa reproduce asexually, some species may also reproduce sexually during a portion of their life cycle. Most protozoa are harmless, although some are of immense clinical concern because they are parasitic and may cause human disease, including African sleeping sickness and malaria.

Table 4.1 Some Representatives of the Protista: Primarily Unicellular Organisms

	Taxa and Representative Kinds	Characteristics
Plant-like	**Chrysophyta**—diatoms and golden algae	Diatom cell walls composed of or impregnated with silica, often with two halves; plastids often golden in Chrysophyta due to pigment composition
	Dinophyta—dinoflagellates	Two flagella in grooves of wall; brownish-gold plastids
Animal-like	**Rhizopoda**—amoebas	Cytoskeleton of microtubules and microfilaments; amoeboid locomotion
	Apicomplexa—sporozoa and *Plasmodium*	Lack locomotor capabilities and contractile vacuoles; mostly parasitic
	Sarcomastigophora—protozoa	Use flagella or pseudopodia to locomote; mostly parasitic
	Euglenophyta—euglenoids	Flagellates containing chloroplasts, lacking typical cell walls
	Ciliophora—ciliates and *Paramecium*	Use cilia to move and feed

Figure 4.1 Illustration of *Amoeba proteus*, a fresh-water protozoan.

Phylum Chrysophyta - diatoms and golden algae

Figure 4.2 *Biddulphia*, a diatom forming colonies. These cells are beginning cell division.

Figure 4.3 Live specimens of pennate diatoms. (a) *Navicula*, and (b) *Cymbella*.
  1. Chloroplast   2. Striae

Figure 4.4 *Hyalodiscus*, a centric (radially symmetrical) diatom, from a freshwater spring in Nevada.
  1. Silica cell wall   2. Chloroplasts

Figure 4.5 *Epithemia*, a distinctive (bilaterally symmetrical) freshwater diatom.

Figure 4.6 *Stephanodiscus*, a centric diatom.

Figure 4.7 Two common freshwater diatoms.
  1. *Cocconeis*   2. *Amphora*

Figure 4.8 *Hantzschia*, one of the most common soil diatoms.

Figure 4.9 Scanning electron micrograph of *Cocconeis*, a common freshwater diatom.
  1. Striae containing pores, or punctae, in the frustule (silicon cell wall).

Figure 4.10 A scanning electron micrograph of the diatom *Achnanthes flexella*.
  1. Raphe   2. Striae

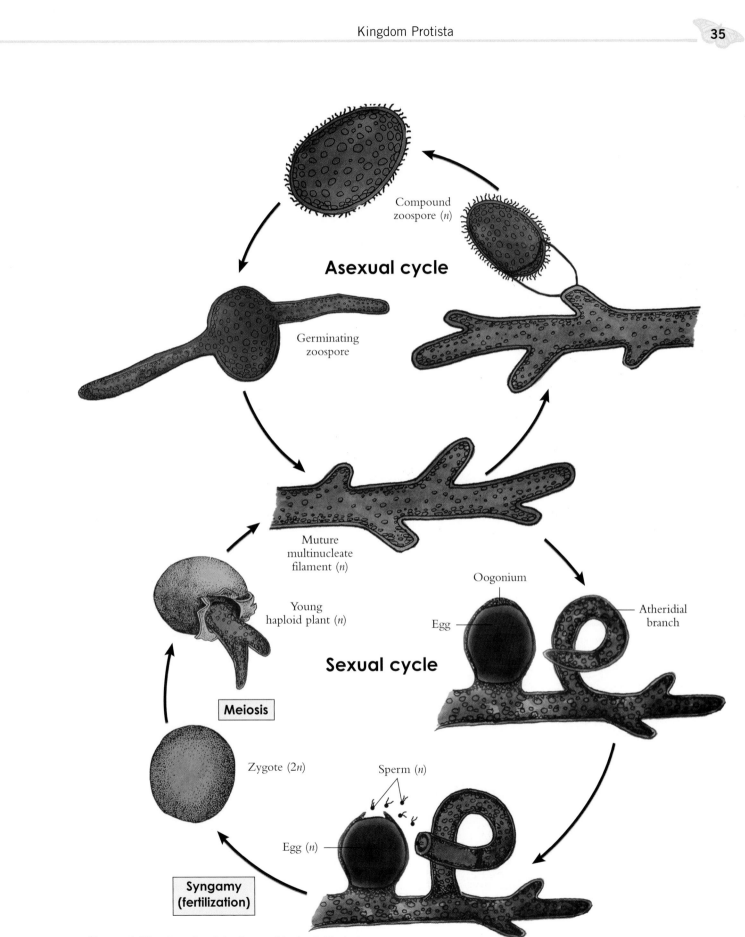

Figure 4.11 Life cycle of the "water felt alga," *Vaucheria*.

Figure 4.12 Filament with immature gametangia of the "water felt" alga, *Vaucheria. Vaucheria* is a chrysophyte that is widespread in fresh-water and marine habitats. It is also found in the mud of brackish areas that periodically become submerged and then exposed to air.

1. Antheridium
2. Developing oogonium

Figure 4.13 *Vaucheria*, with mature gametangia.

1. Fertilization pore
2. Antheridium
3. Chloroplasts
4. Developing oogonium

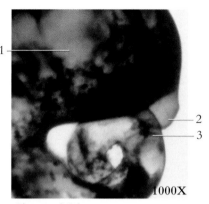

Figure 4.14 *Vaucheria*, with mature gametangia.

1. Oogonium
2. Fertilization pore
3. Antheridium

Phylum Dinophyta (Pyrrhophyta) - dinoflagellates

Figure 4.15 Dinoflagellates, *Peridinium*. (a) Some organisms are living; (b) others are dead and have lost their cytoplasm and consist of resistant cell walls.

1. Dead dinoflagellate
2. Living dinoflagellate
3. Cellulose plate
4. Remnant of cytoplasm

Figure 4.16 Giant clam with bluish coloration due to endosymbiont dinoflagellates.

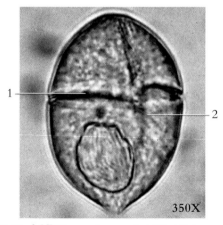

Figure 4.17 Photomicrograph of *Peridinium*. The cell wall of many dinoflagellates is composed of overlapping plates of cellulose, which are evident in this photomicrograph.

1. Transverse groove
2. Wall of cellulose plates

Phylum Rhizopoda - amoebas

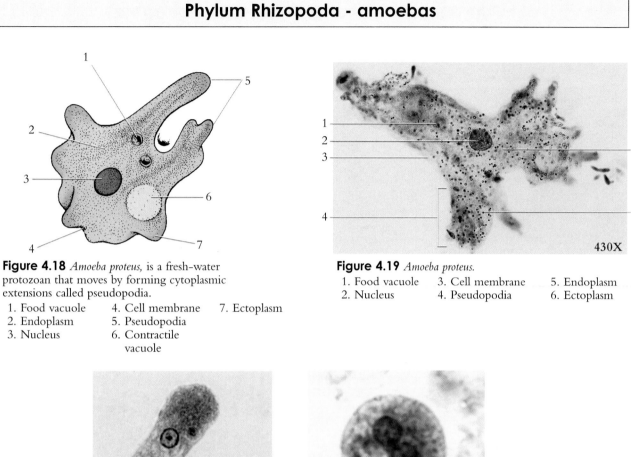

Figure 4.18 *Amoeba proteus,* is a fresh-water protozoan that moves by forming cytoplasmic extensions called pseudopodia.

1. Food vacuole
2. Endoplasm
3. Nucleus
4. Cell membrane
5. Pseudopodia
6. Contractile vacuole
7. Ectoplasm

Figure 4.19 *Amoeba proteus.*

1. Food vacuole
2. Nucleus
3. Cell membrane
4. Pseudopodia
5. Endoplasm
6. Ectoplasm

Figure 4.20 Protozoan *Entamoeba histolytica,* is the causative agent of amebic dysentery, a disease most common in areas with poor sanitation. (a) A trophozoite, and (b) a cyst.

Phylum Apicomplexa - sporazoans and plasmodia

Figure 4.21 Protozoan *Plasmodium falciparum* causes malaria, which is transmitted by the female *Anopheles* mosquito. (a) The ring stage in a red blood cell, (b) a double infection, (c) a developing schizont, and (d) a gametocyte. All 200X

Phylum Sarcomastiphora - flagellated protozoans

430X

Figure 4.22 Protozoan *Trichomonas vaginalis* is the causative agent of trichomoniasis. Trichomoniasis is an inflammation of the genitourinary mucosal surfaces—the urethra, vulva, vagina, and cervix in females and the urethra, prostate, and seminal vesicles in males.

100X

Figure 4.23 Protozoan *Leishmania donovani* is the causative agent of visceral leishmaniasis, or kala-azar disease, in humans. The sandfly is the infectious host of this disease.

100X

Figure 4.24 Flagellated protozoan *Trypanosoma brucei* is the causative agent of African trypanosomiasis, or African sleeping sickness. The tsetse fly is the infectious host of this disease in humans.
1. *Trypanosoma brucei*
2. Red blood cell

Phylum Euglenophyta - euglenoids

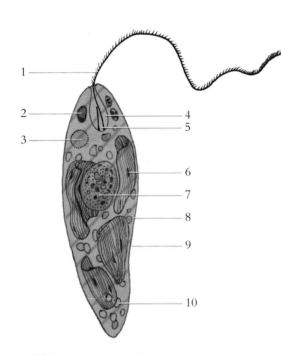

Figure 4.25 Diagram of *Euglena*, which contain flagellates that contain chloroplasts. They are freshwater organisms that have a flexible pellicle rather than a rigid cell wall.

1. Flagellum
2. Photoreceptor (eye spot)
3. Contractile vacuole
4. Reservoir
5. Basal body
6. Chloroplast
7. Nucleus
8. Pellicle
9. Cell membrane
10. Paramylum granule

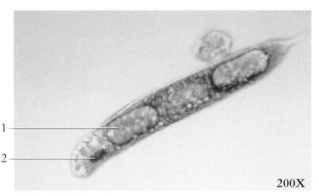

200X

Figure 4.26 Species of *Euglena*.
1. Paramylum body   2. Photoreceptor

200X

Figure 4.27 Species of *Euglena* from a brackish lake in New Mexico.
1. Pellicle   2. Photoreceptor

Phylum Ciliophora - ciliates and paramecia

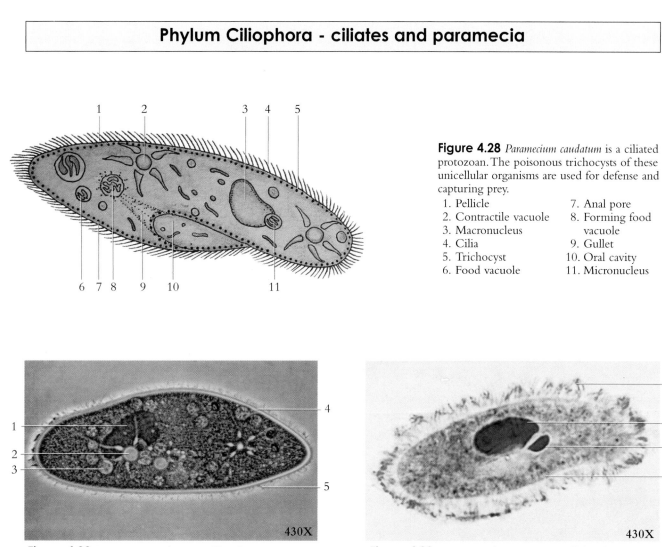

Figure 4.28 *Paramecium caudatum* is a ciliated protozoan. The poisonous trichocysts of these unicellular organisms are used for defense and capturing prey.

1. Pellicle
2. Contractile vacuole
3. Macronucleus
4. Cilia
5. Trichocyst
6. Food vacuole
7. Anal pore
8. Forming food vacuole
9. Gullet
10. Oral cavity
11. Micronucleus

Figure 4.29 *Paramecium caudatum*, a ciliated protozoan.

1. Macronucleus
2. Contractile vacuole
3. Micronucleus
4. Pellicle
5. Cilia

Figure 4.30 *Paramecium busaria* is a unicellular, slipper-shaped organism. Paramecia are usually common in ponds containing decaying organic matter.

1. Cilia
2. Macronucleus
3. Micronucleus
4. Pellicle

Figure 4.31 *Paramecium* in fission.

1. Contractile vacuole
2. Macronucleus
3. Micronucleus

Figure 4.32 *Paramecium* in conjugation.

430X

Figure 4.33 *Balantidium coli* is the causative agent of balantidiasis. Cysts in sewage-contaminated water are the infective form.

150X

Figure 4.34 *Stentor*, a free swimming form which has adopted an oval shape.

Table 4.2 Some Representatives of Protista: Primarily Multicellular Organisms

Phylum and Representative Kinds	Characteristics
Algae	
Phylum Chlorophyta—green algae	Unicellular, colonial, filamentous and multicellular plate-like forms; mosly fresh water; reproduce asexually and sexually
Phylum Phaeophyta—brown algae, giant kelp	Multicellular, mostly marine often in the intertidal zone; most with alternation of generations
Phylum Rhodophyta—red algae	Multicellular, mostly marine; sexual reproduction but with no flagellated cells; alternation of generations common
Protists Resembling Fungi	
Phylum Myxomycota—plasmodial slime molds	Multinucleated continuum of cytoplasm without cell membranes; amoeboid plasmodium during feeding stage; produce asexual fruiting bodies; gametes produced by meiosis
Phylum Dictyosteliomycota—cellular slime molds	Solitary cells during feeding stage; cells aggregate when food is scarce; produce asexual fruiting bodies
Phylum Oomycota—water molds, white rusts and downy mildews	Decomposers or parasitic forms; walls of cellulose, dispersal by non-motile spores or flagellated zoospores, gametes produced by meiosis

Phylum Chlorophyta - green algae

800X

Figure 4.35 *Chlamydomonas*, a common unicellular green alga.

630X

Figure 4.36 *Chlamydomonas nivalis*, the common snow alga.

Figure 4.37 Habitat shot of *Chlamydomonas nivalis* creating "red snow."
1. *Chlamydomonas nivalis*   2. Snow

Figure 4.38 *Gonium* colony. *Gonium* is a 16-celled flat colony of *Chlamydomonas*-like cells.

Figure 4.39 *Pleodorina* species, a multicellular colony (often 64-celled) relative of *Chlamydomonas* and *Volvox*.

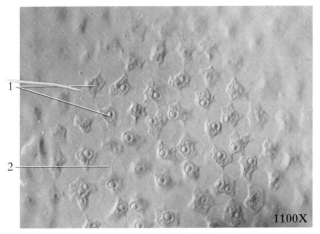

Figure 4.40 Close-up of the surface of *Volvox* showing the interconnections between cells.
1. Vegetative cells   2. Cytoplasmic connection between cells

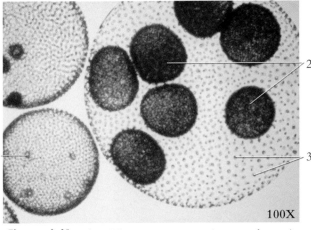

Figure 4.41 *Volvox.* Three separate organisms are shown in this photomicrograph, each containing daughter colonies of various ages.
1. Immature daughter colony   3. Vegetative cells
2. Daughter colonies

Figure 4.42 *Volvox,* a single organism with several large daughter colonies.
1. Daughter colonies

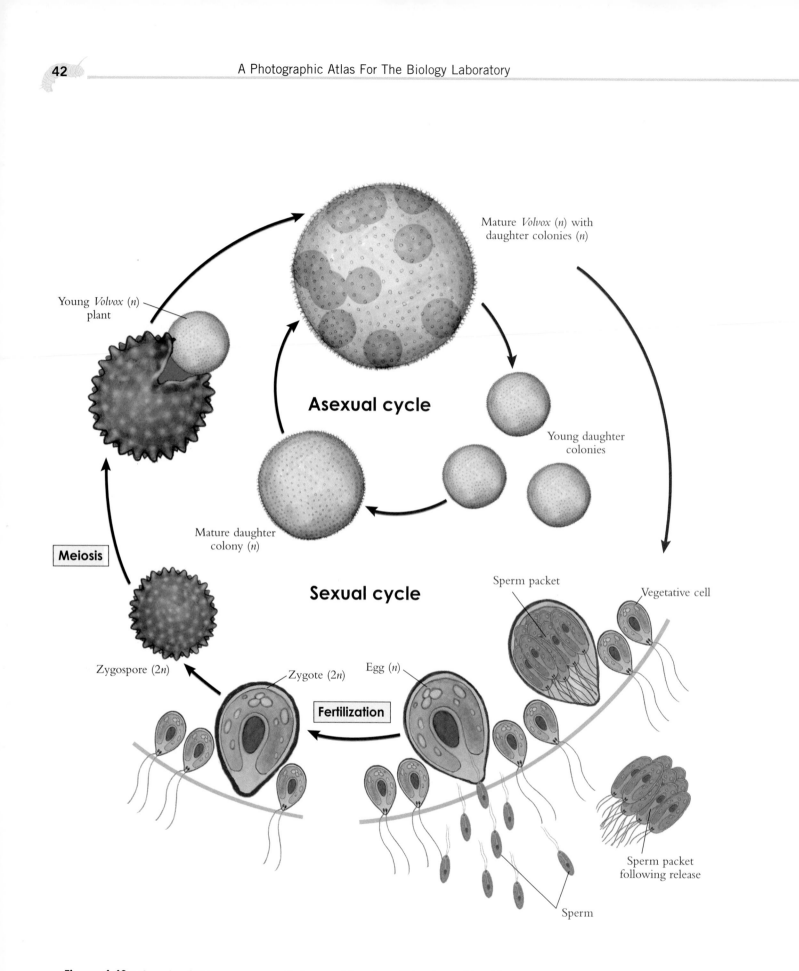

Mature *Volvox* (*n*) with daughter colonies (*n*)

Young *Volvox* (*n*) plant

Asexual cycle

Young daughter colonies

Mature daughter colony (*n*)

Meiosis

Sexual cycle

Sperm packet

Vegetative cell

Zygospore (2*n*)

Zygote (2*n*)

Egg (*n*)

Fertilization

Sperm packet following release

Sperm

Figure 4.43 Life cycle of *Volvox*, a common freshwater chlorophyte. *Volvox* is considered by some to be a colony and by others to be a single, integrated plant.

Figure 4.44 *Volvox,* a single mature specimen with several eggs and zygotes.
1. Zygotes   2. Vegetative cells   3. Egg

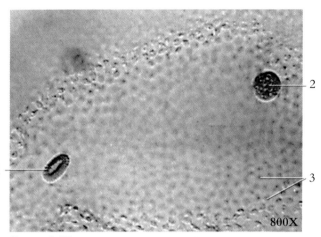

Figure 4.45 Single mature specimen of *Volvox.* This photomicrograph is a highly magnified view of a single organism showing gametes.
1. Sperm packet   3. Vegetative cells
2. Egg

Figure 4.46 *Volvox,* showing a prominent egg at the edge of the organism. This egg will be fertilized to develop a zygote and then a zygospore.
1. Egg   2. Vegetative cells

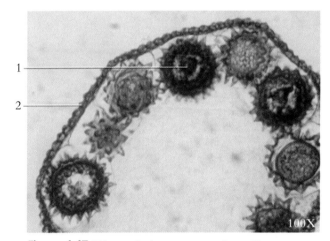

Figure 4.47 *Volvox,* a single mature organism with zygospores.
1. Zygospore
2. Vegetative cells

Figure 4.48 Live specimens of *Ulothrix,* an unbranched, filamentous green alga.

Figure 4.49 *Ulothrix,* an unbranched, filamentous green alga.
1. Zoospores   2. Individual cells (known as sporangia when they produce spores)

Vegetative stained filament   **Stained filament with zoospores**   **Empty filament, after zoospores have been released**

Figure 4.50 Production and release of zoospores in the green alga *Ulothrix*.

1. Filament   2. Chloroplasts   3. Young zoospores   4. Mature zoospores   5. Empty cells following zoospore release

Figure 4.51 *Stigeocolonium*, a close relative of *Ulothrix*, showing a branched thallus.

Figure 4.52 *Oedeogonium* showing the distinctive "apical caps" that accrue from cell division in this genus.
1. Apical caps

Figure 4.53 Young filament of *Oedogonium*.
1. Basal cell
2. Holdfast

Figure 4.54 (a) *Oedogonium*, a filamentous, unbranched, green alga.
(b) Close-up of an oogonium.

1. Oogonia   3. Basal holdfast cell
2. Antheridium   4. Holdfast

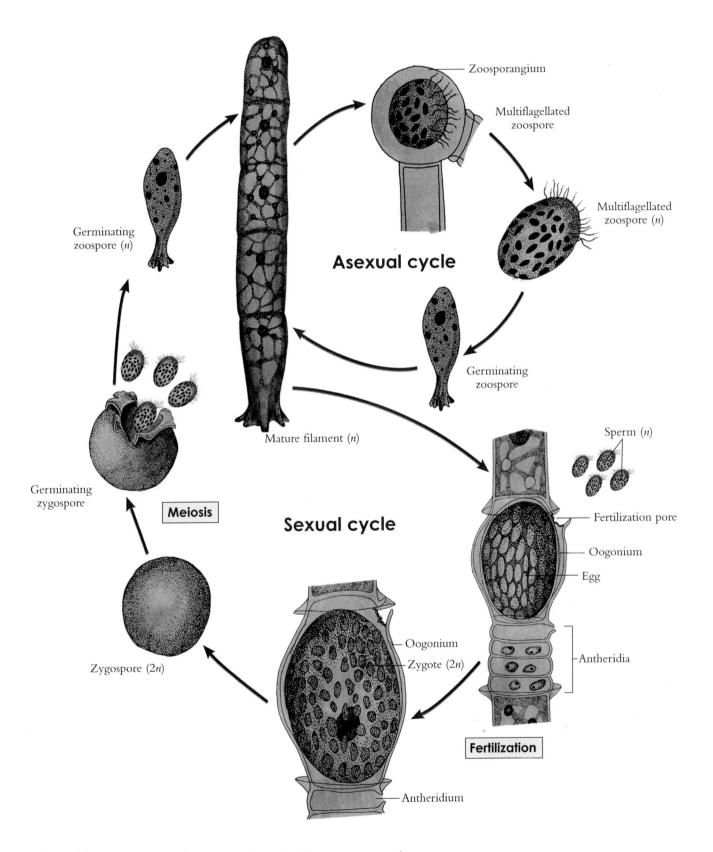

Figure 4.55 Life cycle of *Oedogonium*, an unbranched, filamentous green alga.

Figure 4.56 The oogonium of the unbranched, green alga, *Oedogonium*.
1. Dwarf male filament
2. Oogonium
3. Developing egg
4. Vegetative cell

Figure 4.57 *Oogonium* with mature egg and dwarf male filament.
1. Egg
2. Dwarf male filament

Figure 4.58 Filament of the unbranched green alga, *Oedogonium*.
1. Annular scars from cell division
2. Antheridia
3. Sperm

Figure 4.59 Green alga, *Oedogonium*, showing antheridia between vegetative cells.
1. Sperm within antheridia
2. Nucleus of vegetative cell
3. Vegetative cell

Figure 4.60 Zoosporangium of the unbranched green alga, *Oedogonium*.
1. Zoosporangium
2. Zoospore

Figure 4.61 Species of *Spirogyra* are filamentous green algae commonly found in green masses on the surfaces of ponds and streams. Their chloroplasts are arranged as a spiral within the cell. (a) Several cells comprise a filament. (b) A magnified view of a single filament composed of several cells.
1. Single cell
2. Filaments
3. Cell wall
4. Chloroplast

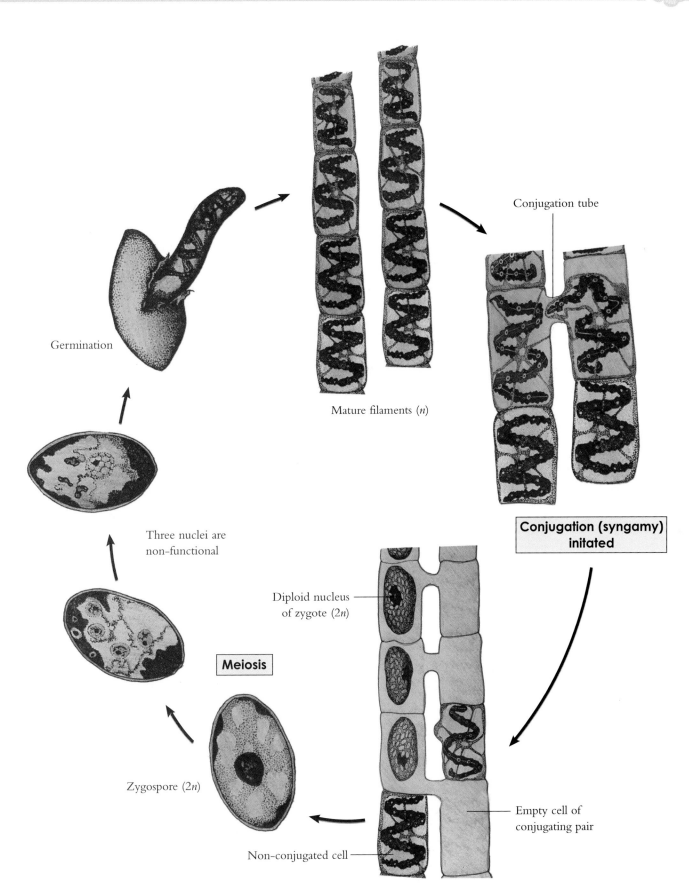

Conjugation tube

Mature filaments (n)

Conjugation (syngamy) initated

Germination

Three nuclei are non-functional

Diploid nucleus of zygote (2n)

Meiosis

Zygospore (2n)

Empty cell of conjugating pair

Non-conjugated cell

Figure 4.62 Life cycle of *Spirogyra*, a common fresh-water green alga.

Figure 4.63 Two filaments of *Spirogyra* with aplanospores.
1. Aplanospore   2. Cell wall

Figure 4.64 *Spirogyra* floating on the surface of a small fresh-water pond.

Figure 4.65 *Zygnema* filament showing the star-shaped chloroplasts.
1. Cell wall   3. Pyrenoid
2. Chloroplast

Figure 4.66 *Zygnema* undergoing conjugation.
1. Zygote   3. Conjugation
2. Cell wall   tube

Figure 4.67 Self–fertile species of *Spirogyra*. A gamete has migrated from the upper cell to form a zygote in the lower cell.
1. Upper cell   4. Conjugation
2. Lower cell   tube
3. Chloroplast   5. Zygote

Figure 4.68 *Zygnema* undergoing conjugation. (a) The filament is just forming conjugation tubes; (b) and two conjugated filaments.
1. Developing gametes   3. Zygotes
2. Developing conjugation tubes   4. Conjugation tube

Figure 4.69 Conjugation in *Spirogyra*.
1. Cell bearing zygote   3. Cell that did
2. Zygote   not conjugate

Figure 4.70 Desmid *Closterium*. Desmids are unicellular, fresh water chlorophyta, which reproduce sexually by conjugation.

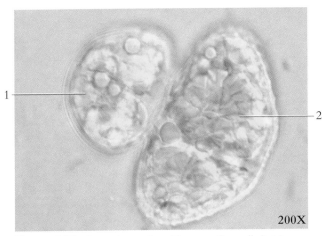

Figure 4.71 *Cosmarium*, a desmid, soon after cell division forming a new semi-cell.
1. New semi-cell   2. Dividing cell

Figure 4.72 Zygospore of the desmid *Cosmarium*.
1. Zygospore   2. Empty cell that has been involved in conjugation

Figure 4.73 Desmid *Micrasterias*.

Figure 4.74 Sea lettuce, *Ulva*, lives as a flat membranous chlorophyte in marine environments.

Figure 4.75 Several green algae are common marine organisms. *Codium* occurs in intertidal zones and is commonly known as dead man's fingers.

Figure 4.76 Branching filaments of *Cladophora glomerata*. This member of class Ulvophyceae is found in both fresh-water and marine habitats.

Figure 4.77 *Hydrodictyon*. The large, multinucleated cells form net-shaped colonies.
1. Individual cell
2. Nuclei of cell

Figure 4.78 (a) *Chara*, inhabits marshes or shallow, temperate lakes, showing characteristic gametangia. (b) A magnified view of the gametangia.

1. Oogonium
2. Antheridium
3. Egg
4. Oogonium
5. Sperm-producing cells (filaments)
6. Antheridium

Phylum Phaeophyta - brown algae and giant kelp

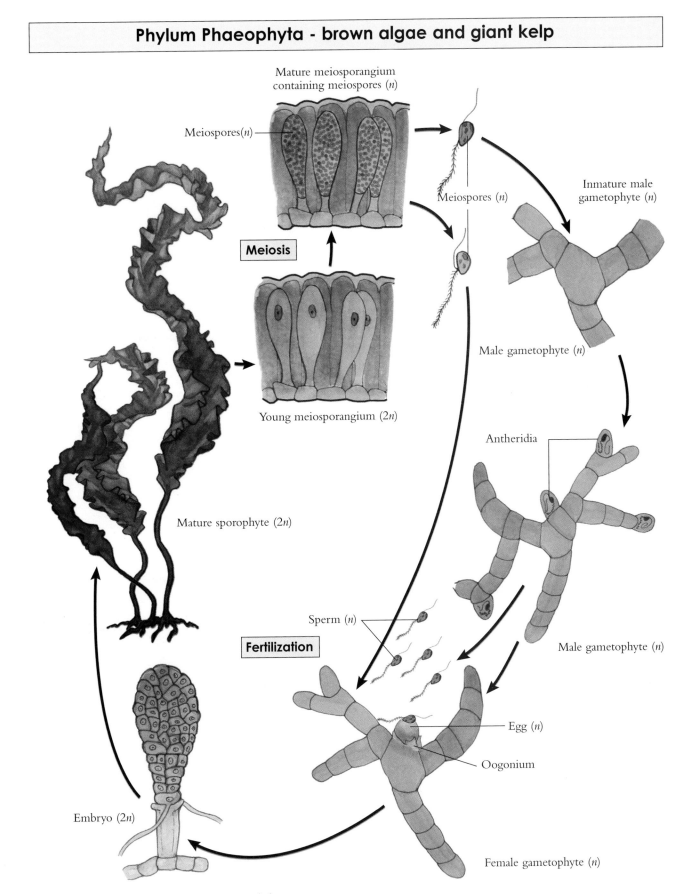

Mature meiosporangium containing meiospores (n)

Meiospores (n)

Meiosis

Young meiosporangium (2n)

Meiospores (n)

Inmature male gametophyte (n)

Male gametophyte (n)

Antheridia

Male gametophyte (n)

Mature sporophyte (2n)

Sperm (n)

Fertilization

Egg (n)

Oogonium

Embryo (2n)

Female gametophyte (n)

Figure 4.79 Life cycle of *Laminaria*, a common kelp.

Figure 4.80 Rocky coast of southern Alaska showing dense growths of the brown alga, *Fucus*.

Figure 4.81 "Sea palm," *Postelsia palmaeformis*, a common brown alga found on the western coast of North America.

Macrocystis

Macrocystis

Macrocystis

Egregia

Figure 4.82 Examples of brown algae, Phaeophyta. These large species are commonly known as kelps.

1. Blade
2. Float (air-filled bladder)
3. Stipe

Figure 4.83 Kelp, *Laminaria*, is one of the common "sea weeds" found along many rocky coasts. Note that the holdfast of this specimen is attached to a mussel shell.

1. Blade   3. Holdfast
2. Stipe   4. Mussel shell

Figure 4.84 Tidal pool with several species of Phaeophyta.

Figure 4.85 Brown alga, *Nereocystis,* has a long stipe and photosynthetic laminae attached to a large float. The holdfast anchors the alga to the ocean floor. This alga and others can grow to lengths of several meters.

1. Floats (air-filled bladders)   3. Holdfasts
2. Stipe   4. Lamina

Figure 4.86 *Sargassum,* a brown alga common in the Sargasso sea.

1. Float   2. Blade   3. Stipe

Figure 4.87 Mixture of kelps washed onto shore to form "windrows" of Phaeophyta.

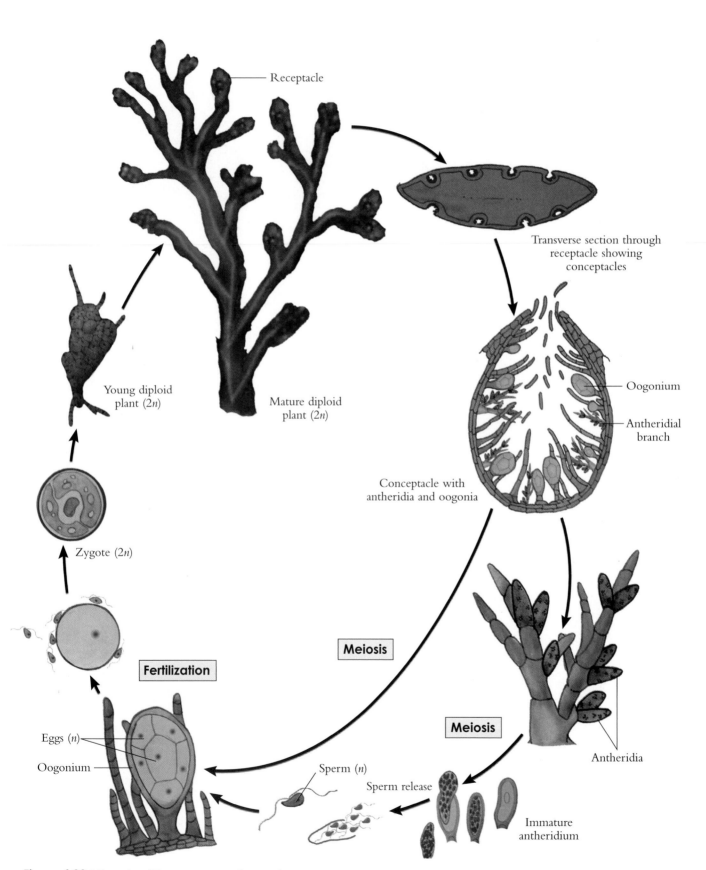

Figure 4.88 Life cycle of *Fucus*, a common brown alga.

Figure 4.89 (a) *Fucus*, a brown alga, commonly called rockweed. (b) An enlargement of a blade supporting the receptacles.
1. Blade
2. Receptacle
3. Conceptacles (light-colored spots) are chambers imbedded in the receptacles
4. Blade

Figure 4.90 Conceptacle of *Fucus*.
1. Sterile paraphases
2. Antheridial branches

Figure 4.91 Close-up of antheridial branch of *Fucus*.
1. Antheridial branch
2. Antheridium

Figure 4.92 Close-up of antheridium of *Fucus*.
1. Sperm within antheridium

Figure 4.93 *Fucus*, conceptacle containing both antheridia and oogonia.
1. Ostiole
2. Paraphyses (sterile hairs)
3. Surface of receptacle
4. Oogonium

Figure 4.94 *Fucus*, closeup of bisexual conceptacle.
1. Nucleus of egg
2. Oogonium
3. Eggs
4. Antheridium
5. Paraphyses

Phylum Rhodophyta - red algae

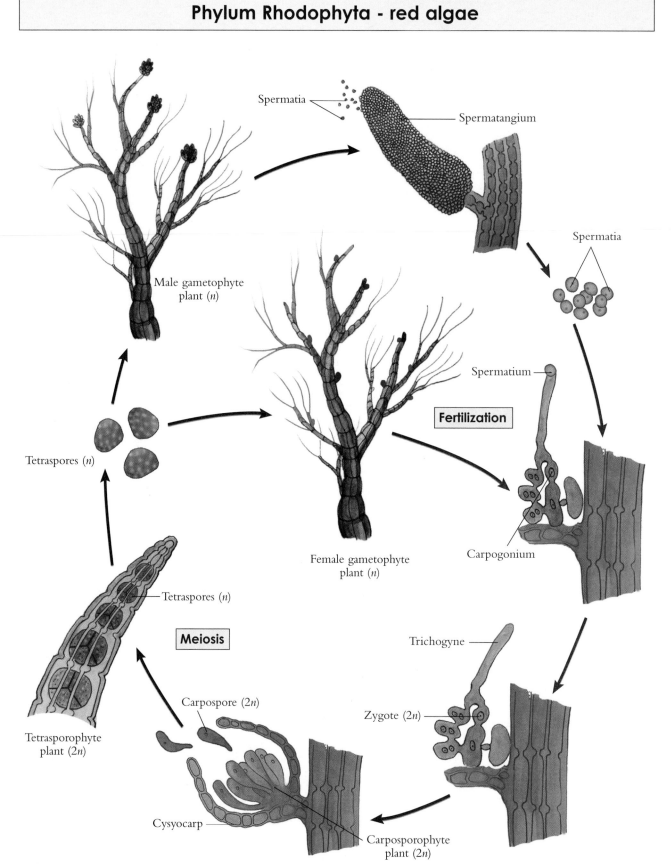

Spermatia

Spermatangium

Male gametophyte
plant (n)

Spermatia

Spermatium

Fertilization

Carpogonium

Female gametophyte
plant (n)

Tetraspores (n)

Tetraspores (n)

Trichogyne

Meiosis

Carpospore (2n)

Zygote (2n)

Tetrasporophyte
plant (2n)

Cysyocarp

Carposporophyte
plant (2n)

Figure 4.95 Life cycle of the red alga, *Polysiphonia*.

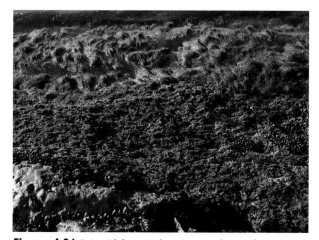

Figure 4.96 Intertidal zone showing a colony of red alga, *Bangia*.

Figure 4.97 Mature plant of the red alga, *Rhodymenia*.

Figure 4.98 Small encrusting colonies of a species of red alga on a stone. The colonies shown are bright red and are only a few millimeters in size.

Figure 4.99 *Batrachospermum*, a common fresh water red alga.

Figure 4.100 *Audouinella* is a fresh water member of Rhodophyta. This organism was collected from a cold-water spring.

Figure 4.101 Mature plant of the common red alga, *Polysiphonia*.

Figure 4.102 Red alga, *Polysiphonia*, has alternation of three generations. (a) Female gametophyte with attached carposporophyte generation. (b) A closeup of the cystocarp plant.
1. Pericarp   2. Carposporophyte producing carpospores

Figure 4.103 *Polysiphonia*, showing the release of carpospores.
1. Carpospores (2*n*)   2. Ruptured cystocarp

Figure 4.104 Tetrasporophyte generation of *Polysiphonia* showing tetraspores (meiospores).
1. Tetraspores   2. Cells of tetrasporophyte plant

Figure 4.105 Close-up of tetrasporophyte plant of *Polysiphonia*.
1. Tetraspore (meiospore)

Figure 4.106 Male gametophyte plant of *Polysiphonia*, showing spermatangia.
1. Spermatangium with spermatia

Phylum Myxomycota - plasmodial slime molds

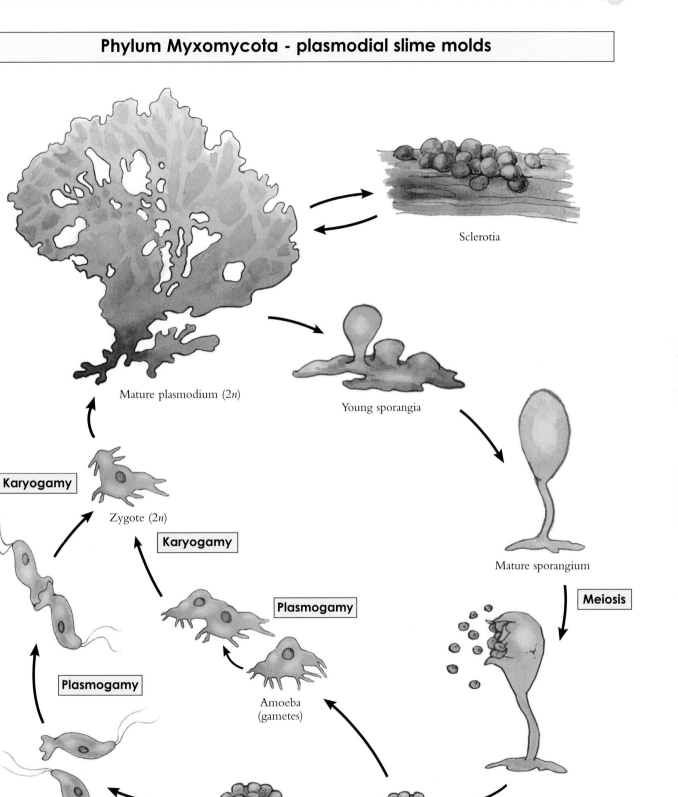

Sclerotia

Mature plasmodium (2*n*)

Young sporangia

Mature sporangium

Karyogamy

Zygote (2*n*)

Karyogamy

Meiosis

Plasmogamy

Amoeba (gametes)

Plasmogamy

Flagellated gametes (*n*) (swarm cells)

Germinating meiospore

Meiospore (*n*)

Figure 4.107 Life cycle of a plasmodial slime mold.

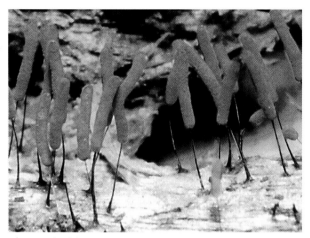

Figure 4.108 Sporangia of the slime mold *Comatricha typhoides*.

Figure 4.109 Longitudinal section through the sporangium of *Stemonitis*.
1. Cellular filaments (capillitum)   2. Columella

Figure 4.110 Close-up through the sporangium of *Stemonitis*.
1. Spores   2. Capillitum

Figure 4.111 *Physarum* plasmodium.

Figure 4.112 Slime mold sporangia vary considerably in size and shape. One species of *Lycogala* is shown here.

Figure 4.113 Slime mold specimen from a high mountain locality.

Phylum Oomycota - water molds, white rusts, and downy mildews

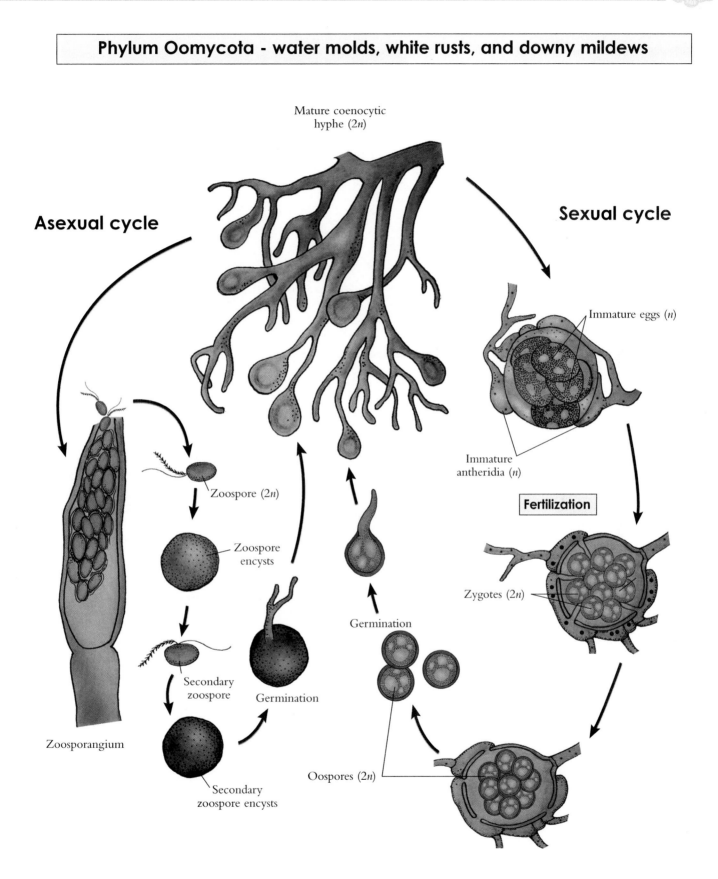

Mature coenocytic
hyphe (2n)

Asexual cycle

Sexual cycle

Immature eggs (n)

Immature
antheridia (n)

Zoospore (2n)

Fertilization

Zoospore
encysts

Zygotes (2n)

Germination

Secondary
zoospore   Germination

Zoosporangium

Secondary
zoospore encysts

Oospores (2n)

Figure 4.114 Life cycle of the water mold *Saprolegnia*.

430X

Figure 4.115 Sporangium of the
water mold *Saprolegnia*.
  1. Zoosporangium
  2. Zoospores

430X

Figure 4.116 Water mold, *Saprolegnia,* showing a
young oogonium before eggs have been formed.

200X

Figure 4.117 Mature oogonia of the water mold *Saprolegnia*.
  1. Oogonium   2. Eggs

Figure 4.118 Skin of this brown trout has been infected by the common water mold, *Saprolegnia*.

Chapter 5

Fungi, Yeasts, Molds, Mushrooms, Rusts, and Lichens

About 250,000 species of fungi are currently extant on Earth. All fungi are heterotrophs; they absorb nutrients through their cell walls and cell membranes. The kingdom Fungi includes the conjugation fungi, yeasts, mushrooms, toadstools, rusts, and lichens. Most are saprobes, absorbing nutrients from dead organic material. Some are parasitic, absorbing nutrients from living hosts. Fungi decompose organic material, helping to recycle nutrients essential for plant growth.

Except for the unicellular yeasts, fungi consist of elongated filaments called *hyphae*. Hyphae begin as cellular extensions of spores that branch as they grow to form a network of hyphae called a *mycelium*. Even the body of a mushroom consists of a mass of tightly packed hyphae attached to an underground mycelium. Fungi are nonmotile and reproduce by means of spores, produced sexually or asexually.

Many species of fungi are commercially important. Some are used as food, such as mushrooms; or in the production of foods, such as bread, cheese, beer, and wine. Other species are important in medicine, for example, in the production of the antibiotic penicillin. Many other species of fungi are of medical and economic concern because they cause plant and animal diseases and destroy crops and stored goods.

Table 5.1 Some Representatives of Fungi

Phyla and Representative Kinds	Characteristics
Zygomycota — conjugation fungi	Hyphae lack cross walls along filaments; sexual reproduction by conjugation
Ascomycota — yeasts, molds, morels, and truffles	Septate hyphae; reproductive structure contains meiospores within asci in fruiting bodies known as ascocarps (ascoma); asexual reproduction by budding or conidia
Basidiomycota — mushrooms, toadstools, rusts, and smuts	Septate hyphae; four meiospores produced externally on cells called basidia contained in basidiocarp (basidioma)
Lichens — not a phylum, but a symbiotic association of an alga and a fungus	Algal component (usually a green alga) provides food from photosynthesis; fungal component (usually an ascomycete) may provide anchorage, water retention, and/or nutrient absorbance

Figure 5.1 Examples of common fungi. (a) A cup fungus, *Peziza*, a common ascomycete, and (b) oyster mushrooms, *Pleurotus*.

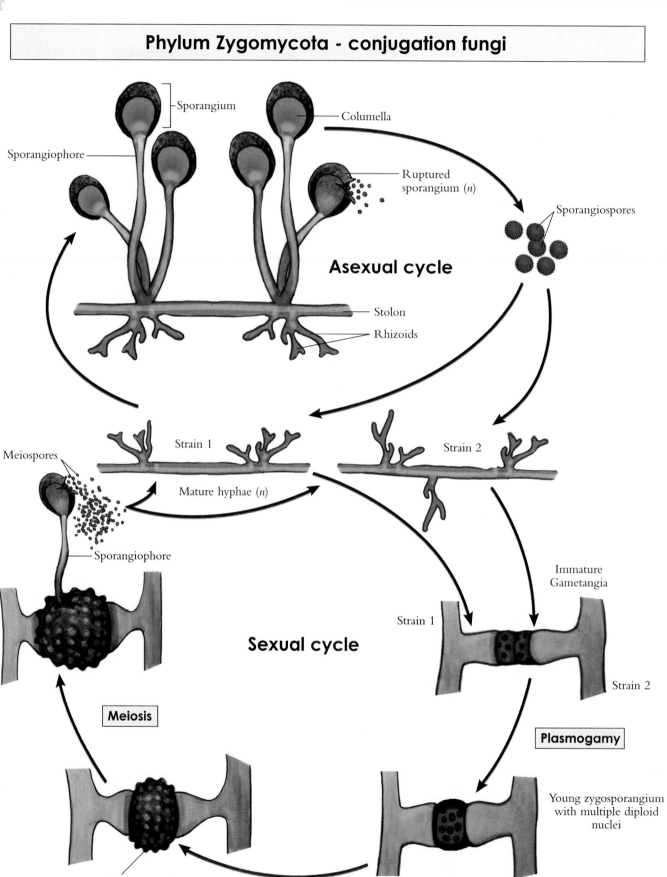

Phylum Zygomycota - conjugation fungi

Sporangium

Columella

Sporangiophore

Ruptured sporangium (*n*)

Sporangiospores

Asexual cycle

Stolon

Rhizoids

Meiospores

Strain 1

Strain 2

Mature hyphae (*n*)

Sporangiophore

Immature Gametangia

Strain 1

Sexual cycle

Strain 2

Meiosis

Plasmogamy

Young zygosporangium with multiple diploid nuclei

Zygosporangium

Figure 5.2 Life cycle of *Rhizopus*, the common bread mold.

Figure 5.3 *Rhizopus* species growing on a slice of bread.
1. Sporangia
2. Hyphae (stolon)

Figure 5.4 Whole mount of the bread mold, *Rhizopus.*
1. Sporangium
2. Spores
3. Columella
4. Sporangiophore
5. Hyphae

Figure 5.5 Mature sporangium in the asexual reproductive cycle of the bread mold, *Rhizopus.*
1. Sporangium
2. Sporangiophore
3. Spores
4. Columella

Figure 5.6 Young gametangia of *Rhizopus* contacting prior to plasmogamy.
1. Immature gametangia
2. Suspensor cell

Figure 5.7 Immature *Rhizopus* zygospore following plasmogamy.
1. Immature zygospore

Figure 5.8 Mature *Rhizopus* zygospore.
1. Zygospore
2. Suspensor cell

Phylum Ascomycota -yeasts, molds, morels, and truffles

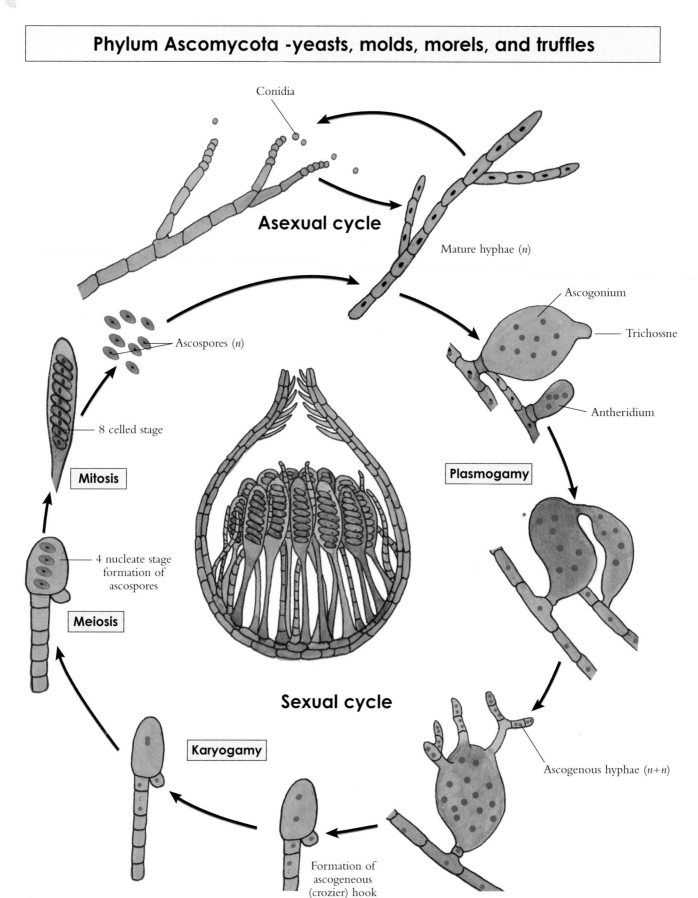

Conidia

Asexual cycle

Mature hyphae (*n*)

Ascogonium

Trichossne

Ascospores (*n*)

Antheridium

8 celled stage

Mitosis

Plasmogamy

4 nucleate stage
formation of
ascospores

Sexual cycle

Meiosis

Ascogenous hyphae (*n+n*)

Karyogamy

Formation of
ascogeneous
(crozier) hook

Figure 5.9 Life cycle of an ascomycete.

Figure 5.10 Baker's yeast, *Saccharomyces cerevisiae*. The ascospores of this unicellular ascomycete are characteristically spheroidal or ellipsoidal in shape.

Figure 5.11 Close-up of the parasitic ascomycete, *Hypoxylon*, showing imbedded perithecia.
1. Perithecium   2. Hymenium

Figure 5.12 Parasitic ascomycete, *Dibotryon morbosum*, on a branch of a chokecherry, *Prunus virginiana*.
1. Chokecherry stem   2. Fungus

Figure 5.13 Cleistothecuium (ascocarp or ascoma) of the ascomycete *Penicillium*.
1. Cleistothecium
2. Hyphae

Peziza repanda   *Monilinia fructicola*   *Morchella esculenta*   *Helvella*

Figure 5.14 Fruiting bodies (ascocarps or ascoma) of common ascomycetes. *Peziza repanda* is a common woodland cup fungus. *Monilinia fructicola* is an important plant pathogen causing brown rot of fruit. *Morchella esculenta* is a common edible morel. *Helvella* is sometimes known as a saddle fungus since the fruiting body is thought by some to resemble a saddle.
1. Pit of fruit

(a)   100X

(b)   250X

Figure 5.15 Ascomycete, *Claviceps purpurea.*
(a) Longitudinal section through stroma showing ascocarps (ascoma). (b)Enlargement of three perithecia. This fungus causes serious plant diseases and is toxic to humans.

1. Perithecia
2. Stroma within multiple perithecia

3. Perithecia containing asci
4. Ostiole

430X

Figure 5.16 Section through the hymenial layer of the apothecium of *Peziza*, showing asci with ascospores.
1. Hymenial layer
2. Ascus with ascospores

3. Ascocarp (ascoma) mycelium

3X

Figure 5.17 Section through an ascocarp (ascoma) of the morel, *Morchella.* True morels are prized for their excellent flavor.
1. Convoluted fruiting body
2. Hollow "stalk"

3. Hymenium

800X   1200X

Figure 5.18 Scanning electron micrographs of the powdery mildew, *Erysiphe graminis*, on the surface of wheat. As the mycelium develops, it produces spores (conidia) that give a powdery appearance to the wheat.
1. Conidia
2. Wheat host

3. Hyphae of the fungus

Photograph courtesy of: James V. Allen

1800X

Figure 5.19 Scanning electron micrograph of a germinating spore (conidium) of the powdery mildew, *Erysiphe graminis.* The spore develops into a mycelium that penetrates the epidermis and then spreads over the host plant producing a powdery appearance.

Figure 5.20 Fungus *Penicillium* causes economic damage as a mold but is also the source of important antibiotics. (a) A colony of *Penicillium,* and (b) a closeup of a conidiophore with chains of asexual spores (conidia) at the end.

  1. Conidia   2. Conidiophore   3. Conidia

Figure 5.21 Common mold, *Aspergillus.*

  1. Conidia (spores)   3. Cleistothecium
  2. Conidiophore   4. Hyphae

Figure 5.22 Common mold, *Aspergillus.*

  1. Conidia   2. Conidiophores

Figure 5.23 Closeup of sporangia of the mold, *Aspergillus.* The conidia, or spores, of this genus are produced in a characteristic radiate pattern.

  1. Conidia (spores)   3. Developing conidiophore
  2. Conidiophore

Figure 5.24 Electron micrograph of an *Aspergillus* spore. Note the rodlet pattern on the spore wall.

Photograph courtesy of: James V. Allen

Phylum Basidiomycota - mushrooms, toadstools, rusts, and smuts

Polyporus

Hericium

Coriolus

Astreus

Coprinus

Amanita

Cortinarius

Ananita

Nidularia

Boletus

Figure 5.25 Representative basidocarps (basidiomas or fruiting bodies) of basidiomycetes.

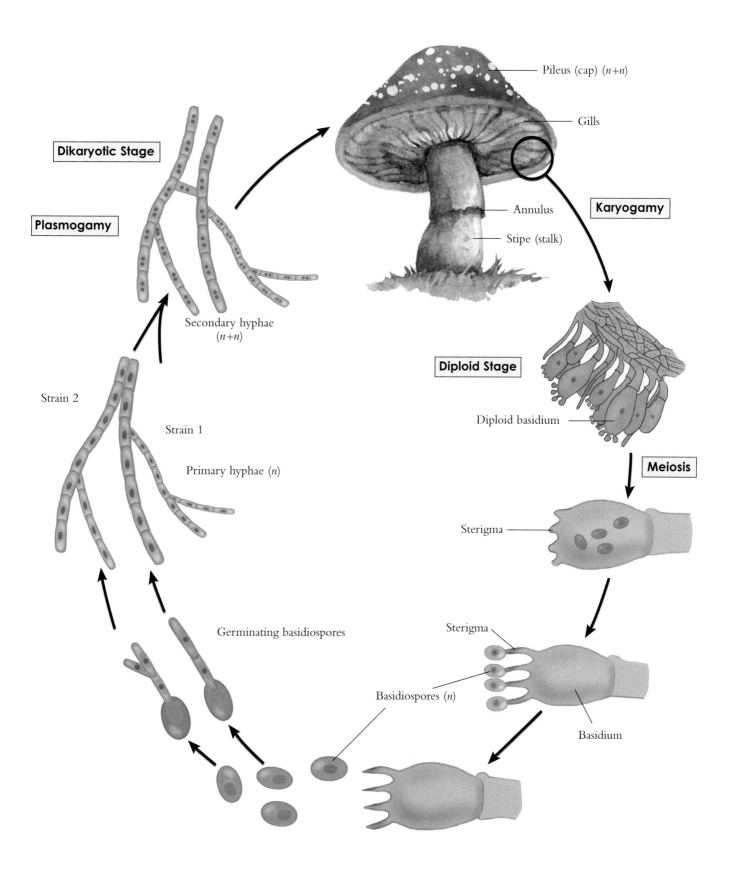

Figure 5.26 Life cycle of a "typical" basidiomycete (mushroom).

(a)   (b)   (c)   (d)

Figure 5.27 Structure of a mushroom. (a) An inferior view with the annulus intact, (b) an inferior view with the annulus removed to show the gills, (c) a lateral view, and (d) a longitudinal section.

1. Pileus (cap)   4. Stipe (stalk)   7. Pileus (cap)
2. Veil   5. Annulus   8. Gills
3. Gills   6. Stipe (stalk)

Figure 5.28 Basidiomycete puffballs growing on a decaying log.

Figure 5.29 Herbarium specimen of the wood fungus, *Stropharia semiglobata*. Growing on decaying wood and other organic matter, basidiomycetes are important decomposers in forest communities.

(a)   40X   (b)   430X

Figure 5.30 Gills of the mushroom *Coprinus*. (a) A closeup of several gills, and (b) a closeup of a single gill.

1. Hyphae comprising the gills   4. Immature basidia   7. Basidiospore
2. Gill   5. Gill (comprised of hyphae)
3. Basidiospores   6. Sterigma

Basidiospores germinate on barberry leaf

Basidiospores (*n*)

Carried to barberry where they germinate

Basidium

Meiosis

Germinating teliospore

Teliospores (2*n*) in telium on wheat plant

Karyogamy

Wheat stem with teliosporangia

Late season

Teliosporangium

Pycnium (spermagonium) with receptive hyphae and spermatia

Barberry plant

Plasmogamy

Aecium with aeciospores (*n+n*)

Urediniosporangium

Urediniospores (*n+n*)

Reinfect wheat plant

Early season

Wheat stem with uredinosporangia

Close-up of wheat plant with urediniosporangia contaning urediniospores (uredospores)

Figure 5.31 Life cycle of wheat rust, *Puccinia graminis.*

240X

Figure 5.32 Wheat rust, *Puccinia graminis*, pycnidium on barberry leaf.
1. Barberry leaf   2. Pycnidium

240X

Figure 5.33 *Puccinia graminis*, aecium on barberry leaf.
1. Aecuim   2. Aeciospores

180X

Figure 5.34 Uredium of *Puccinia* on wheat leaf.
1. Uredium   2. Uredospore

Figure 5.35 Black stem wheat rust, *Puccinia graminis*, on the lower surface of barberry leaves.
1. Clusters of aecia

Figure 5.36 Corn plant, *Zea mays*, infected by the smut *Ustilago maydis*, which destroyed the fruit (ear).
1. Corn ear destroyed by the fungus
2. Corn stalk

Figure 5.37 Smut-infected brome grass. The grains have been destroyed by the smut fungus.

Photo courtesy of James V. Allen

2000X

Figure 5.38 Scanning electron micrograph of teliospores of a wheat smut fungus.

Lichens (symbiotic associations of fungi and algae)

Figure 5.39 Lichens are often separated informally on the basis of their form. (a) Crustose lichen, (b) foliose lichen, and (c) fruticose lichen.

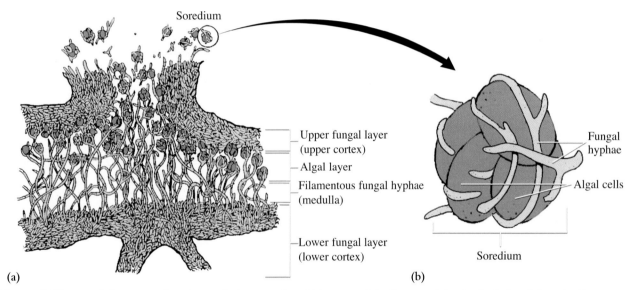

Figure 5.40 Many lichens reproduce by producing soredia, which are small bodies containing both algal and fungal cells. (a) Lichen thallus, and (b) soredium.

Figure 5.41 Transverse section through a lichen thallus.
1. Algal cells   2. Fungal hyphae

Figure 5.42 Lichen thallus consist of distinct algal and fungal layers. This transverse section of a lichen thallus clearly shows these layers.
1. Upper fungal layer (upper cortex)
2. Algal layer
3. Loose filamentous fungal hyphae (medulla)
4. Lower fungal layer (lower cortex)

125X

Figure 5.43 Transverse section through a lichen thallus.
1. Fungal hyphae   3. Lower cortex
2. Medulla   4. Algal layer (upper cortex)

Figure 5.44 Foliose lichen of the bark of a tree.
1. Lichen   2. Bark

Figure 5.45 Folios lichens growing on sandstone in an arid southern Utah environment.

Figure 5.46 Crustose lichens growing in the Southwest.

Figure 5.47 Cryptogamic soil replete with lichens. Lichen in such habitats contribute to soil stability.
1. Lichen

Figure 5.48 Foliose and crustose lichens on volcanic stones in Hawaii.
1. Foliose lichen   2. Crustose lichen

Plants are photosynthetic, multicellular eukaryotes. *Cellulose* in their cell walls provides protection and rigidity, while the *pores* or *stomata,* and *cuticle* of stems and leaves regulate gas exchange. Mitosis and meiosis are characteristic of all plants. Jacketed sex organs, called *gametangia,* protect the gametes and embryos from desiccation. Most plants have heteromorphic alternation of generations with distinctive haploid *gametophyte* and diploid *sporophyte* forms. Photosynthetic cells within plants contain *chloroplasts* with the pigments chlorophyll *a,* chlorophyll *b,* and a variety of carotenoids. Carbohydrates are produced by plants and stored in the form of starch.

Reproduction in seed plants is well adapted to a land existence. The conifers produce their seeds in protective *cones,* and the angiosperms produce their seeds in protective *fruits.* In the life cycle of a conifer, such as a pine, the mature *sporophyte* (tree) has female cones which produce *megaspores* that develop into the female gametophyte generation, and male cones which produce *microspores* that develop into the male gametophyte generation (mature pollen grains). Following fertilization, immature sporophyte generations are present in seeds located on the female cones. The female cone opens and the *seeds* (pine nuts) disperse to the ground and germinate if the conditions are right. Reproduction in angiosperms is similar to gymnosperms except that the angiosperm pollen and ovules are produced in flowers, rather than in cones and a fruit is formed.

Table 6.1 Some Representatives of Plantea

Phyla and Representative Kinds	Characteristics
Bryophyta — liverworts, hornworts, and mosses	Flattened and waxy leaflike cuticles that lack vascular tissue; rootlike rhizomes supporting rhizoids; homosporous
Psilotophyta (Psilophyta) — wisk ferns	True roots and leaves are absent, but vascular tissue present; rhizome and rhizoids present
Lycophyta (Lycopodiophyta) — clubmosses and quillworts	Sporangia borne on sporophylls; homosporous (bisexual gametophyte); many are epiphytes
Sphenophyta (Equisetophyta) — horsetails	Epidermis embedded with silica; tips of stems bear conelike structures containing sporangia; most homosporous
Pterophyta (Polypodiophyta) — ferns	Nonseed producing, vascular plants; fronds as leaves, underground rhizome as roots; homosporous
Cycadophyta — cycads	Heterosporous, pollen and seed cones borne of different plants; large pith
Ginkgophyta — ginkgo	Deciduous, fan-shaped leaves; seed-producing; heterosporous
Coniferophyta (Pinophyta) — conifers	Woody plants that produce their seeds in air spaces, and the stoma are sunken
Anthophyta (Magnoliophyta) — angiosperms (monocots and dicots)	Flowering plants that produce their seeds enclosed in fruit; heterosporous; most are free-living, some are saprophytic or parasitic

Table 6.2 Some Representatives of the Phylum Bryophyta

Phyla and Representative Kinds	Characteristics
Hepatophyta — liverworts	Flat or leafy gametophytes; single-celled rhizoids; simple sporophytes and elaters present; stomata and columella absent
Antherocophyta — hornworts	Flat, lobed gametophytes; more complex sporophytes with stomata; pseudoelaters and columella present
Bryophyta — mosses	Leafy gametophytes, multicellular rhizoids; sporophytes with stomata, columella, peristome teeth and/or operculum present

Phylum Hepatophyta - liverworts

Lepidozia   *Blepharostoma*   *Plectocolea*

Figure 6.1 Illustration of three genera of leafy liverworts, showing the gametophyte with an attached sporophyte. The perianth contains the archegonium and the developing sporophyte.

Figure 6.2 Sporophyte plants attached to gametophytes of the liverwort *Conocephalum*.

Figure 6.3 Liverwort *Calopegia*. A gametophyte plant showing the "leafy" thallus.

Figure 6.4 Gemmae cups of the liverwort *Lunaria*.

110X

Figure 6.5 Sporophyte (capsule) of the leafy liverwort, *Pelia*.

  1. Capsule   2. Sporogenous tissue

430X

Figure 6.6 Capsule from the leafy liverwort, *Pelia*, in longitudinal view.

  1. Spores   2. Elaters

Antheridiophore

Male gametophyte
with receptacles

Antheridium

Transverse section through
male receptacle showing
antheridia

Sperm

Meiospores

Meiosis

Archegoniophore

Female gametophyte
with receptacles

Transverse section through
female receptacle showing
archegonia

Sperm

Foot

Seta (stalk)

Capsule

Meiospores

Elaters

Archegonium

Muture sporophyte

Young embryo

Fertilization

Archegonium

Zygote

Figure 6.7 Life cycle of the thalloid liverwort, *Marchantia*.

Figure 6.8 *Marchantia* with prominent male antheridial receptacles.
1. Antheridial receptacle
2. Gametophyte thallus

Figure 6.9 Dorsal view of a female gametophyte of the liverwort *Marchantia*, showing archegonial receptacles.
1. Archegonial receptacles

Figure 6.10 *Marchantia* gametophyte plants with prominent gemmae cupules.
1. Gemmae cup with gemmae

Figure 6.11 Transverse section through a gemmae capule of *Marchantia*.
1. Gemmae capule   2. Gemmae

Figure 6.12 Lateral view of the liverwort *Marchantia* showing rhiziods.
1. Rhizoids

Photo courtesy of James V. Allen

1000X

Figure 6.13 Scanning electron micrograph of the thallus of *Marchantia*.
1. Air pore

Figure 6.14 (a) Archegonial receptacle of a liverwort, *Marchantia*, in a longitudinal section. (b) Archegonium with egg.

1. Archegonial receptacle
2. Eggs
3. Neck of archegonium
4. Base of archegonium
5. Egg
6. Venter of archegonium
7. Neck canal
8. Neck of archegonium

Figure 6.15 Young sporophyte of *Marchantia*.

1. Young embryo

Figure 6.16 Young sporophyte of *Marchantia*, in longitudinal section.

1. Foot
2. Seta (stalk)
3. Capsule
4. Sporogenous tissue (*2n*)
5. Enlarged archegonium (calyptra)
6. Neck of archegonium

Figure 6.17 Immature and mature sporophytes.

1. Foot
2. Seta (stalk)
3. Sporangium (capsule)
4. Spores (*n*) and elaters (*2n*)

Figure 6.18 (a) Male receptacle with antheridia of a liverwort, *Marchantia*, in a longitudinal section. (b) Antheridial head showing a developing antheridium.

1. Antheridia
2. Spermatogenous tissue
3. Antheridium

Phylum Antherocophyta - hornworts

Sporophyte

Gametophyte

(a)

Sporophyte

Gametophyte

(b)

Figure 6.19 Comparison of the sporophytes and gametophytes of (a) the liverwort, *Marchantia*, and (b) the hornwort, *Anthoceros*.

Figure 6.20 Longitudinal section of a portion of the sporophyte of the hornwort, *Anthoceros*.

1. Meristematic region of sporophyte
2. Foot
3. Gametophyte

Figure 6.21 Longitudinal section of the sporangium of a sporophyte from the hornwort, *Anthoceros*.

1. Spores
2. Elater-like structures (pseudoelaters)
3. Capsule

Figure 6.22 Transverse section through the capsule of a sporophyte of the hornwort, *Anthoceros*.

1. Epidermis
2. Photosynthetic tissue
3. Columella
4. Tetrad of spores
5. Pore (stomate)

Phylum Bryophyta - mosses

Figure 6.23 *Sphanuum* bog in the high Rocky Mountains. This lake has nearly been filled in with dense growths of *Sphagnum*.

Figure 6.24 Researcher examining a plug from a core taken from a *Sphagnum* bog. Examining this sample will provide a glimpse of the past environment due to preserved pollen grains and diatoms.

Figure 6.25 Gametophyte plants of peat moss, *Sphagnum*, showing attached sporophytes.
  1. Sporophyte   3. Gametophytes
  2. Pseudopodium

Figure 6.26 Longitudinal section of *Sphagnum* gametophyte showing antheridia.
  1. "leaf"
  2. Antheridium

Figure 6.27 (a) Gametophyte of peat moss, *Sphagnum*. (b) A magnified view of a "leaf", showing the dead cell chambers that aid in water storage.
  1. Leaves   2. Photosynthetic cells   3. Dead cells

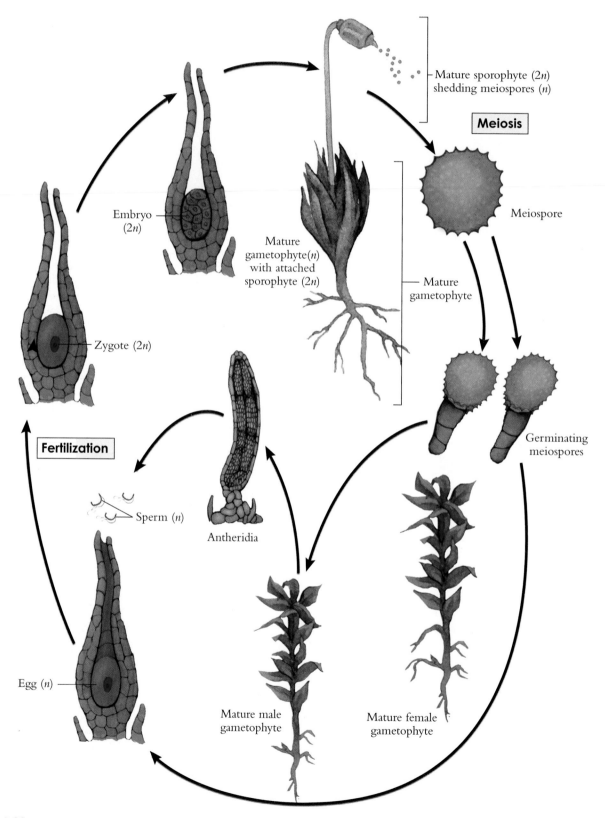

Figure 6.28 Life cycle of a moss (Bryophyta).

Figure 6.29 Habitat of a moss growing in a wooded environment.
1. Moss
2. Vascular plants

Figure 6.30 Moss-covered sand stone. under dry conditions, mosses may become dormant and lose their intense green.
1. Stone   2. Moss

Figure 6.31 Moss growing on the shaded side of a volcanic rock.
1. Moss
2. Lichen

Figure 6.32 Some mosses are aquatic or require very wet environments.

Figure 6.33 Protonemata and bulbills of a moss. The bulbills will grow to become a new gametophyte plant.
1. Protonema
2. Bulbill

Figure 6.34 Gametophyte plants with sporophyte plants attached.
1. Capsule of sporophyte   3. Gametophyte
2. Stalk (seta)

Figure 6.35 Longitudinal section of the archegonial head of the moss *Mnium*. The paraphyses are non-reproductive filaments that support the archegonia.

1. Egg
2. Neck
3. Paraphyses
4. Venter
5. Stalk

Figure 6.36 Longitudinal section of the antheridial head of the moss *Mnium*.

1. Spermatogenous tissue
2. Sterile jacket layer
3. Stalk
4. Male gametophyte (*n*)
5. Paraphyses (sterile filaments)
6. Antheridium (*n*)

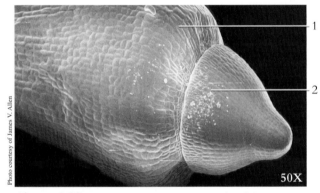

Figure 6.37 Close up of *Mnium*.

1. Antheridium (*n*)
2. Speratogenous tissue
3. Paraphes

Figure 6.38 Scanning electron micrograph of the sporophyte capsule of the moss *Mnium*.

1. Capsule
2. Operculum

Photo courtesy of James V. Allen

Photo courtesy of James V. Allen

Figure 6.39 Scanning electron micrograph of the peristome of the moss *Mnium*. The operculum is absent in the specimen.

1. Peristone
2. Capsule

Figure 6.40 Scanning electron micrograph of the peristome of the moss *Mnium*.

1. Outer teeth of peristome
2. Inner teeth of peristome
3. Capsule

Phylum Psilotophyta (Psilophyta) - whisk ferns

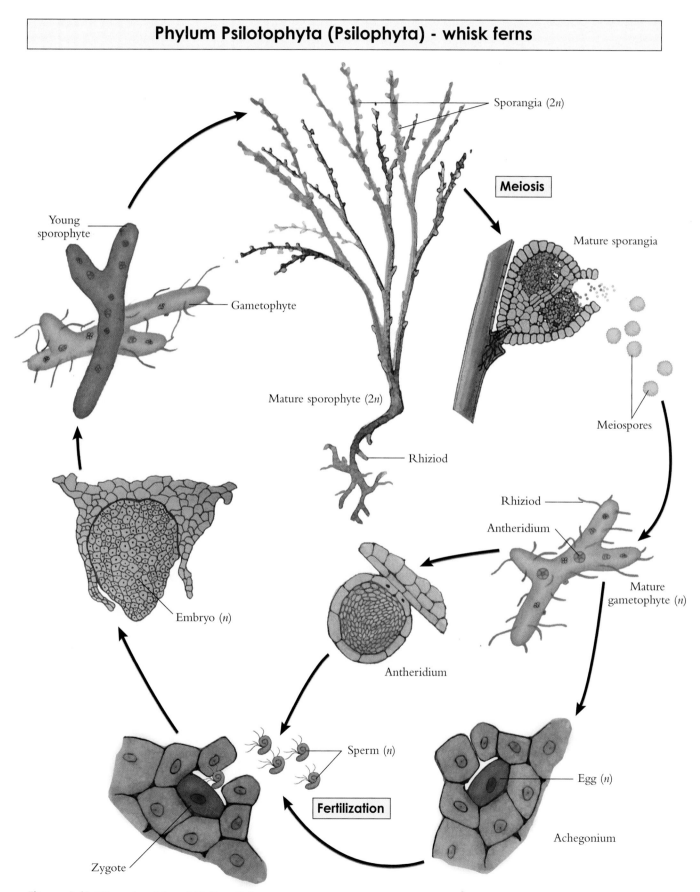

Figure 6.41 Life cycle of the whisk fern, *Psilotum*.

Figure 6.42 Whisk fern, *Psilotum nudum,* is a simple vascular plant lacking true leaves and roots.

Figure 6.43 Branches (axes) of *Psilotum nuda.*
1. Rhizome   2. Aerial stem

Figure 6.44 Sporophyte of the whisk fern, *Psilotum nudum.* The axes of the sporophyte support sporangia (synangia), which produce the spores.
1. Branch (axis)   2. Sporangia (synangia)

Figure 6.45 Scanning electron micrograph of a ruptured synangium (3 fused sporangia) of *Psilotum,* which is spilling spores.
1. Sporangium (often   2. Axis   3. Spores
   called synagia)

Figure 6.46 Longitudinal section through a stem and sporangium (synagium) of *Psilotum.*
1. Axis   2. Sporangia (synangium)

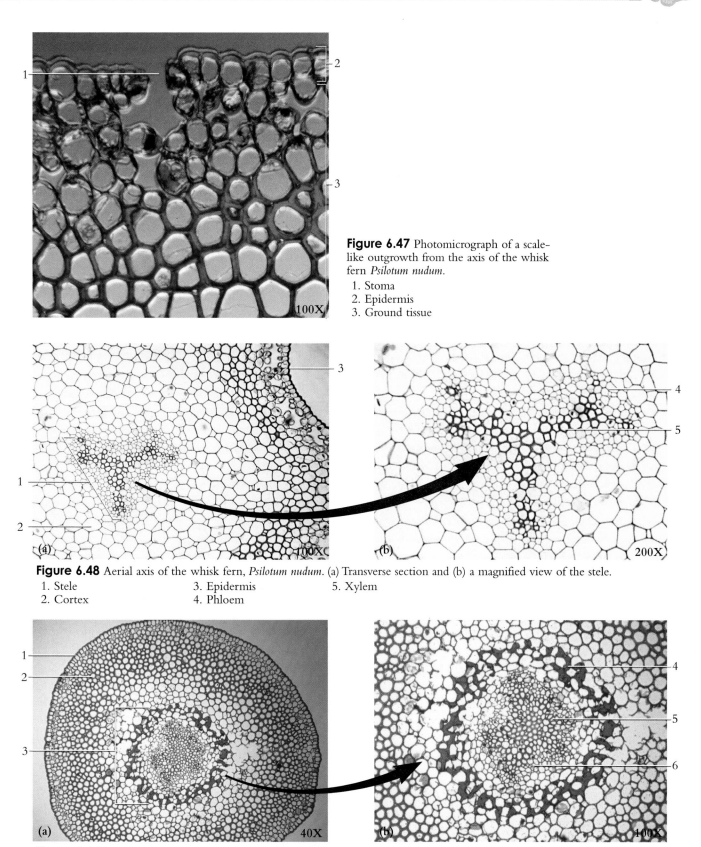

Figure 6.47 Photomicrograph of a scale-like outgrowth from the axis of the whisk fern *Psilotum nudum*.
1. Stoma
2. Epidermis
3. Ground tissue

Figure 6.48 Aerial axis of the whisk fern, *Psilotum nudum*. (a) Transverse section and (b) a magnified view of the stele.
1. Stele   3. Epidermis   5. Xylem
2. Cortex   4. Phloem

Figure 6.49 Aerial axis of the whisk fern, *Tmesipteris*. The genus *Tmesipteris* is restricted to distribution in Australia, New Zealand, New Caledonia, and other South Pacific islands. (a) Axis arising from the aerial axis and (b) a magnified view of the stele.
1. Epidermis   3. Stele   5. Xylem
2. Cortex   4. Endodermis   6. Phloem

Lycophyta (Lycopodiophyta) - club mosses, quillworts, and spike mosses

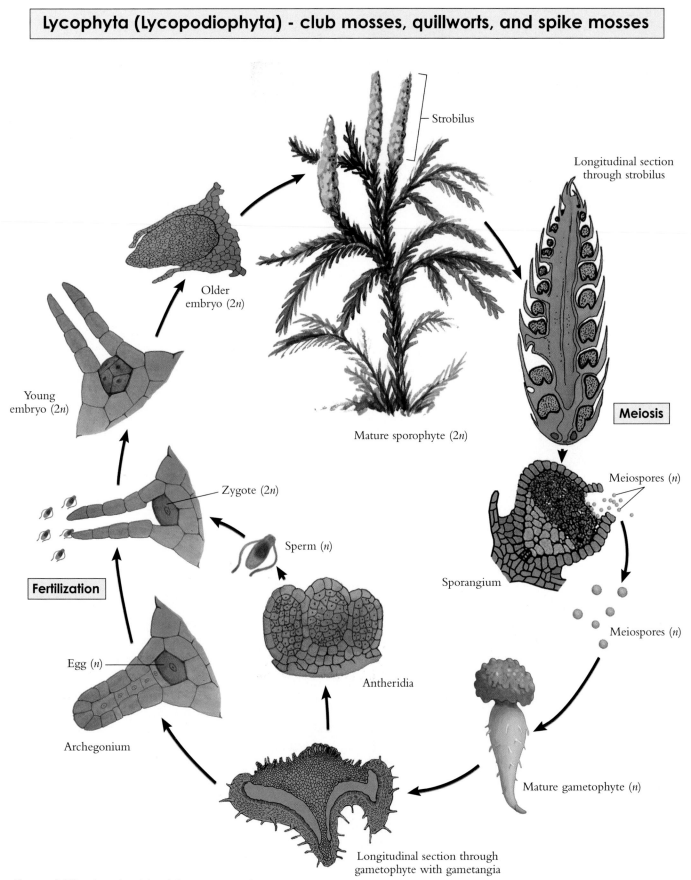

Figure 6.50 Life cycle of the club moss, *Lycopodium*.

Figure 6.51 Specimen of a lycopod, *Lycopodium clavatum.*
Lycopodium occurs from the arctic to the tropics.
1. Strobilus
2. Stem

Figure 6.52 Enlargement of a specimen of *Lycopodium,*
showing branch tip with sporangia.
1. Sporangia
2. Sporophylls (leaves with attached sporangia)

Figure 6.53 (a) Transverse view of an aerial stem of the club moss, *Lycopodium.* (b) A magnified view of the stele.

1. Leaves (microphylls)	4. Epidermis	7. Phloem
2. Stele	5. Leaf trace	8. Pericycle
3. Cortex	6. Xylem	9. Endodermis

Figure 6.54 (a) Longitudinal section of the strobilus (cone) of the club moss
Lycopodium, and (b) a magnified view of the strobilus showing sporangia.
1. Sporangia   3. Sporangium
2. Sporophyll   4. Sporophyll

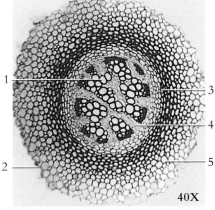

Figure 6.55 Transverse section of a
rhizome of *Lycopodium.* The rhizome
of *Lycopodium* is similar to an aerial
stem, but it lacks the microphylls.
1. Xylem   4. Phloem
2. Epidermis   5. Cortex
3. Endodermis

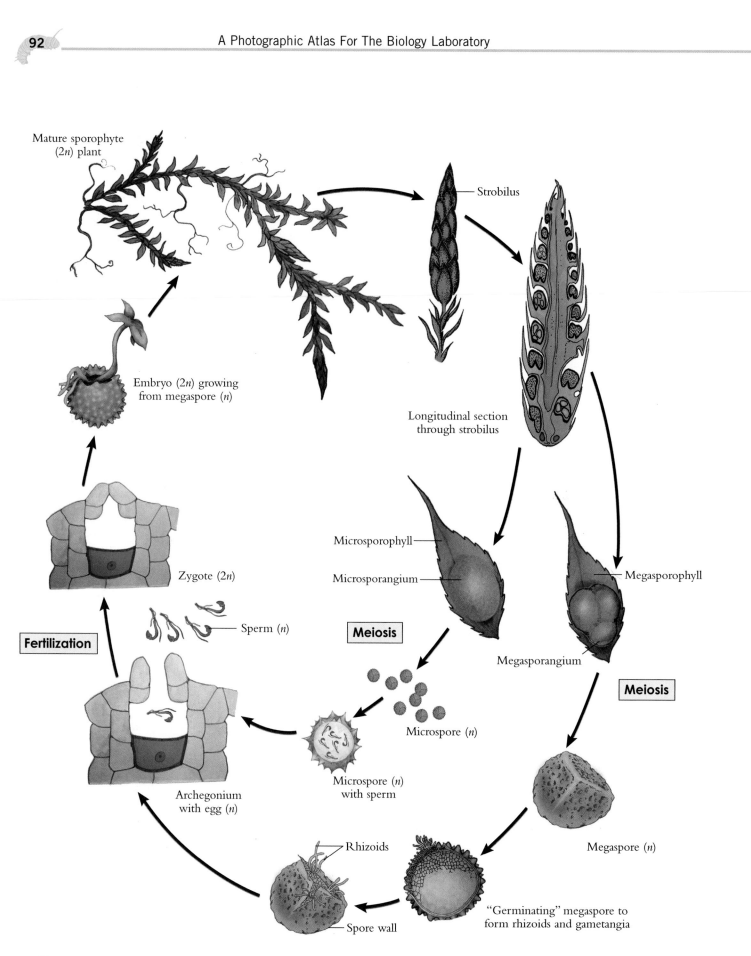

Mature sporophyte (2n) plant

Strobilus

Longitudinal section through strobilus

Microsporophyll

Microsporangium

Megasporophyll

Megasporangium

Meiosis

Meiosis

Embryo (2n) growing from megaspore (n)

Microspore (n)

Zygote (2n)

Fertilization

Sperm (n)

Microspore (n) with sperm

Megaspore (n)

Archegonium with egg (n)

Rhizoids

"Germinating" megaspore to form rhizoids and gametangia

Spore wall

Figure 6.56 Life cycle of *Selaginella*.

Figure 6.57 Young sporophyte plant of *Selaginlla* attached to the gametophyte.
1. Megaspore
2. Leaves

Figure 6.58 Mature *Selaginella* sporophyte.

Figure 6.59 Section through the megaspore, *Selaginella*.
1. Spore wall
2. Megagametophyte tissue

Figure 6.60 Herbarium specimen of a quillwort, *Isoetes melanopoda*. The aquatic quillwort has a small underground stem and quill-like leaves. It is heterosporous and the megasporangia and microsporangia are located at the bases of diffeent leaves.

Figure 6.61 Longitudinal section of *Isoetes*, an aquatic, lycopod that superficially resembles grass.
1. Megasporangium   3. Corm (stem)
2. Microsporangium

Figure 6.62 Longitudinal view of the surface of the fossil lycophyte *Lepidodendron*, a common lycopod from perhaps 300 million years ago.

Figure 6.63 Longitudinal section through a fossil strobilus of the lycophyte *Lepidostrobus*, from approximately 300 million years ago.
1. Sporangium   2. Sporangenous tissue

Phylum Sphenophyta (Equisetophyta) - horsetails

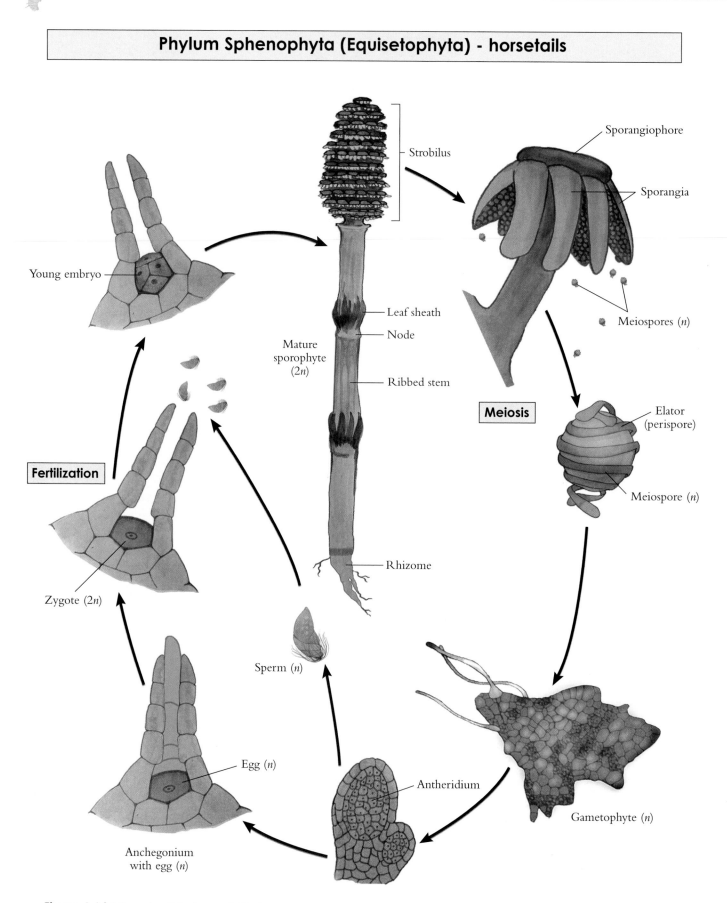

Figure 6.64 Life cycle of the horsetail, *Equisetum*.

Figure 6.65 *Equisetum* plants in natural habitat.

Figure 6.66 Close-up of several stems of *Equisetum*.

Figure 6.67 Stem of *Equisetum* showing a prominent leaf sheath at the node.
1. Stem
2. Leaf sheath

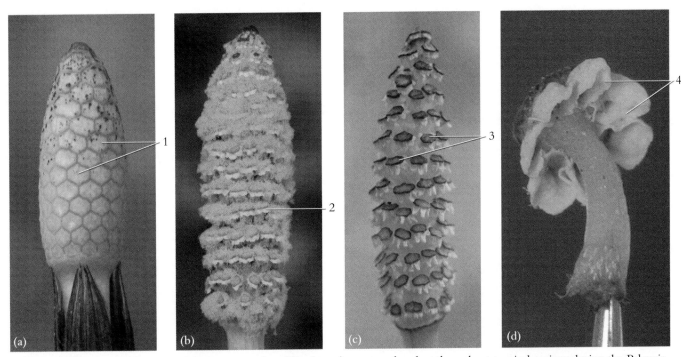

Figure 6.68 Horsetail, *Equisetum*. Numerous species of Equisetophyta were abundant throughout tropical regions during the Palezoic Era, some 300 million years ago. Currently, Equisetophyta are represented by this single genus. The meadow horsetail, *Equisetum*, showing (a) an immature strobilus, (b) a mature strobilus, shedding spores (c) an open stobilus, and (d) a sporangiophore with its spores released.

1. Sporangiophores
2. Separated sporangiophores revealing sporangia
3. Sporangiophores after spores are shed
4. Open sporangia with spores shed

Figure 6.69 Longitudinal section of the strobilus of *Equisetum*.
1. Sporangiophore   3. Strobilus axis
2. Sporangium

12X

Figure 6.70 Longitudinal section through the strobilus of *Equisetum*.
1. Axis of the strobilus   3. Sporangium
2. Sporangiophore

20X

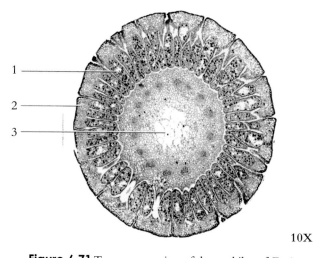

Figure 6.71 Transverse section of the strobilus of *Equisetum*.
1. Sporangium   3. Strobilus axis
2. Sporangiophore

10X

Figure 6.72 Transverse section of the stem of *Equisetum* just above a node.
1. Leaf sheath   3. Branch
2. Main stem

10X

Figure 6.73 Meiospores of *Equisetum*.
1. Meiospore   2. Perisore (elater)

900X

Figure 6.74 Surface longitudinal view of a fossel stem impression of *Calamites* a close relative of *Equisetum;* common perhaps 300 million years ago.
1. Ribbed stem   2. Node

Phylum Pterophyta (Polypodiophyta) - ferns

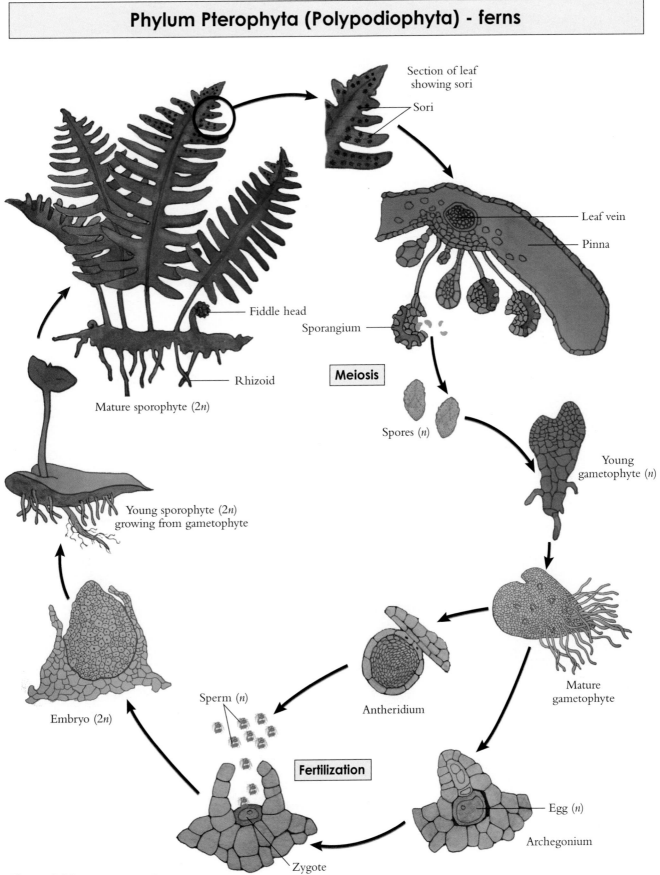

Section of leaf showing sori

Sori

Leaf vein

Pinna

Fiddle head

Sporangium

Meiosis

Rhizoid

Spores (n)

Mature sporophyte (2n)

Young gametophyte (n)

Young sporophyte (2n) growing from gametophyte

Mature gametophyte

Embryo (2n)

Sperm (n)

Antheridium

Fertilization

Egg (n)

Archegonium

Zygote

Figure 6.75 Life cycle of a fern.

Figure 6.76 Water fern, *Azolla*, is a floating fresh-water plant found throughout Europe and the United States. *Azolla* may become bright orange or red during fall.

Figure 6.77 View of a new fern leaf showing circinate venation forming a fiddle-head.

1. Mature leaf   2. Immature leaf (fiddle head)

Figure 6.78 Fronds of the staghorn fern, *Platycerium alcicorne.*

Figure 6.79 Pinnate leaf showing pinnate venation in the leaflets of a fern.

1. Leaf   3. Venation
2. Pinna

Figure 6.80 Leaf of a holly fern, *Phanerophlebia.*

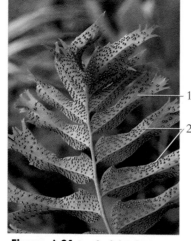

Figure 6.81 Leaf of the fern *Phanerophlebia*, showing sori (groups of sporangia).

1. Pinna
2. Sori

Figure 6.82 Close-up of the fern leaf of *Phanerophlebia* (scale in mm).

1. Sorus with indusium
2. Sorus with indusium shed

Figure 6.83 Holly fern, *Polypodium*. (a) Sori on the undersurface of the pinnae, and (b) a scanning electron micrograph of a sorus.

1. Pinna 2. Sori 3. Annulus 4. Sporangium

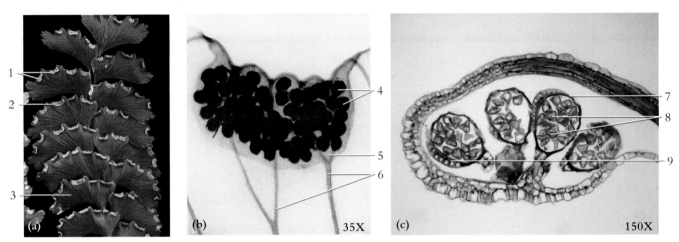

Figure 6.84 Maidenhair fern, *Adiantum*. (a) Pinnae and sori. (b) Magnified view of the tip of a pinna folded under to form a false indusium that encloses the sorus. (c) Sporangia with spores.

1. Sori 3. Pinna 5. False indusium enclosing a sorus 7. Sporangium 9. Annulus
2. False indusium 4. Sporangia with spores 6. Vascular tissue (veins)of the pinna 8. Spores

Figure 6.85 Sorus of a homosporous fern, *Cyrtomium falcatum*.

1. Sporangium ($2n$) 3. Indusium ($2n$) 5. Spores
2. Annulus 4. Pinna tissue

Figure 6.86 Sporangium of the fern *Cyrtomium*, discharging spores.

1. Spore (n) 3. Annulus
2. Lip cell

Figure 6.87 (a) Fern gametophyte showing antheridia, and (b) a magnified view of an archegonium with an egg.
1. Rhizoids
2. Antheridia with sperm
3. Gametophyte (prothallus)
4. Archegonium
5. Egg

Figure 6.88 Fern gametophyte with a young sporophyte attached.
1. Gametophyte   2. Young sporophyte

Figure 6.89 Maidenhair fern, *Adiantum capillus*, indigenous to Hawaii.

Figure 6.90 Transverse section of the stem of *Polytrichum*.
1. Epidermus
2. Leaf trace (vascular tissue)
3. Cortex

Figure 6.91 Transverse section of a fertile pinnule (soro-carp) of the water fern, *Marsilea*, which is one of the two living orders of heterosporous ferns.
1. Microsporangum with microspores
2. Megasporangia with megaspores

Phylum Cycadophyta - cycads

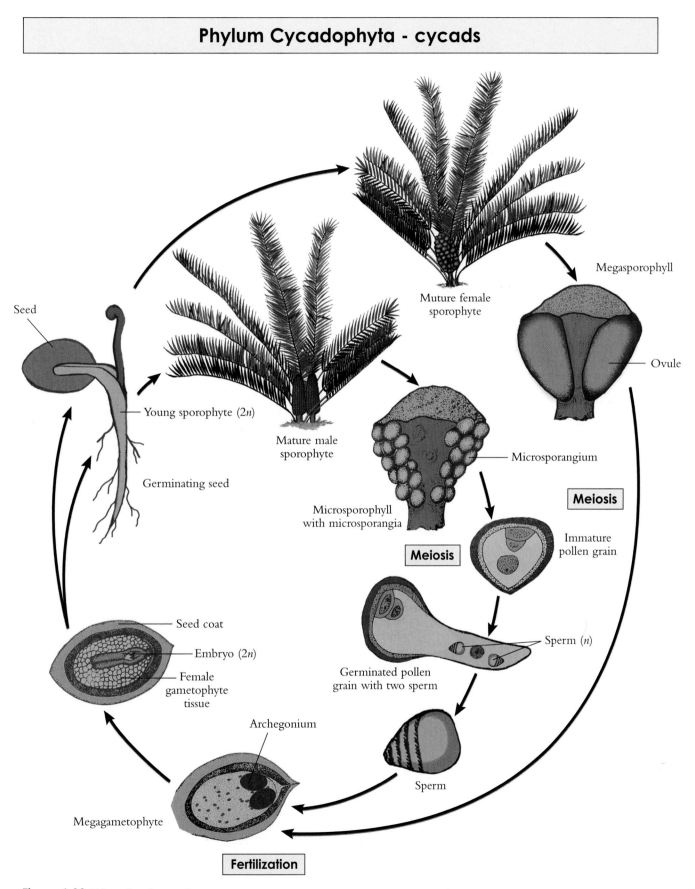

Megasporophyll

Muture female
sporophyte

Ovule

Seed

Young sporophyte (2n)

Mature male
sporophyte

Microsporangium

Germinating seed

Microsporophyll
with microsporangia

Meiosis

Meiosis

Immature
pollen grain

Sperm (n)

Germinated pollen
grain with two sperm

Seed coat

Embryo (2n)

Female
gametophyte
tissue

Archegonium

Sperm

Megagametophyte

Fertilization

Figure 6.92 Life cycle of a cycad.

Figure 6.93 *Cycas revoluta.* Cycads were abundant during the Mesozoic Era. Currently, there are 10 living genera, with about 100 species, that are mainly found in tropical and subtropical areas. The trunk of many cycads is densely covered with petioles of shed leaves.

Figure 6.94 *Cycas revoluta* showing a female cone.
1. Cone

Figure 6.95 *Cycas revoluta* showing a close up view of a female cone with developing seeds.
1. Seeds　　2. Megasporophyll

Figure 6.96 *Cycas revoluta* showing a close up view of a female cone duing seed dispersal.
1. Seeds

Figure 6.97 Male cone of *Cycas revoluta.*
1. Cone

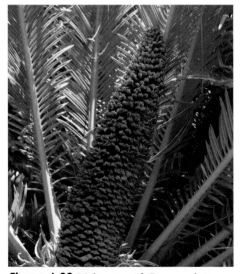

Figure 6.98 Male cone of *Cycas revoluta* after release of pollen.

Figure 6.99 Young plant of the cycad *Zamia pumila*. Found in Florida, this cycad is the only species native to the United States. The rootstocks and stems of this plant were an important source of food for some Native Americans.

Figure 6.100 Microsporangiate cones of the cycad *Zamia*.

Figure 6.101 *Encephalartos villosus*, a non-threatened species of cycad native to southeastern Africa.

Figure 6.102 Maturing female cone of *Encephalartos villosus*.

Figure 6.103 Transverse section of the leaf of the cycad *Zamia*.
  1. Upper epidermis
  2. Palisade mesophyl
  3. Vascular bundle (vein)

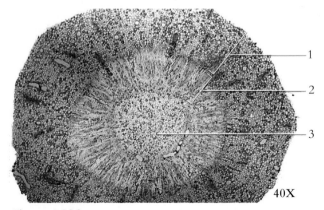

Figure 6.104 Transverse section of the stem of the cycad *Zamia*.
  1. Cortex   3. Pith
  2. Vascular tissue

Figure 6.105 Microsporangiate cone of the cycad, *Zamia*. The cone on the right (b) is longitudinally sectioned.
1. Microsporangia   2. Microsporophyll

Figure 6.106 Transverse sections of (a) a microsporangiate cone, and (b) a megasporangiate cone of the cycad *Zamia*.
1. Ovule   3. Microsporangia
2. Megasporophyll   4. Microsporophyll

Figure 6.107 Transverse section of a microsporophyll of the cycad *Cycas*. Note the microsporangia develop on the undersurface of the microsporophyll.
1. Microsporophyll
2. Microsporangia

Figure 6.108 Megasporophyll and ovules of *Cycas revoluta*.
1. Megasporophyll   2. Ovules

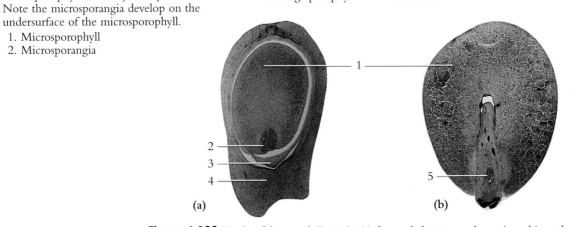

Figure 6.109 Ovule of the cycad *Zamia*. In (a) the ovule has two archegonia and is ready to be fertilized. In (b) the ovule has been fertilized and contains an embryo. The seed coat has been removed from this specimen.
1. Female gametophyte   4. Integument (will become seed coat)
2. Archegonium   5. Embryo
3. Megasporangium (nucellus)

Phylum Ginkgophyta - ginkgo

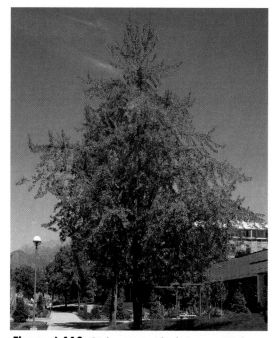

Figure 6.110 *Ginkgo*, or maidenhair tree, *Ginkgo biloba*. Consisting of a central trunk with lateral branches, a mature *Ginkgo* grows to 100 feet tall. Native to China, *Ginkgo biloba* has been introduced into countries with temperate climates throughout the world as an interesting and hardy ornamental tree.

Figure 6.112 Fossil *Ginkgo* leaf impression from Paleocene sediment. This specimen was found in Morton County, North Dakota.

Figure 6.114 Branch of a *Ginkgo* tree supporting a mature seed.

  1. Long shoot   3. Mature seed
  2. Short shoot (spur)

Figure 6.111 Leaf from the *Ginkgo* tree. The fan-shaped leaf is characteristic of this species.

Figure 6.113 As the sole member of the phylum Ginkgophyta, *Ginkgo biloba is a*ble to withstand air polution. Ginkos are often used as ornamental trees within city parks. *Ginkgo biloba* may have the longest genetic lineage among seed plants.

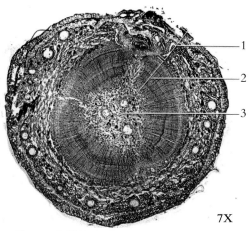

7X

Figure 6.115 Transverse section of a short branch from *Ginkgo biloba*.

  1. Cortex   3. Pith
  2. Vascular tissue

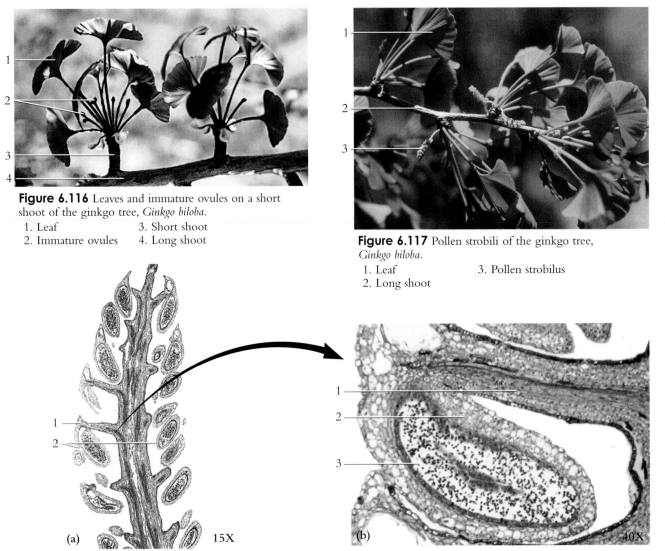

Figure 6.116 Leaves and immature ovules on a short shoot of the ginkgo tree, *Ginkgo biloba.*
1. Leaf
2. Immature ovules
3. Short shoot
4. Long shoot

Figure 6.117 Pollen strobili of the ginkgo tree, *Ginkgo biloba.*
1. Leaf
2. Long shoot
3. Pollen strobilus

(a)   15X   (b)   40X

Figure 6.118 Microsporangiate strobilus of the ginkgo tree. (a) A longitudinal section and (b) a magnified view showing a microsporangium.
1. Sporophyll
2. Microsporangium
3. Pollen

Figure 6.119 Mature seed of *Ginkgo*, hanging from a short shoot of the tree.

Figure 6.120 Mature seed of *Ginkgo* with the outer layer of the seed coat removed, exposing the stony layer of the seed

Figure 6.121 Longitudinal section of an ovule of *Ginkgo* prior to fertilization.
1. Megagametophyte
2. Integument
3. Pollen chamber
4. Nucellus
5. Micropyle

Figure 6.122 Longitudinal section of a seed of *Ginkgo*, with the seed coat removed.
1. Megagametophyte
2. Developing embryo

Coniferophyta (Pinophyta) - conifers

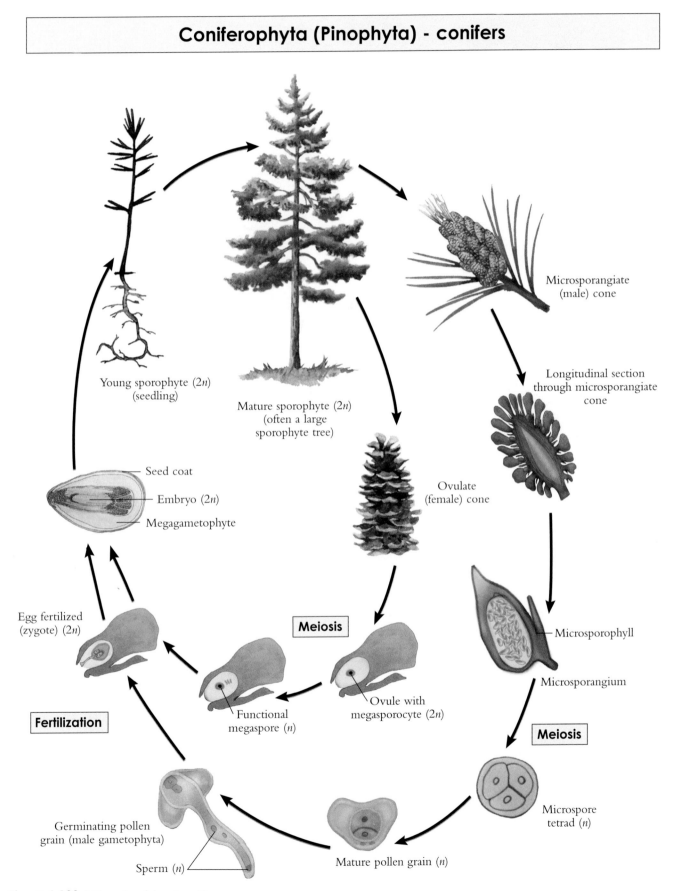

Figure 6.123 Life cycle of the pine, *Pinus*.

Courtesy of *Champion Paper Company, Inc.*

Figure 6.124 Diagram of the tissues in the stem (trunk) of a conifer. The periderm and dead secondary phloem (outer bark) protects the tree against water lost and the infestation of insects and fungi. The cells of the phloem (inner bark) compress and become nonfunctional after a relatively short period. The vascular cambium annually produces new phloem and xylem and accounts for the growth rings in the wood. The secondary xylem is a water transporting layer of the stem and provides structural support to the tree.

1. Outer bark
2. Phloem
3. Cambium
4. Secondary xylem

Courtesy of *Champion Paper Company, Inc.*

Figure 6.125 Stem (trunk) of a pine tree that was harvested in the year 2000 when the tree was 62 years old. The growth rings of a tree indicate environmental conditions that occurred during the tree's life.

1. **1939**—A pine seedling.
2. **1944**—Healthy, undisturbed growth indicated by broad and evenly spaced rings.
3. **1949**—Growth disparity probably due to the falling of a dead tree onto the young healthy six-year old tree. The wider "reaction rings" on the lower side help support the tree.
4. **1959**—The tree is growing straight again, but the narrow rings indicate competition for sunlight and moisture from neighboring trees.
5. **1962**—The surrounding trees are harvested, thus permitting rapid growth once again.
6. **1965**—A burn scar from a fire that quickly scorched the forest.
7. **1977**—Narrow growth rings resulting from a prolonged drought.
8. **1992**—Narrow growth rings, resulting from a sawfly insect infestation, whose larvae eat the needles and buds of many kinds of conifers.

Figure 6.126 Leaves of most species of conifers are needle-shaped such as those of the blue spruce, *Picea pungens* (a). *Araucaria heterophyla,* Norfolk Island pine, however, (b) has awl-shaped leaves, and *Podocarpus* (c) has strap-shaped leaves.

Figure 6.127 Lodgepole pine, *Pinus contorta* Native to northwestern United States. Lodgepole pines grow to 100 feet in height.

Figure 6.128 Enlarged view of the stem of *Pinus* showing tissues following secondary growth.

1. Late secondary xylem (wood)
2. Early secondary xylem (wood)
3. Seondary phloem
4. Vascular cambium
5. Resin duct
6. Periderm
7. Epidermis

Figure 6.129 Radial longitudinal section through the phloem of *Pinus*.

1. Sieve areas on a sieve cell
2. Storage parenchyma
3. Sieve cell

Figure 6.130 Radial longitudinal section through a stem of *Pinus*, cut through the xylem tissue.

1. Ray parenchyma
2. Tracheids
3. Vascular cambium
4. Sieve cells

Figure 6.131 Growth rings in *Pinus*. (a) Transverse section through a stem; and (b) radial longitudinal section through a stem.
1. Early wood   2. Late wood

Figure 6.132 Transverse section of a leaf (needle) of *Pinus*.

1. Stoma	5. Epidermis
2. Endodermis	6. Phloem
3. Resin duct	7. Xylem
4. Photosynthetic mesophyll	8. Transfusion tissue

Figure 6.133 Transverse section through the leaf (needle) of *Pinus*

1. Xylem	5. Sub-stomatal chamber
2. Phloem	6. Resin duct
3. Endodermis	7. Transfusion tissue (surrounding
4. Sunken stoma	vascular tissue)

Figure 6.134 Megasporangiate cones from various species of conifers. (a) Southern hemisphere pine, *Araucaria*; (b) pinyon pine, *Pinus edulis*; and (c) sugar pine, *Pinus lambertiana*. (Not to the same scale.)

Figure 6.135 First-year ovulate cone in *Pinus*.
1. Pollen cones   2. First-year ovulate cone

Figure 6.136 Transeverse section through a first-year ovulate cone in *Pseuotsuga*.
1. Cone scale bracts   2. Immature ovule

(a)   20X   (b)   10X

Figure 6.137 Ovulate cones of a *Pinus*. (a) Transverse section, and (b) longitudinal section.
1. Ovuliferous scale   2. Ovule   3. Cone axis

Figure 6.138 Close up view of a *Pinus* ovule.
1. Nucellus   3. Integument
2. Ovule   4. Cone scale

Figure 6.139 Close up view of an ovule of *Pinus* with pollen grains in the pollen chamber.
1. Nucellus   3. Pollen chamber
2. Pollen grain   4. Integument

Figure 6.140 Microsporangiate cones of a conifer. The staminate cones are at the end of a branch.
1. Needle-like leaves   3. Pollen cone
2. Sporophylls

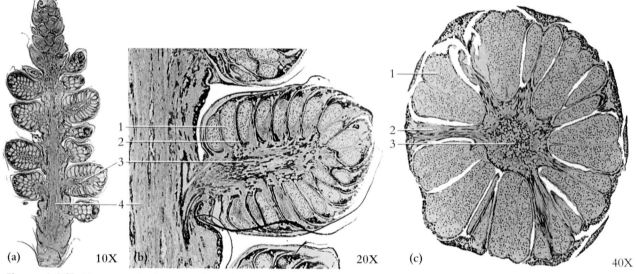

(a)   10X   (b)   20X   (c)   40X

Figure 6.141 (a) Longitudinal section through a branch tip of microsporangiate cones; (b) a longitudinal section through a single cone; and (c) a transverse section through a single cone.
1. Microsporangium   2. Sporophyll   3. Cone axis   4. Branch tip

Figure 6.142 Close up of a microsporangiate cone scale and microsporangiate of *Pinus*.
1. Microsporangium with   2. Microsporophyll
   pollen grains

Photo courtesy of James V. Allen

Figure 6.143 Scanning electron micrograph of a *Pinus* pollen grain with inflated bladder-like wings.
1. Pollen body   2. Wings

Figure 6.144 Close up of an ovulate cone scale in *Pinus*.

1. Ovulate cone scale
2. Mature ovules (wings)
3. Seed (containing embryo within seed coat)

Figure 6.145 Young sporophyte (seedling) of a pine, *Pinus*.

1. Seed coat
2. Seedling leaves (needles)
3. Young stem

Courtesy of *Champion Paper Company, Inc.*

Figure 6.146 Diagram of pinyon pine seed germination producing a young sporophyte. (a) The seeds are protected inside the cone, two seeds formed on each scale. (b) A sectioned seed showing an embryo embedded in the endosperm. (c) The growing embryo splits the shell of the seed, enabling the root to grow toward the soil. (d) As soon as the tiny root tip penetrates and anchors into the soil, water, and nutrients are absorbed. (e) The cotyledons emerge from the seed coat and create a supply of chlorophyll. Now the sporophyte can manufacture its own food from water and nutrients in the soil and carbon dioxide in the air. (f) Growth occurs at the terminal buds at the base of the leaves.

Phylum Anthophyta (Magnoliophyta) – angiosperms: monocots and dicots

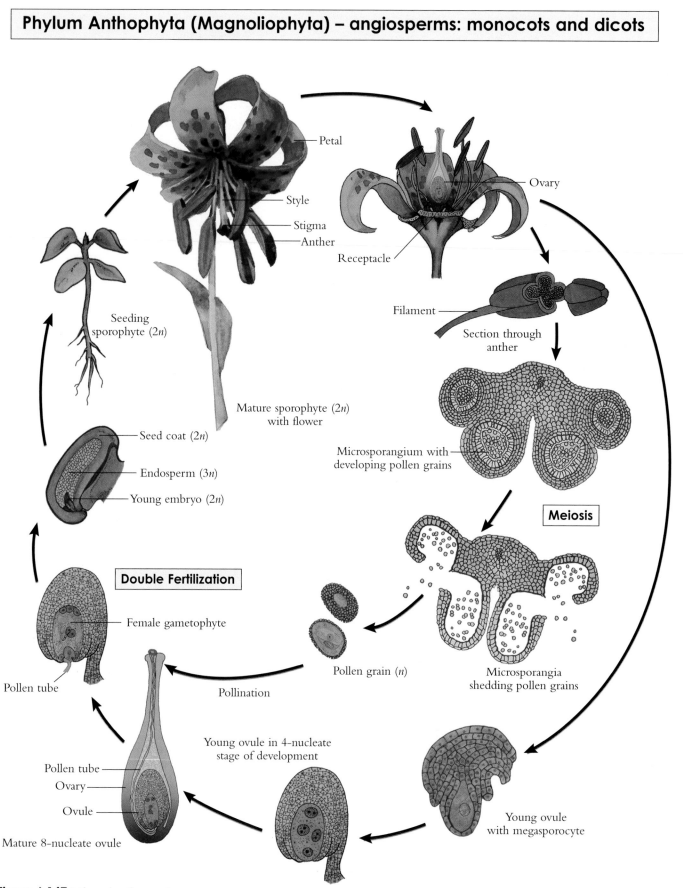

Petal

Style

Stigma

Anther

Ovary

Receptacle

Filament

Section through anther

Seeding sporophyte (2n)

Mature sporophyte (2n) with flower

Microsporangium with developing pollen grains

Meiosis

Seed coat (2n)

Endosperm (3n)

Young embryo (2n)

Double Fertilization

Female gametophyte

Pollen tube

Pollen grain (n)

Pollination

Microsporangia shedding pollen grains

Young ovule in 4-nucleate stage of development

Pollen tube

Ovary

Ovule

Mature 8-nucleate ovule

Young ovule with megasporocyte

Figure 6.147 Life cycle of an angiosperm.

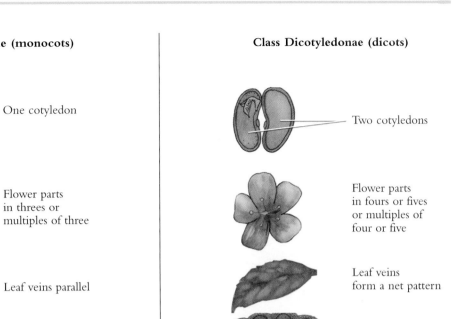

Class Monocotyledonae (monocots)

One cotyledon

Flower parts
in threes or
multiples of three

Leaf veins parallel

Vascular bundles
scattered

Class Dicotyledonae (dicots)

Two cotyledons

Flower parts
in fours or fives
or multiples of
four or five

Leaf veins
form a net pattern

Vascular bundles
arranged in a ring

Some examples of monocots

Wheat

Corn

Cattail

Iris

Some examples of dicots

Water lily

Columbine

Rose

Sunflower

Figure 6.148 Comparison and examples of monocots and dicots.

Roots of Angiosperms

Fibrous root system (grasses)   **Taproot** (shrubs)   **Modified taproot** (carrot)   **Prop roots** (corn)   **Aerial roots** (orchid)

Figure 6.149 Root systems of angiosperms.

Figure 6.150 Root system of an orchid (monocot) (a) showing aerial roots and an avocado (dicot) (b) showing prop roots. Monocot roots are fibrous, with many roots of more or less equal size. Dicots usually have a taproot system, consisting of a long central root with smaller, secondary roots branching from it.

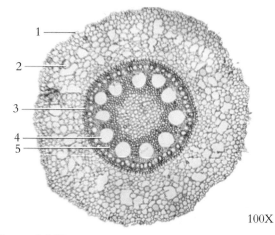

100X

Figure 6.151 Transverse section of the root of the monocot *Smilax*.
1. Epidermis   4. Xylem
2. Cortex   5. Phloem
3. Endodermis

430X

Figure 6.152 Close up of a root of the monocot *Smilax*.
1. Cortex   2. Endodermis
3. Xylem   4. Phloem

Figure 6.153 Prop roots of the corn plant, *Zea mays.*
1. Stem   2. Prop roots

Figure 6.154 Photomicrograph of a young root of wheat, *Triticum*, showing root hairs.

1. Root hair   5. Endodermis
2. Epidermis   6. Primary xylem
3. Stele   7. Primary phloem
4. Cortex

Figure 6.155 Longitudinal section of a willow species showing lateral root formation.
1. Lateral root   3. Cortex
2. Epidermis   4. Vascular tissue

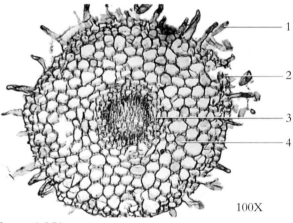

Figure 6.156 Transverse section of the root of a pea plant showing prominent root hairs.
1. Root hair   3. Vascular tissue (stele)
2. Epidermis   4. Cortex

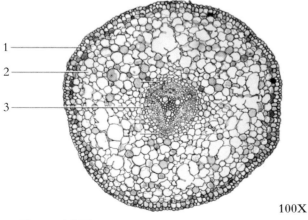

Figure 6.157 Transverse section of a young root of *Salix*.
1. Epidermis   3. Stele
2. Cortex

Figure 6.158 Transverse section of an older root of *Salix*, showing early secondary growth.
1. Epidermis   3. Vascular tissue
2. Cortex

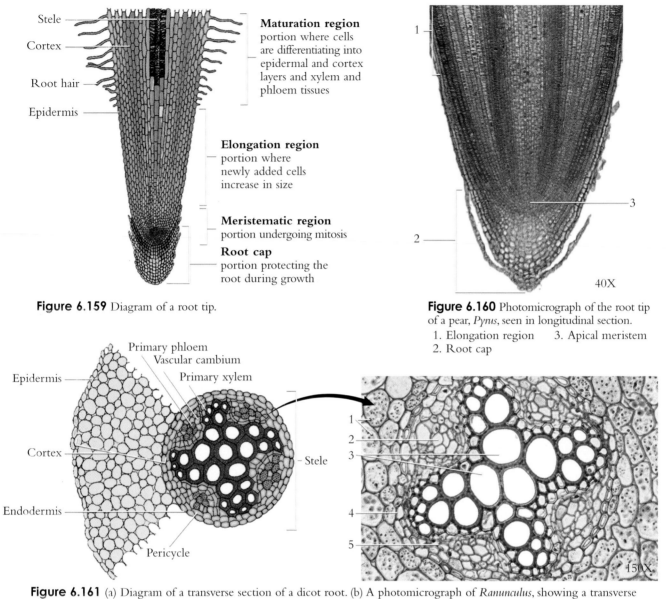

Stele

Cortex

Root hair

Epidermis

Maturation region
portion where cells
are differentiating into
epidermal and cortex
layers and xylem and
phloem tissues

Elongation region
portion where
newly added cells
increase in size

Meristematic region
portion undergoing mitosis

Root cap
portion protecting the
root during growth

Figure 6.159 Diagram of a root tip.

1

3

2

40X

Figure 6.160 Photomicrograph of the root tip
of a pear, *Pyrus*, seen in longitudinal section.
  1. Elongation region   3. Apical meristem
  2. Root cap

Primary phloem
Vascular cambium
Primary xylem

Epidermis

Cortex

Endodermis

Pericycle

Stele

1
2
3

4

5

150X

Figure 6.161 (a) Diagram of a transverse section of a dicot root. (b) A photomicrograph of *Ranunculus*, showing a transverse
section of the stele.
  1. Starch grains within parenchyma cells   3. Primary xylem   5. Pericycle
  2. Primary phloem   4. Endodermis

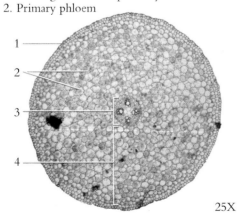

1

2

3

4

25X

Figure 6.162 Root of a buttercup, *Ranunculus*.
  1. Epidermis   3. Stele
  2. Parenchyma cells of cortex   4. Cortex

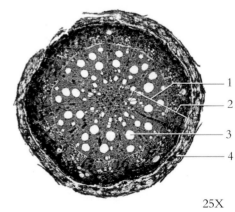

1

2

3

4

25X

Figure 6.163 Transverse section of the root of *Tilia*
showing secondary growth.
  1. Secondary xylem   3. Vessel element
  2. Secondary phloem   4. Periderm

Stems of Angiosperms

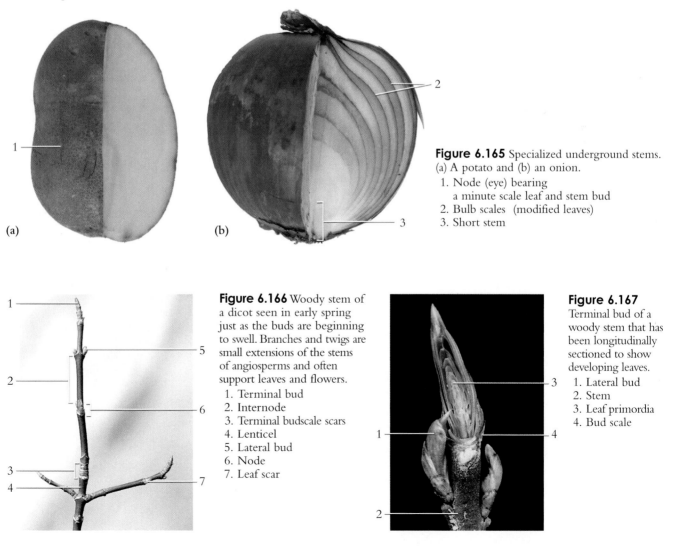

Tuber (Potato)

Rhizome (*Iris*)

Bulb (Onion)

Tendril (Grape)

Corm (Gladiolus)

Terminal bud
Lateral bud
Lenticel

Terminal budscale scar

Leaf scar

Woody stem

Figure 6.164 Examples of the variety and specialization of angiosperm stems. The stem of an angiosperm is often the ascending portion of the plant specialized to produce and support leaves and flowers, transport and store water and nutrients, and provide growth through cell division. Stems of plants are utilized extensively by humans in products including paper, building materials, furniture, and fuel. In addition, the stems of potatoes, onions, cabbage, and other plants are important food crops.

(a)

(b)

Figure 6.165 Specialized underground stems. (a) A potato and (b) an onion.
1. Node (eye) bearing a minute scale leaf and stem bud
2. Bulb scales (modified leaves)
3. Short stem

Figure 6.166 Woody stem of a dicot seen in early spring just as the buds are beginning to swell. Branches and twigs are small extensions of the stems of angiosperms and often support leaves and flowers.
1. Terminal bud
2. Internode
3. Terminal budscale scars
4. Lenticel
5. Lateral bud
6. Node
7. Leaf scar

Figure 6.167 Terminal bud of a woody stem that has been longitudinally sectioned to show developing leaves.
1. Lateral bud
2. Stem
3. Leaf primordia
4. Bud scale

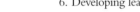

Figure 6.168 Longitudinal section of the stem tip of the common houseplant *Coleus*.

1. Procambium
2. Ground meristem
3. Leaf gap
4. Trichome
5. Apical meristem
6. Developing leaf primordia
7. Leaf primordium
8. Axillary bud
9. Developing vascular tissue

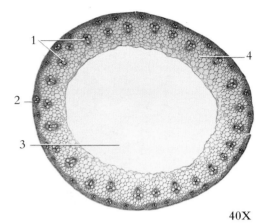

Figure 6.169 Transverse section through the stem of a monocot, *Triticum*, wheat.

1. Vascular bundles
2. Epidermis
3. Ground tissue cavity
4. Parenchyma cells

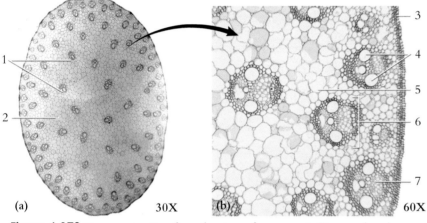

Figure 6.170 Transverse section from the stem of a monocot, *Zea mays* (corn).

1. Vascular bundles with primary xylem and phloem
2. The pattern of vascular bundles in a monocot is known as an atactostele
3. Epidermis
4. Vessel elements of primary xylem
5. Parenchyma cells
6. Vascular bundle
7. Primary phloem

Figure 6.171 Vascular bundle of a fossil palm plant.

1. Bundle cap (fibers)
2. Phloem
3. Vessel elements
4. Ground tissue (parenchyma)

Figure 6.172 Transverse section through a stem of clover, *Trifolium,* showing an eustele.

1. Epidermis
2. Cortex
3. Pith
4. Interfascicular region
5. Vascular bundles with caps of phloem fibers

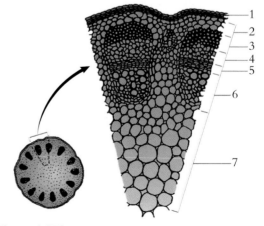

Figure 6.173 Diagram of vascular bundles from the stem of a dicot showing the eustele.

1. Early periderm
2. Cortex
3. Phloem fibers
4. Phloem
5. Vascular cambium
6. Xylem
7. Pith

"Woody" monocot   Woody dicot

Figure 6.174 Comparison of the transverse sections of stems of a "woody" monocot and a woody dicot. The stem of the "woody" monocot is rigid because of the fibrous nature of the numerous vascular bundles. The stem of the woody dicot is rigid because of the compact xylem cells impregnated with lignin forming the dense, hardened wood, seen as annual rings.

1. Bark   2. Annual rings

Figure 6.175 Transverse section of a *Vitus* stem showing secondary tissues.

1. Bark   4. Sieve tube elements
2. Secondary phloem   5. Vessel
3. Secondary xylem

Figure 6.176 Transverse section of a *Vitus* stem.

1. Sieve tube element   4. Secondary phloem
2. Phloem fibers   5. Secondary xylem
3. Parenchyma cells

Figure 6.177 Transverse section through one-year-old *Fraxinus* stem showing secondary growth.

1. Periderm   4. Secondary phloem
2. Cortex   5. Secondary xylem
3. Phloem fibers   6. Pith

Figure 6.178 *Aristolochia* stem with healing wound.

1. Callus tissue   3. Vascular bundle
2. Wound

(a)　　　　(b)　　　　(c)　　　　(d)　　　　(e)　　　　(f)

Figure 6.179 Samples of bark patterns of representative conifers and angiosperms
(a) **Redwood**—The tough, fibrous bark of a redwood tree may be a 30 cm thick. It is highly resistant to fire and insect infestation.
(b) **Ponderosa pine**—The mosaic-like pattern of the bark of mature ponderosa pine is resistant to fire.
(c) **White birch**—The surface texture of bark on the white birch is like white paper. The bark of the white birch was used by Indians in Eastern United States for making canoes.
(d) **Sycamore**—The mottled color of the sycamore bark is due to a tendency for large, thin, brittle plates to peel off, revealing lighter areas beneath. These areas grow darker with exposure, until they, too, peel off.
(e) **Mangrove**—The leathery bark of a mangrove tree is adaptive to brackish water in tropical or semi-tropical regions.
(f) **Shagbark hickory**—The strips of bark in a mature shagbark hickory tree gives this tree its common name.

Figure 6.180 Angiosperm, *Ruscus aculeatus*, is characterized by stems (a) that resemble leaves in form and function. Note the true leaf (b) arising from the leaf-like stem.
1. Stem　　　2. Leaf　　　3. Flower bud

Figure 6.181 Bark of a cherry tree, *Prunus*, showing lenticels. Lenticels are spongy areas in the cork surfaces that permit gas exchange between the internal tissues and the atmosphere.
1. Lenticels

Figure 6.182 Transverse section of a dicot stem showing a lenticel and stem tissues.
1. Lenticel　　3. Periderm
2. Cortex　　　4. Vascular tissue

Figure 6.183 Gall on an oak, *Quercus*, stem. The feeding of a gall wasp larva causes abnormal growth and the formation of a gall. The wasp larva feeds upon the gall tissue, pupates within this enclosure, and then chews an exit to emerge.
1. Gall　　　2. Stem

Leaves of Angiosperms

Venation	Margin	Complexity	Arrangement on Stem

Pinnate

Entire

Palmately compound

Opposite

Parallel

Pinnately lobed

Simple

Alternate

Palmate

Serrate

Pinnately compound

Whorled

Figure 6.184 Several representative angiosperm leaf types. Leaves comprise the foliage of plants, which provide habitat and a food source for many animals including humans. Leaves also provide protective ground cover and are the portion of the plant most responsible for oxygen replenishment into the atmosphere.

(a) (b) (c)

Figure 6.185 Shape of the leaf (a) is of adaptive value to withstand wind. As the speed of the wind increases (b) and (c), the leaf rolls into a tight cone shape, avoiding damage.

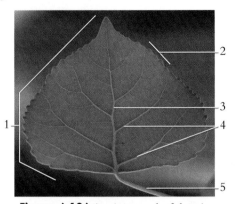

Figure 6.186 Angiosperm leaf showing characteristic surface features. Leaves are organs modified to carry out photosynthesis. Photosynthesis is the manufacture of food (sugar) from carbon dioxide and water, with sunlight providing energy.

1. Lamina (blade)
2. Serrate margin
3. Midrib
4. Veins
5. Petiole

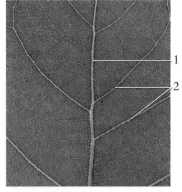

Figure 6.187 Undersurface of an angiosperm leaf showing the vascular tissue lacing through the lamina, or blade, of the leaf.

1. Midrib
2. Veins

Figure 6.188 Organic decomposition of a leaf is a gradual process begining with the softer tissues of the lamina, leaving only the vascular tissues of the midrib and the veins, as seen in this photograph. With time, these will also decompose.

Figure 6.189 Brilliant autumn colors of leaves come about when colorless flavonols are converted into anthocyanins as the chlorophyll breaks down.

Figure 6.190 Transverse section of tomato leaf.

1. Upper epidermis
2. Palisade mesophyll
3. Spongy mesophyll
4. Leaf vein (vascular bundle)
5. Xylem
6. Phloem

Figure 6.191 Transverse section through the leaf of the common hedge privet *Ligustrum*. The typical tissue arrangement of a leaf includes an upper epidermis, a lower epidermis, and the centrally located mesophyll. Containing chloroplasts, the cells of the mesophyll are often divided into palisade mesophyll and spongy mesophyll. Veins within the mesophyll conduct material through the leaf.

1. Upper epidermis
2. Palisade mesophyll
3. Trichome (leaf hair)
4. Bundle sheath
5. Xylem
6. Phloem
7. Spongy mesophyll
8. Lower epidermis

Figure 6.192 Transverse section through the leaf of *Tilia*.

1. Upper epidermis
2. Mesophyll
3. Lower epidermis
4. Leaf vein (midrib)
5. Phloem
6. Xylem

100X

Figure 6.193 Transverse section through the leaf of *Curcurbita*.

1. Palisade mesophyll
2. Spongy mesophyll
3. Leaf vein (midrib)
4. Trichome

100X

1500X   1500X

High humidity
Light
Low CO2

High Water loss Moderate
Stoma closed   Potential   Stoma open

Darkness
High CO2
Low humidity

Figure 6.194 Guard cells in many plants regulate the opening of the stomata according to the environmental factors, as indicated in this diagram. (a) Face view of a closed stoma of a geranium, and (b) an open stoma.

40X

Figure 6.195 Surface view of the leaf epidermis of *Tradescantia*.

1. Epidermal cells
2. Guard cells surrounding stomata
3. Subsidiary cells

40X

Figure 6.196 Surface view of the epidermis of *Allium*. Note the twin guard cells with the stoma opened.

1. Lower epidermis
2. Guard cell
3. Stomate

Flowers of Angiosperms

Structure of a flower

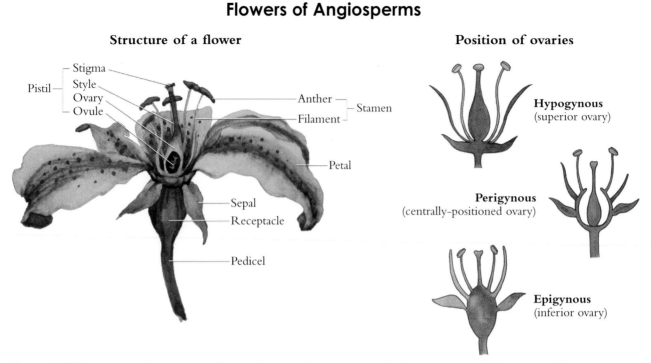

Pistil
— Stigma
— Style
— Ovary
— Ovule

Anther — Stamen
Filament

Petal

Sepal
Receptacle

Pedicel

Position of ovaries

Hypogynous
(superior ovary)

Perigynous
(centrally-positioned ovary)

Epigynous
(inferior ovary)

Figure 6.197 Diagrams of angiosperm flowers showing the structure and relative position of the ovaries. The angiosperm flower is typically composed of sepals, petals, stamens, and one or more pistils. The sepals are the outermost circle of protective leaf-like structures. They are usually green and are collectively called the calyx. The stamens and the pistils are the reproductive parts of the flower. A stamen consists of the filament (stalk) and the anther, where pollen is produced. The pistil consists of a sticky stigma at the tip that receives pollen and a style that leads to the ovary.

Crown of thorns

Foxglove

Orchid

Bird of Paradise

Columbine

Hibiscus

Figure 6.198 Flowers of representative angiosperms.

Figure 6.199 Floral structure of a tulip.

Figure 6.200 Structure of a dissected cherry, showing a perigynous flower.

Figure 6.201 Structure of a dissected *Pyrus*, showing an epigynous flower.

Figure 6.202 Dissected quince, *Chaenomeles japonica*, showing an epigynous flower.

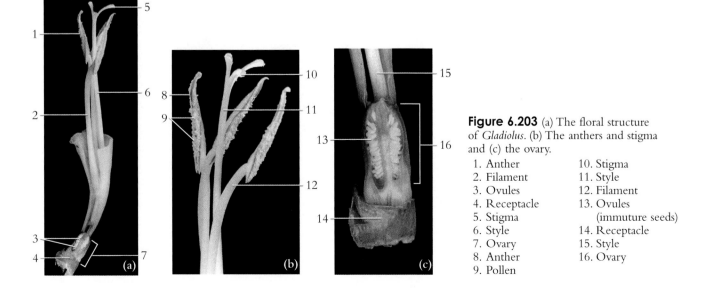

Figure 6.203 (a) The floral structure of *Gladiolus*. (b) The anthers and stigma and (c) the ovary.

1. Anther
2. Filament
3. Ovules
4. Receptacle
5. Stigma
6. Style
7. Ovary
8. Anther
9. Pollen
10. Stigma
11. Style
12. Filament
13. Ovules (immuture seeds)
14. Receptacle
15. Style
16. Ovary

Figure 6.204 Scanning electron micrograph of the stigma of an angiosperm pistil. The stigma is the location where pollen grains adhere and germinate to produce a pollen tube.

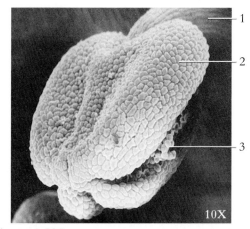

Figure 6.205 Scanning electron micrograph of the anther of candy tuft, *Lobularia*. The anther has ruptured, resulting in the release of pollen grains.

1. Filament   3. Pollen grains
2. Anther

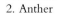

Figure 6.206 Floral structure of grasses.

Figure 6.207 Floral parts of a grass, *Elymus flavescens*, showing spikelets with six florets.

Figure 6.208 Grass, wheat, *Triticum*, is *e*conomically important.

Figure 6.209 Bamboo is an important grass of commerce. It is also important in many natural ecosystems.

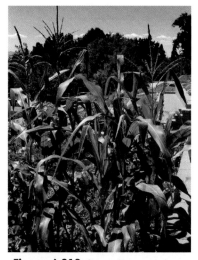

Figure 6.210 Corn, *Zea mays,* is a New World grass important as food for humans and livestock.

Figure 6.211 Flowers of the family Asteraceae are usually produced in tight heads resembling single large flowers. One of these inflorescences can contain hundreds of individual flowers. Examples of this family include dandelions, sunflowers, asters, and marigolds.

Figure 6.212 Dissected inflorescence a member of the Asteraceae, *Balsamorhiza sagittata*.
1. Ray flower   3. Receptacle
1. Disk flower

Figure 6.213 Strawberry, *Fragaria*, showing (a) the flower, (b) immature aggregate fruits, and (c) a ripening fruit.

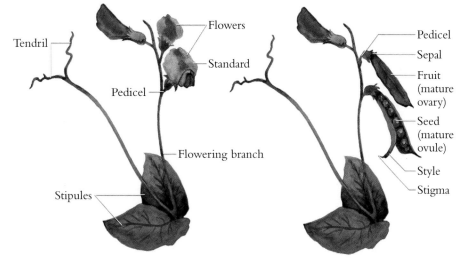

Figure 6.214 Flower and fruit of the pea, *Pisum*.

Figure 6.215 Seeds in the receptacle of the giant sunflower.

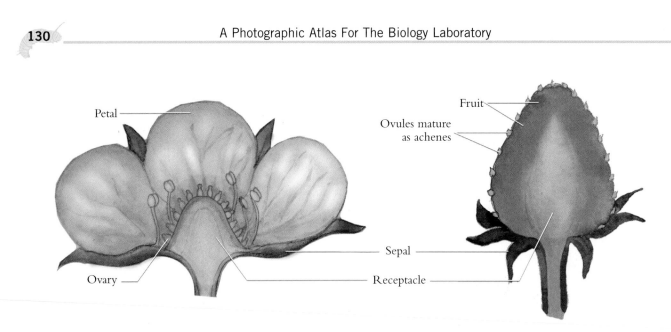

Figure 6.216 Flower and fruit of the strawberry, *Fragaria*. The strawberry has an aggregate fruit.

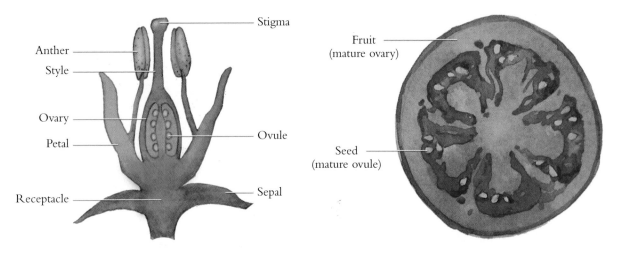

Figure 6.217 Illustration of a flower and fruit of a tomato, *Lycopersicon esculentum*. A tomato fruit is a berry.

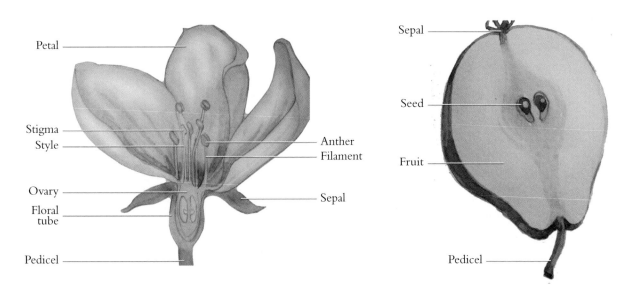

Figure 6.218 Flower and fruit of the pear *Pyrus*. The pear fruit develops from the floral tube (fused perianth) as well as the ovary.

Seeds, Fruits and Seed Germination of Angiosperms

Figure 6.219 Pollen grains of the dicot pigweed, *Amaranthus*.

Figure 6.220 Pollen grains of a lilic, *Syringa*.

Figure 6.223 Pollen grains of a lily. The pollen grain at the top of the photo has germinated to produce a pollen tube.
1. Pollen grain   2. Pollen tube

Figure 6.221 Pollen grains of the dicot arrowroot, *Balsamorhiza*.

Figure 6.222 Pollen grain of hibiscus, *Hibiscus*.

Figure 6.224 Diagram showing the process of pollination.

Anther splits open freeing pollen grains

Anther

Stigma

Style

Filament

Intact pollen grain

Sperm nucleus

Tube nucleus

Dissected pollen grain

Pollen grains

Stigma

Pollen tube

Sperm travels through pollen tube to ovule

Style

Ovule

Ovary

Antipodals

Polar nuclei

Synergid

Egg

120X

Figure 6.225 Photomicrograph of a developing dicot embryo from a shepherd's purse, *Capsella bursa-pastoris*.

1. Endothelium
2. Cellular endosperm
3. Endosperm
4. Developing embryo
5. Basal cell

120X

Figure 6.226 Photomicrograph of a mature dicot embryo from a shepherd's purse, *Capsella bursa-pastoris*.

1. Apical meristem
2. Seed coat
3. Cotyledons
4. Hypocotyl (embryonic root axis)
5. Root tip
6. Basal cell

200X

Figure 6.227 Photomicrograph of a mature grain, or kernel, of wheat, *Triticum aestivum*.

1. Pericarp
2. Starchy endosperm
3. Scutellum
4. Coleoptile
5. Shoot apex
6. Radicle
7. Coleorhiza
8. Embryo

75X

Figure 6.228 Transverse section of a mature ovary of a lily, *Lilium*.

1. Developing ovules

200X

Figure 6.229 Transverse section of an eight–nucleate embryo sac of an ovule from a lily, *Lilium*.

1. Locule
2. Megagametophyte
3. Funiculus
4. Wall of ovary
5. Chalaza
6. Antipodal cells (n)
7. Polar nuclei (n)
8. Outer integument ($2n$)
9. Inner integument ($2n$)
10. Synergid cells (n)
11. Egg (n)
12. Micropyle (pollen tube entrance)

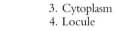

Figure 6.230 Transverse section of a megaspore mother cell from a lily, *Lilium*.

1. Megaspore
2. Nucleus
3. Cytoplasm
4. Locule

Figure 6.231 Transverse section of a mature anther from a lily, *Lilium*.

1. Pollen grains
2. Filament

Figure 6.232 Flower (a) and the fruits (b and c) of the dandelion, *Taraxacum*. The dandelion has a composite flower. The wind-borne fruit (containing one seed) of a dandelion, and many other members of the family Asteraceae, develop a plumelike pappus, which enables the light fruit to float in the air.

1. Pappus
2. Ovary wall, with one seed inside

Figure 6.233 Dissected legume, garden bean, *Phaseolus*.

1. Pedicel
2. Seeds
3. Fruit
4. Stigma

Figure 6.234 Lima bean. (a) The entire bean seed and (b) a longitudinally sectioned seed

1. Integument (seed coat)
2. Hilum
3. Radicle
4. Hypocotyl
5. Epicotyl (plume)
6. Cotyledon

Figure 6.235 Photomicrograph of the seed coat of the garden bean, *Phaseolus*, showing the sclerified epidermis

1. Macrosclerids
2. Subepidermal sclereids

Figure 6.236 Cob of corn from *Zea mays*. Corn was domesticated approximately 7,000 years ago from a Mexican grass, family Poaceae.

Figure 6.237 Fruit and seed of a peanut plant.

1. Cotyledon
2. Integument (seed coat)
3. Plumule
4. Embryo axis
5. Interior of fruit
6. Mesocarp
7. Radicle
8. Cotyledon
9. Fruit wall

Figure 6.238 Longitudinal section of an apple fruit (pome).

1. Pedicel
2. Mature floral tube
3. Seed (mature ovule)
4. Remnants of floral parts
5. Ovary wall
6. Mature ovary (2 & 6 comprise the fruit)

Figure 6.239 Transverse section through a grapefruit fruit (hesperidium).

1. Exocarp
2. Mesocarp
3. Endocarp
4. Pericarp
5. Seed

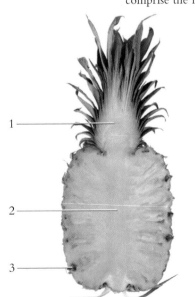

Figure 6.240 Longitudinal section of a pineapple fruit.

1. Shoot apex
2. Central axis
3. Floral parts

Figure 6.241 Longitudinal section of a tomato fruit (berry).

1. Pedicel
2. Pericarp
3. Locule
4. Placenta
5. Seed
6. Mature ovary (fruit)

Figure 6.242 Examples of seed dispersal.

(a) Maple—The winged seeds of a maple fall with a spinning motion that may carry it hundreds of yards from the parent tree.
(b) White pine—The second-year cones of a white pine open to expose the winged seeds to the wind.
(c) Willow—The airborne seeds of a willow may be dispersed over long distances.
(d) Witch hazel—Mature seeds of the witch hazel tree are dispersed up to 10 feet by forceful discharge.
(e) Mangrove—The fruits of this tropical tree begin to germinate while still on the branch, forming pointed roots. When the seeds drop from the tree, they may float to a muddy area where the roots take hold.
(f) Coconut—The buoyant, fibrous husk of a coconut permits dispersal from one island or land mass to another by ocean currents.

(g) Pecan—The seed husk of a pecan provides buoyancy and protection as it is dispersed by water.
(h) Black walnut—The encapsulated seed of the black walnut is dispersed through burial by a squirrel or floating in a stream.
(i) Apple—The seeds of an apple tree may be dispersed by animals that ingest the fruit and pass the undigested seeds hours later in their feces.
(j) Cherry—Moderate-sized birds, such as robins, may carry a ripe cherry to an eating site where the juicy pulp is eaten and the hard seed is discarded.
(k) Beech—Seeds from a beech tree are dispersed by mammals as the spiny husks adhere to their hair. In addition, many mammals ingest these seeds and disperse them in their feces.
(l) Oak—An oak seed may be dispersed through burial by a squirrel or jay.

Figure 6.243 (a) Mature milkweed, *Asclepias*; (b) milkweed pods; and (c) seeds ready for airborne dispersal.

Forcible discharge dispersal

Touch-me-not

Water dispersal

Coconut

Animal dispersal

Burdock   Cocklebur

Blueberries

Wind dispersal

Dandelion   Poppy

Maple

Figure 6.244 Several fruits and seeds to illustrate seed dispersal.

Chapter 7
Animalia

Animals are multicellular, heterotrophic eukaryotes that ingest food materials and store carbohydrate reserves as glycogen or fat. The cells of animals lack cell walls, but do contain intercellular connections including desmosomes, gap junctions, and tight junctions. Animal cells are also highly specialized into the specific kinds of tissues described in chapter 1. Most animals are motile through the contraction of muscle fibers containing actin and myosin proteins. The complex body systems of animals include elaborate sensory and neuromotor specializations that accommodate dynamic behavioral mechanisms.

Reproduction in animals is primarily sexual, with the diploid stage generally dominating the life cycle. Primary sex organs, or *gonads*, produce the haploid gametes called *sperm* and *ova*. Propagation begins as a small flagellated sperm fertilizes a larger, nonmotile egg forming a diploid zygote that has genetic traits of both parents. The zygote then undergoes a succession of mitotic divisions called *cleavage*. In most animals, cleavage is followed by the formation of a multicellular stage called a *blastula*. With further development, the *germ layers* form which eventually give rise to each of the body organs. The developmental cycle of many animals includes *larval forms*, which are still developing, free-living, and sexually immature. Larvae usually have different food and habitat requirements from those of the adults. Larvae eventually undergo metamorphoses that transform them into sexually mature adults.

Animals inhabit nearly all aquatic and terrestrial habitats of the biosphere. The greatest number of animals are marine, where the first animals probably evolved. Depending on the classification scheme, animals may be grouped into as many as 35 phyla. The most commonly known phylum is *Chordata* (table 7.1) that includes the subphylum *Vertebrata*, or the backboned animals. Chordates, however, comprise only about 5% of all the animal species. All other animals are frequently referred to as *invertebrates*, and they account for approximately 95% of the animal species.

Table 7.1 Some Representatives of the Kingdom Animalia

Phylum and Representative Kinds	Characteristics
Porifera — sponges	Multicellular, aquatic animals, with stiff skeletons and bodies perforated by pores
Cnidaria — corals, hydra, and jellyfish	Aquatic animals, radially symmetrical, mouth surrounded by tentacles bearing cnidocytes (stinging cells); body composed of epidermis and gastrodermis, separated by mesoglea
Platyhelminthes — flatworms	Elongated, flattened, and bilaterally symmetrical; distinct head containing ganglia; nerve cords; protonephridia or flame cells
Mollusca — clams, snails, and squids	Bilaterally symmetrical with a true coelom, containing a mantle; many have muscular foot and protective shell
Annelida — segmented worms	Body segmented (except leeches); a series of hearts; hydrostatic skeleton and circular and longitudinal muscles
Nematoda — round worms	Mostly microscopic, unsegmented wormlike; body enclosed in cuticle; whip-like body movement
Arthropoda — crustaceans, insects, and spiders	Body segmented; paired and jointed appendages; chitinous exoskeleton; hemocoel for blood flow
Echinodermata — sea stars and sea urchins	Larvae have bilateral symmetry; adults have pentaradial symmetry; coelom, most contain a complete digestive tract; regeneration of body parts
Chordata — lancelets, tunicates, and vertebrates	Fibrous notochord, pharyngeal gill pouches, dorsal hollow nerve cord, and postanal tail present at some stage in their life cycle

Phylum Porifera

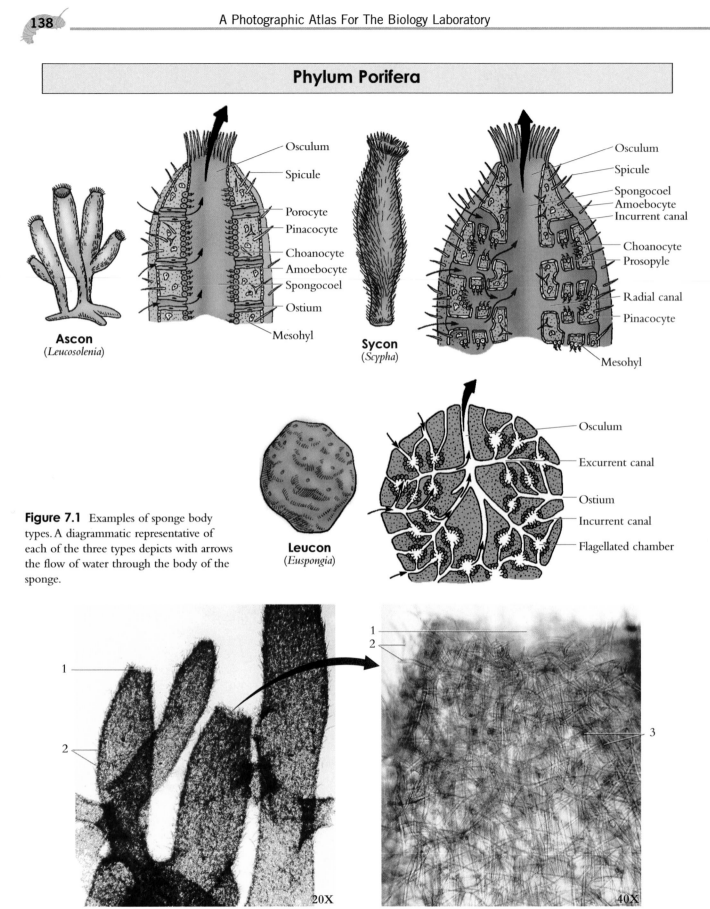

Ascon
(*Leucosolenia*)

Osculum
Spicule
Porocyte
Pinacocyte
Choanocyte
Amoebocyte
Spongocoel
Ostium
Mesohyl

Sycon
(*Scypha*)

Osculum
Spicule
Spongocoel
Amoebocyte
Incurrent canal
Choanocyte
Prosopyle
Radial canal
Pinacocyte
Mesohyl

Leucon
(*Euspongia*)

Osculum
Excurrent canal
Ostium
Incurrent canal
Flagellated chamber

Figure 7.1 Examples of sponge body types. A diagrammatic representative of each of the three types depicts with arrows the flow of water through the body of the sponge.

Figure 7.2 (a) *Leucosolenia* has an ascon body type.
1. Osculum   2. Spicules

20X

Figure 7.3 Higher magnification of the spicules and ostia.
1. Osculum   2. Spicules   3. Ostia

40X

Figure 7.4 Transverse sections of the sponge, *Grantia* (*Scypha*). (a) Low magnification and (b) high magnification.

1. Spongocoel
2. Incurrent canal
3. Radial canal
4. Choanocytes (collar cells)
5. Incurrent canal
6. Apopyle
7. Ostium
8. Pinacocytes
9. Radial canal
10. Mesohyl

Figure 7.5 Bath sponge, class Demospongiae, has a leuconoid body structure.

1. Ostia
2. Osculum

Figure 7.6 Branched silica spicules of a freshwater sponge.

Figure 7.7 Yellow ball sponge, *Cinachyra allocladia* a leucon type sponge.

Phylum Cnidaria

Table 7.2 Representatives of the Phylum Cnidaria

Classes and Representative Kinds	Characteristics
Hydrozoa — hydra, *Obelia,* and Portuguese man-of-war	Mainly marine; both polyp and medusa stage (polyp form only in hydra); polyp colonies in most
Scyphozoa — jellyfish	Marine coastal waters; polyp stage restricted to small larval forms
Cubozoa — box jellies	Marine coastal waters; polyp and medusa stage; square shaped when veiwed from above
Anthozoa — sea anemones, corals, and sea fans	Marine coastal waters; solitary or colonial polyps no medusa stage; partitioned gastrovascular cavity

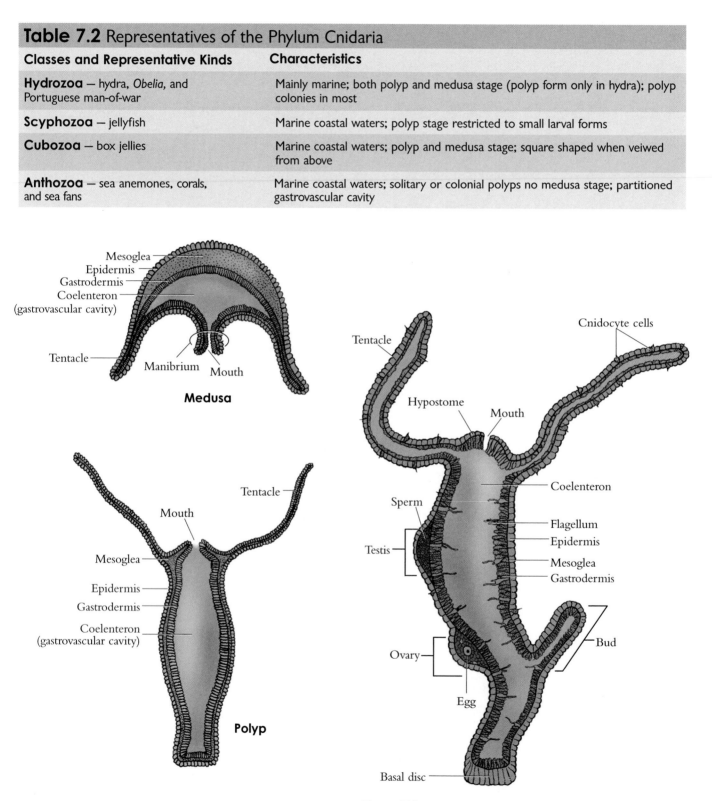

Figure 7.8 General body type of cnidarians.

Figure 7.9 Longitudinal section of a hydra.

Figure 7.10 Budding hydra.
1. Tentacles   3. Hypostome
2. Bud   4. Basal disc (foot)

Figure 7.11 Anterior end of a hydra.
1. Cnidocytes   3. Tentacles
2. Hypostome   4. Mouth

Figure 7.12 Transverse section of a female hydra.
1. Epidermis (ectoderm)   4. Gastrodermis
2. Coelenteron   (endoderm)
3. Mesoglea

Figure 7.13 Transverse section of a male hydra.
1. Coelenteron   4. Gastrodermis
2. Testes   (endoderm)
3. Epidermis (ectoderm)

Figure 7.14 Longitudinal section of a hydra.
1. Hypostome   5. Mesoglea
2. Epidermis (ectoderm)   6. Gastrodermis
3. Coelenteron   (endoderm)
4. Basal disc

Figure 7.15 Male hydra.
1. Tentacles
2. Testes

40X

Figure 7.16 Female hydra.
1. Tentacles
2. Ovary
3. Basal disc (foot)

40X

Figure 7.17 Life cycle of *Obelia*.

Female medusa
Male medusa
Sperm
Egg
Zygote
Blastula
Swimming planula larva
Developing polyp
Young colony
Medusa buds
Gonangium (reproductive polyp)
Hydranth (feeding polyp)

Figure 7.18 *Obelia* colony.
1. Coenosarc
2. Hydranth (feeding polyp)
3. Gonangium (reproductive polyp)

15X

Figure 7.19 Detail of *Obelia* colony.
1. Tentacles
2. Perisarc
3. Coenosarc
4. Medusa buds
5. Hydranth (feeding polyp)
6. Gonangium (reproductive polyp)
7. Gonotheca
8. Blastostyle
9. Hypostome

40X

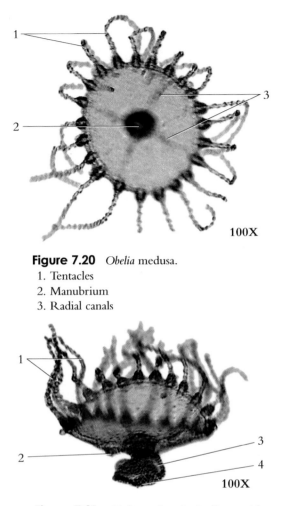

Figure 7.20 *Obelia* medusa.
1. Tentacles
2. Manubrium
3. Radial canals

100X

Figure 7.22 Portuguese man-of-war, *Physalia*, is actually a colony of medusae and polyps acting as a single organism. The tentacles are comprised of three types of polyps: the gastrozooids (feeding polyps), the dactylozooids (stinging polyps), and the gonozooids (reproductive polyps).
　1. Pneumatophore (float)　　　2. Tentacles

100X

Figure 7.21 *Obelia* medusa in feeding position.
1. Tentacles　　　3. Manubrium
2. Gonad　　　　4. Mouth

40X

Figure 7.23 *Aurelia* planula larva develops from a fertilized egg that may be retained on the oral arm of the medusa.

40X

Figure 7.24 *Aurelia* scyphistoma. The polyp is a developmental stage in the life cycle of the jellyfish.

40X

Figure 7.25 *Aurelia* strobila. Under favorable conditions, the scyphistoma develops into the strobila.
　1. Developing ephyrae

40X

Figure 7.26 *Aurelia* ephyra larva, which gradually develops into adult jellyfish.
1. Rhopalia (sense organs)
2. Gonads

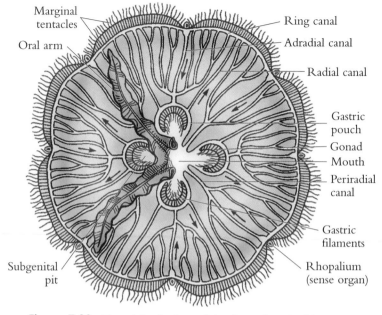

Figure 7.27 Ventral (oral) view of *Aurelia* medusa.
1. Ring canal
2. Gonad
3. Marginal tentacles
4. Radial canals
5. Subgenital pit
6. Oral arm

Figure 7.28 Ventral (oral) view of *Aurelia* medusa. In this diagram, the right oral arms have been removed. The arrows depict circulation through the canal system.

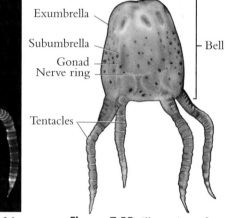

Figure 7.29 Sea nettle, *Chrysaora fuscescens*, often mass in large swarms off the Pacific coast where they feed on zooplankton.

Figure 7.30 Red-striped jellyfish, *Chrysaora melanaster*, are common near the surface of the Bering sea.

Figure 7.31 Box jellyfish, *Carybdea sivickisi*, are named from their cube-shaped bell. All cubozoans have four tentacles.

Figure 7.32 Illustration of box jellyfish, *Carybdea sivickisi*, showing basic external structures.

Figure 7.33 Sunburst anemone, *Anthopleura sola*, gets its green coloration from symbiotic algae within it.

Figure 7.34 Two examples of anemone, disk anemones and a yellow anemone.

Figure 7.35 Disk anemones, *Actinodiscus*, form large colonies.

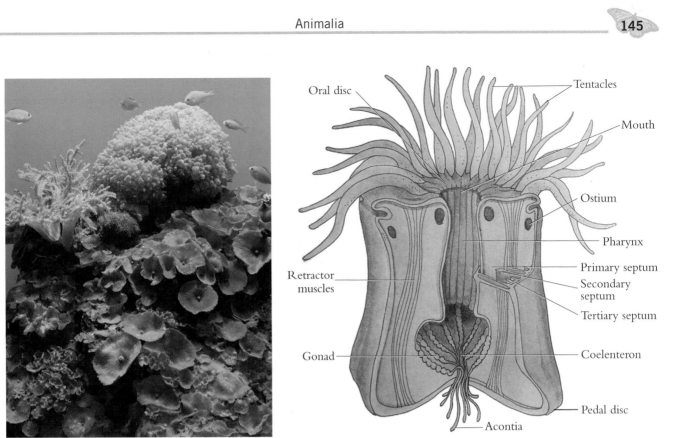

Oral disc

Tentacles

Mouth

Ostium

Pharynx

Primary septum

Secondary septum

Tertiary septum

Retractor muscles

Gonad

Coelenteron

Pedal disc

Acontia

Figure 7.36 Diagram of a partially dissected sea anemone, *Metridium*.

Figure 7.37 Brain coral, *Goniastrea*.

Figure 7.38 Skeletal structure of brain coral, *Goniastrea*.

Figure 7.39 Mushroom coral, *Rhodactis*.

Figure 7.40 Skeletal structure of mushroom coral, *Rhodactis*.

Figure 7.41 Elkshorn coral, *Acropora*.

Figure 7.42 Skeletal structure of elkshorn coral, *Acropora*.

Figure 7.43 Detailed view of the polyps of candy cane coral, *Caulastrea furcata*.

Figure 7.44 Detailed view of the polyps of glove xenia, *Xenia umbellata*.

Phylum Platyhelminthes

Table 7.3 Some Representatives of the Phylum Platyhelminthes

Classes and Representative Kinds	Characteristics
Turbellaria — planarians	Mostly free-living, carnivorous, aquatic forms; body covered by ciliated epidermis
Trematoda — flukes (schistosomes)	Parasitic with wide range of invertebrate and vertebrate hosts; suckers for attachment to host
Cestoda — tapeworms	Parasitic in many vertebrate hosts; complex life cycle with intermediate hosts; suckers or hooks on scolex for attachment to host; eggs are produced and shed within proglottids

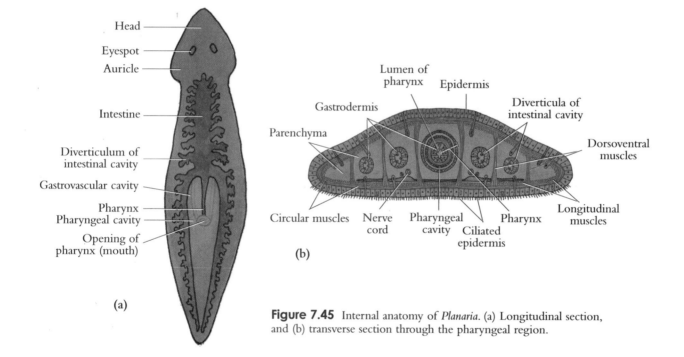

(a)

(b)

Figure 7.45 Internal anatomy of *Planaria*. (a) Longitudinal section, and (b) transverse section through the pharyngeal region.

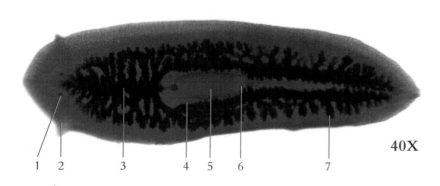

40X

Figure 7.46 *Planaria.*
1. Eyespot
2. Auricle
3. Gastrovascular cavity
4. Pharyngeal cavity
5. Pharynx
6. Opening of pharynx (mouth)
7. Diverticulum of intestinal cavity

Figure 7.47 Transverse section through the pharyngeal region of *Planaria*.

1. Epidermis
2. Intestinal cavity
3. Testis
4. Cilia
5. Pharyngeal cavity
6. Dorsoventral muscles
7. Gastrodermis (endoderm)
8. Pharynx

Figure 7.48 Transverse section through the posterior region of *Planaria*.

1. Epidermis
2. Intestinal cavity
3. Mesenchyme
4. Dorsoventral muscles
5. Endoderm

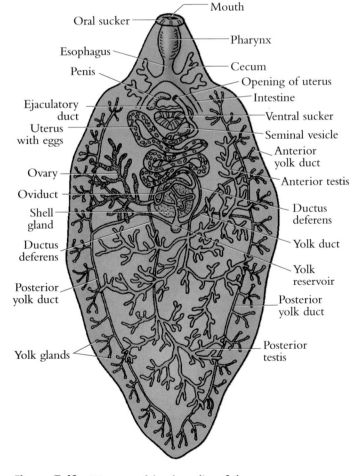

Figure 7.49 Diagram of the sheep liver fluke, *Fasciola hepatica*.

Figure 7.50 Cow liver fluke, *Fasciola magna*, is one of the largest flukes, measuring about 3 inches.

1. Yolk gland
2. Ventral sucker
3. Oral sucker

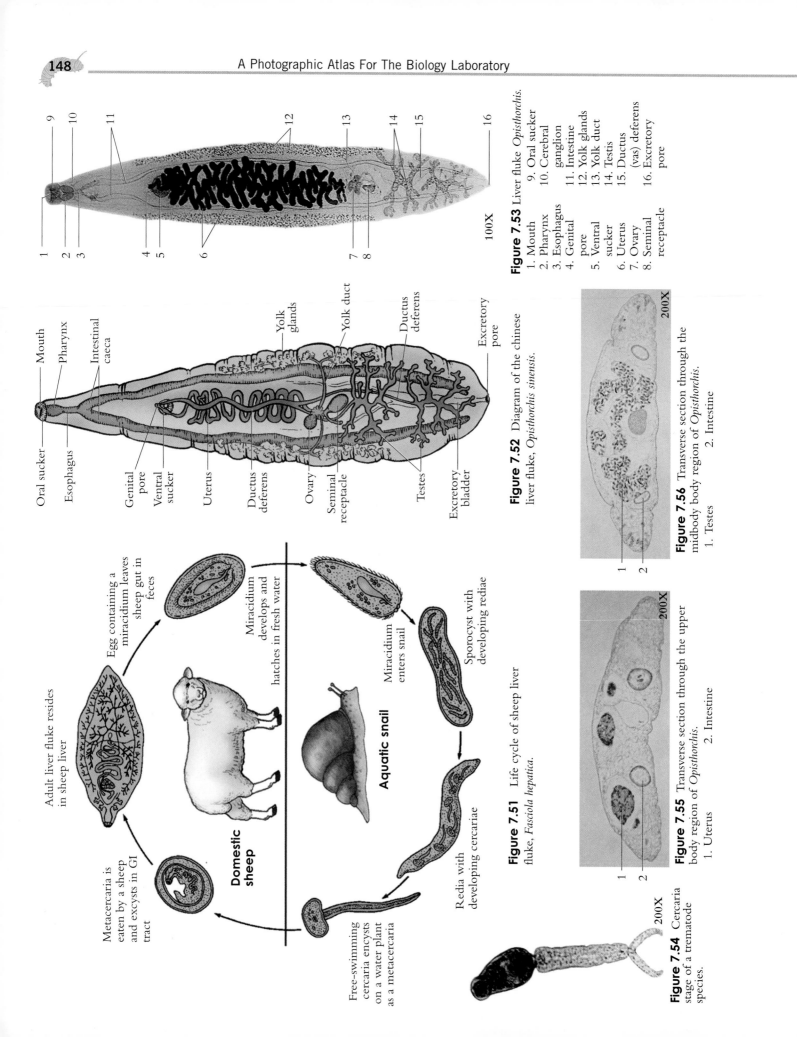

Figure 7.53 Liver fluke *Opisthorchis*.

1. Mouth	9. Oral sucker
2. Pharynx	10. Cerebral
3. Esophagus	ganglion
4. Genital	11. Intestine
pore	12. Yolk glands
5. Ventral	13. Yolk duct
sucker	14. Testis
6. Uterus	15. Ductus
7. Ovary	(vas) deferens
8. Seminal	16. Excretory
receptacle	pore

100X

Figure 7.52 Diagram of the chinese liver fluke, *Opisthorchis sinensis*.

Mouth

Pharynx

Intestinal caeca

Yolk glands

Yolk duct

Ductus deferens

Excretory pore

Oral sucker

Esophagus

Genital pore

Ventral sucker

Uterus

Ductus deferens

Ovary

Seminal receptacle

Testes

Excretory bladder

Figure 7.56 Transverse section through the midbody body region of *Opisthorchis*.
1. Testes   2. Intestine

200X

Figure 7.55 Transverse section through the upper body region of *Opisthorchis*.
1. Uterus   2. Intestine

200X

Egg containing a miracidium leaves sheep gut in feces

Miracidium develops and hatches in fresh water

Adult liver fluke resides in sheep liver

Miracidium enters snail

Domestic sheep

Sporocyst with developing rediae

Aquatic snail

Metacercaria is eaten by a sheep and excysts in GI tract

Redia with developing cercariae

Free-swimming cercaria encysts on a water plant as a metacercaria

Figure 7.51 Life cycle of sheep liver fluke, *Fasciola hepatica*.

Figure 7.54 Cercaria stage of a trematode species.

200X

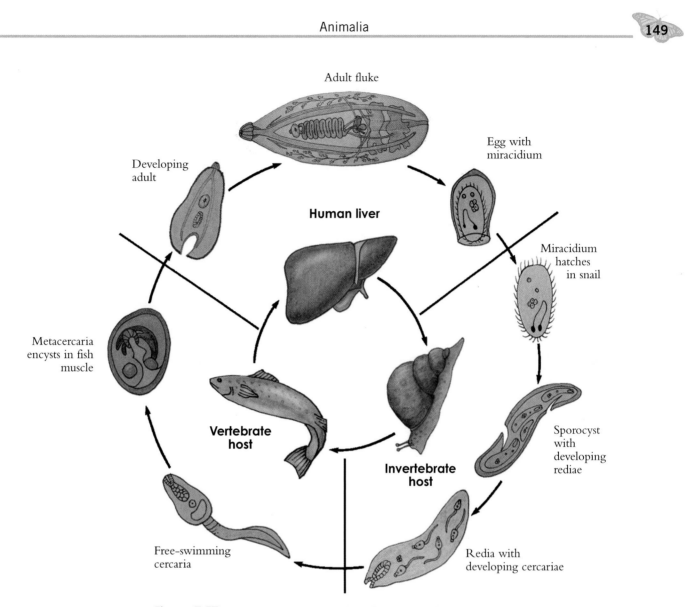

Figure 7.57 Life cycle of the human liver fluke, *Clonorchis sinesis*.

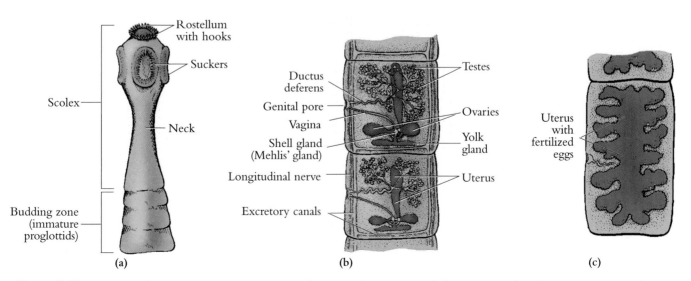

Figure 7.58 Diagrams of a parasitic tapeworm, *Taenia pisiformis*. (a) The anterior end, (b) mature proglottids, and (c) a ripe proglottid.

Figure 7.59 Scolex of *Taenia pisiformis*.
1. Hooks
2. Rostellum
3. Suckers

Figure 7.60 Immature proglottids
of *Taenia pisiformis*,
1. Early ovary
2. Early testes
3. Excretory canal
4. Immature vagina and ductus deferens

Figure 7.61 Mature proglottid of *Taenia pisiformis*.
1. Uterus   4. Excretory canal   7. Cirrus
2. Ovary   5. Testes   8. Genital pore
3. Yolk gland 6. Ductus deferens   9. Vagina

Figure 7.62 *Taenia pisiformis*, ripe proglottid.
1. Zygotes in branched uterus   2. Genital pore

Phylum Mollusca

Table 7.4 Representatives of the Phylum Mollusca

Classes and Representative Kinds	Characteristics
Polyplacophora — chitons	Marine; shell of 8 dorsal plates; broad foot
Gastropoda — snails and slugs	Marine, freshwater, and terrestrial; coiled shell; prominent head with tentacles and eyes
Bivalvia — clams, oysters, and mussels	Marine, freshwater; body compressed between two hinged shells; hatchet-shaped foot
Cephalopoda — squids and octopi	Marine; excellent swimmers, predatory; foot separated into tentacles which may contain suckers; well-developed eyes

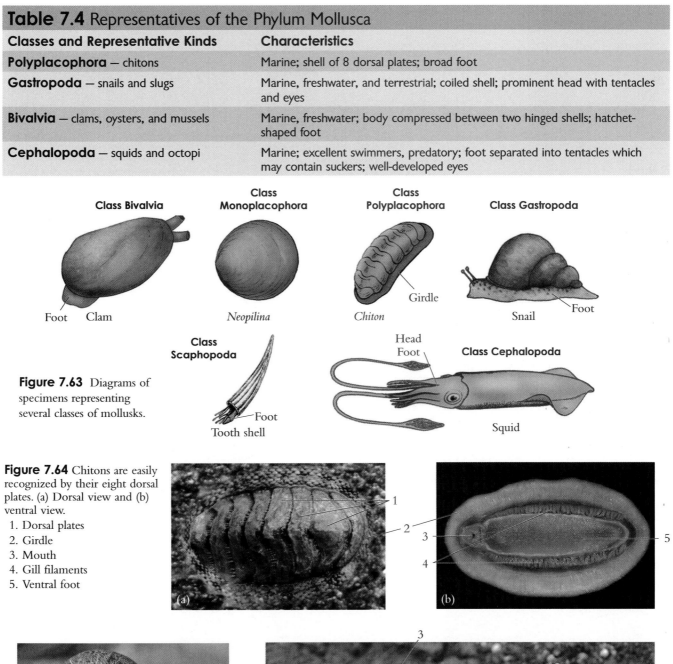

Figure 7.63 Diagrams of specimens representing several classes of mollusks.

Figure 7.64 Chitons are easily recognized by their eight dorsal plates. (a) Dorsal view and (b) ventral view.
1. Dorsal plates
2. Girdle
3. Mouth
4. Gill filaments
5. Ventral foot

Figure 7.65 Snail.
1. Shell   4. Head
2. Foot   5. Tentacle
3. Eye

Figure 7.66 Locomotion of the slug, class Gastropoda, requires the production of mucus. Slugs differ from snails in that a shell is absent.
1. Head   3. Mantle   5. Foot
2. Tentacle   4. Mucus

Figure 7.67 Snail radule, is made up of small horny teeth made of chitin, called denticles

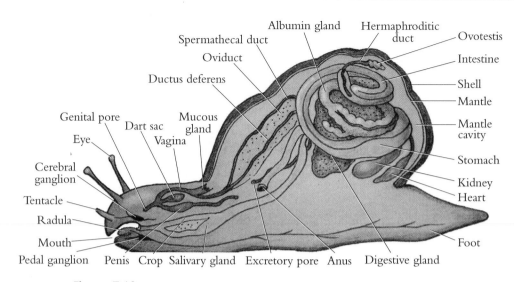

Figure 7.68 Diagram of pulmonate snail anatomy.

Albumin gland
Hermaphroditic duct
Ovotestis
Spermathecal duct
Oviduct
Intestine
Ductus deferens
Shell
Mantle
Genital pore
Mucous gland
Mantle cavity
Dart sac
Eye
Vagina
Stomach
Cerebral ganglion
Kidney
Heart
Tentacle
Radula
Mouth
Foot
Pedal ganglion
Penis
Crop
Salivary gland
Excretory pore
Anus
Digestive gland

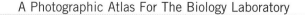

DORSAL

1
2

ANTERIOR

POSTERIOR

(a)

3

(b)

VENTRAL

Figure 7.69 External view of a bivalve (clam) shell. Bivalves have two shells (valves) that are laterally compressed and dorsally hinged. (a) Dorsal view and (b) left valve.

1. Umbo   2. Hinge ligament   3. Growth lines

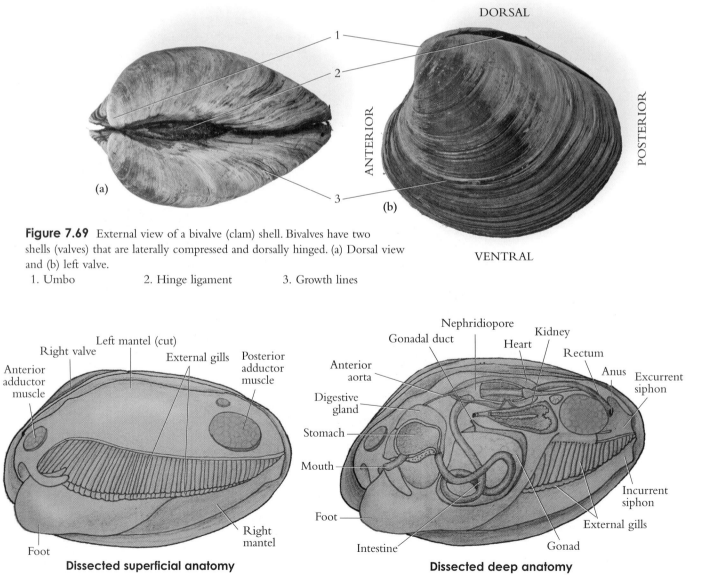

Left mantel (cut)
Right valve
External gills
Posterior adductor muscle
Anterior adductor muscle
Foot
Right mantel

Dissected superficial anatomy

Nephridiopore
Gonadal duct
Heart
Kidney
Anterior aorta
Rectum
Anus
Excurrent siphon
Digestive gland
Stomach
Mouth
Incurrent siphon
Foot
External gills
Intestine
Gonad

Dissected deep anatomy

Figure 7.70 Internal anatomy of a freshwater clam.

Figure 7.71 Diagram of the circulatory and respiratory systems of a freshwater clam.

Labels in Figure 7.71: Intestine, Ventricle, Auricle, Suprabranchial chamber, Non-glandular kidney, Adductor muscle, Glandular kidney, Efferent vessel, Excurrent siphon, Afferent vessel, Direction of water flow, Gonad, Incurrent siphon, Intestine, Gill pores, Gill bars, Foot, Mantel, Shell

Figure 7.72 Lateral view of a clam.

1. Pericardium
2. Ventricle of heart
3. Anus
4. Posterior retractor muscle
5. Posterior adductor muscle
6. Excurrent siphon
7. Nephridium (kidney)
8. Incurrent siphon
9. Atrium of heart
10. Gills
11. Anterior retractor muscle
12. Labial palps
13. Anterior adductor muscle
14. Foot
15. Mantle

Figure 7.73 Lateral view of a clam, foot cut.

1. Hinge ligament
2. Hinge
3. Ventricle of heart
4. Posterior aorta
5. Posterior retractor muscle
6. Nephridium (kidney)
7. Posterior adductor muscle
8. Gonad
9. Foot
10. Umbo
11. Intestine
12. Opening between atrium and ventricle
13. Esophagus
14. Anterior retractor muscle
15. Mouth
16. Anterior adductor muscle
17. Digestive gland
18. Intestine

(a)   (b)

Figure 7.74 *Nautilus*, a cephalopod, has gas-filled chambers within its shell, as seen in the dissected specimen (b). These chambers regulate buoyancy.

Figure 7.75 Dorsal view of an octopus collected in the Sea of Cortez, San Carlos, Mexico.
1. Body   2. Tentacles

Figure 7.76 Ventral view of an octopus.
1. Suction cups   3. Mouth
2. Tentacles

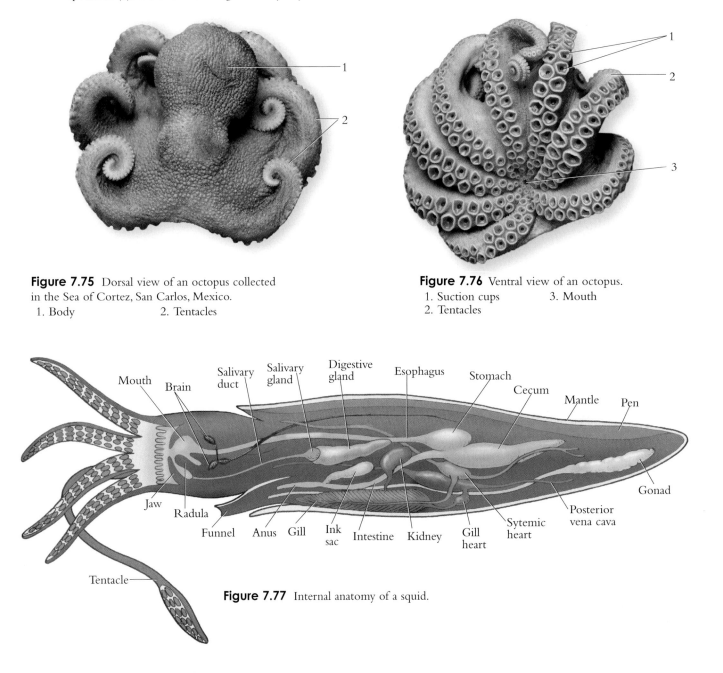

Figure 7.77 Internal anatomy of a squid.

Figure 7.78 External anatomy of the squid, *Loligo*.

1. Tentacles
2. Arms
3. Eye
4. Funnel
5. Collar
6. Mantle (body tube)
7. Fin

Figure 7.79 Internal anatomy of the head region of the squid.

1. Gill
2. Esophagus
3. Pleural nerve
4. Eye
5. Radula
6. Ligula
7. Beak
8. Pen
9. Cephalic aorta
10. Visceral ganglion
11. Pedal ganglion
12. Buccal bulb

Figure 7.80 Internal anatomy of the squid.

1. Testis
2. Spermatophoric duct
3. Penis
4. Kidney
5. Branchial vein
6. Gill
7. Ink sac
8. Funnel retractor muscle
9. Rectum
10. Stomach
11. Posterior vena cava
12. Branchial heart
13. Pancreas
14. Liver
15. Funnel retractor muscle
16. Anterior vena cava
17. Anus
18. Funnel

A Photographic Atlas For The Biology Laboratory

Phylum Annelida

Table 7.5 Some Representatives of the Phylum Annelida

Classes and Representative Kinds	Characteristics
Polychaeta – tubeworms and sandworms	Mostly marine; segments with parapodia
Oligochaeta – earthworms	Freshwater and burrowing terrestrial forms; small setae; poorly developed head
Hirudinea – leaches	Freshwater; some are blood-sucking parasites and others are predators; lack setae; prominent muscular suckers

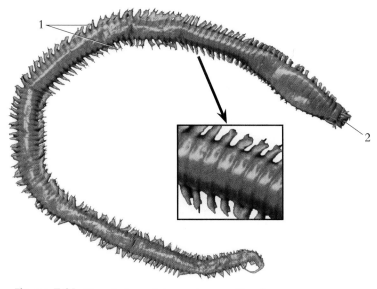

Figure 7.81 Dorsal view of the sandworm, *Neanthes*.

1. Parapodia 2. Mouth

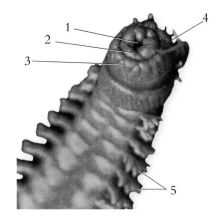

Figure 7.82 View of the head of the sandworm, *Neanthes*.

1. Mouth 4. Prostomium
2. Everted pharynx 5. Parapodia
3. Peristomium

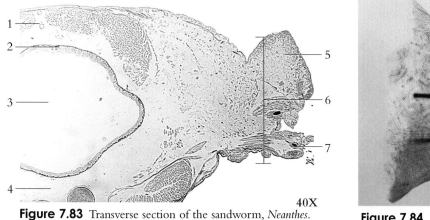

40X

Figure 7.83 Transverse section of the sandworm, *Neanthes*.

1. Dorsal blood vessel 5. Notopodium
2. Intestine 6. Parapodium
3. Lumen of intestine 7. Neuropodium
4. Coelom

100X

Figure 7.84 Parapodium of the sandworm, *Neanthes*.

1. Dorsal cirrus 3. Striae
2. Notopodium 4. Neuropodium

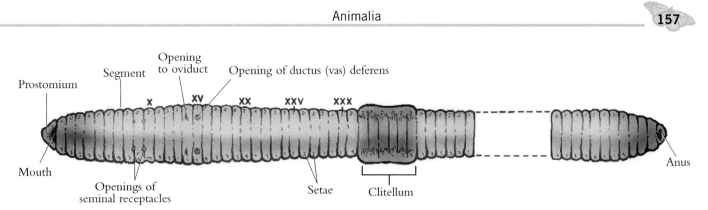

Figure 7.85 Ventral view diagram of the earthworm, *Lumbricus*.

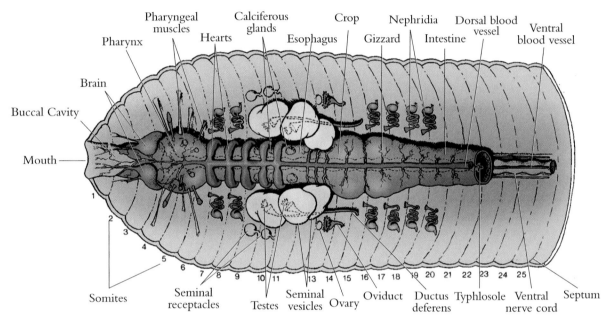

Figure 7.86 Diagram of the anterior end of the earthworm, *Lumbricus*.

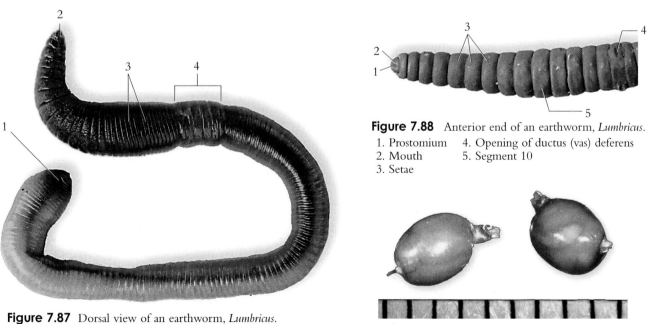

Figure 7.87 Dorsal view of an earthworm, *Lumbricus*.

1. Pygidium   3. Segments, or metameres
2. Prostomium   4. Clitellum

Figure 7.88 Anterior end of an earthworm, *Lumbricus*.

1. Prostomium   4. Opening of ductus (vas) deferens
2. Mouth   5. Segment 10
3. Setae

Figure 7.89 Earthworm cocoon (each line represents 1 mm).

Figure 7.91 Internal anatomy of the posterior end of an earthworm with part of the intestine removed.

1. Intestine
2. Septae
3. Nephridia
4. Ventral blood vessel

Figure 7.92 Transverse section of an earthworm posterior to the clitellum.

1. Dorsal blood vessel
2. Peritoneum
3. Typhlosole
4. Lumen of intestine
5. Intestine
6. Coelom
7. Ventral nerve cord
8. Epidermis
9. Circular muscles
10. Longitudinal muscles
11. Intestinal epithelium
12. Nephridium
13. Ventral blood vessel
14. Subneural blood vessel

Figure 7.90 Internal anatomy of the anterior end of an earthworm, *Lumbricus.*

1. Brain
2. Pharynx
3. Hearts
4. Seminal vesicles
5. Dorsal blood vessel
6. Seminal recepticles
7. Crop
8. Gizzard
9. Intestine

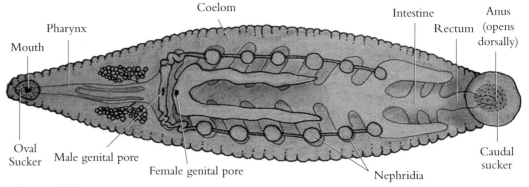

Figure 9.93 Diagram of a leech.

Mouth
Pharynx
Coelom
Intestine
Rectum
Anus (opens dorsally)
Oval Sucker
Male genital pore
Female genital pore
Nephridia
Caudal sucker

Figure 7.94 Leeches are more specialized than other annelids. They have lost their setae and developed suckers for attachment while sucking blood.

Phylum Nematoda

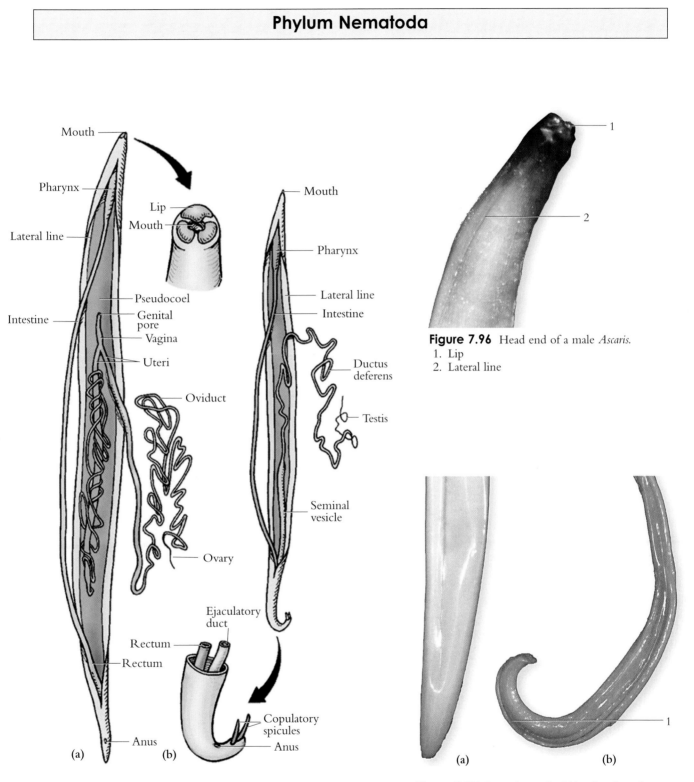

Figure 7.96 Head end of a male *Ascaris.*
1. Lip
2. Lateral line

Figure 7.95 Diagrams of the internal anatomy of (a) a female and (b) a male *Ascaris.*

Figure 7.97 Posterior end of (a) a female and (b) a male *Ascaris.*
1. Ejaculatory duct

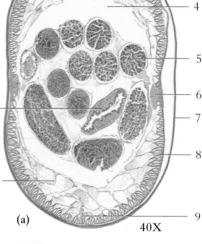

(a)

40X

Figure 7.100 Transverse sections of a male *Ascaris*.

1. Dorsal nerve cord
2. Intestine
3. Longitudinal muscle cell body
4. Pseudocoel
5. Testis
6. Lateral line
7. Cuticle
8. Contractile sheath of muscle cell
9. Ventral nerve cord

Figure 7.98 Internal anatomy of a male *Ascaris*.

1. Seminal vesicle
2. Intestine
3. Ductus deferens
4. Testes
5. Lateral line

Figure 7.99 Internal anatomy of a female *Ascaris*.

1. Intestine
2. Genital pore
3. Vagina
4. Uteri (Y-shaped)
5. Lateral line
6. Oviducts

(b)

40X

Figure 7.101 Transverse sections of a female *Ascaris*.

1. Dorsal nerve cord
2. Pseudocoel
3. Oviduct
4. Uterus
5. Cuticle
6. Eggs
7. Lumen of intestine
8. Lateral line
9. Intestine
10. Ovary
11. Longitudinal muscles
12. Ventral nerve cord

Figure 7.102 Dog heart infested with heartworm, *Dirofilaria immitis.*

Figure 7.103 Photomicrograph of *Trichinella spiralis* encysted in muscle.
1. Cyst   3. Larva
2. Muscle

Phylum Rotifera

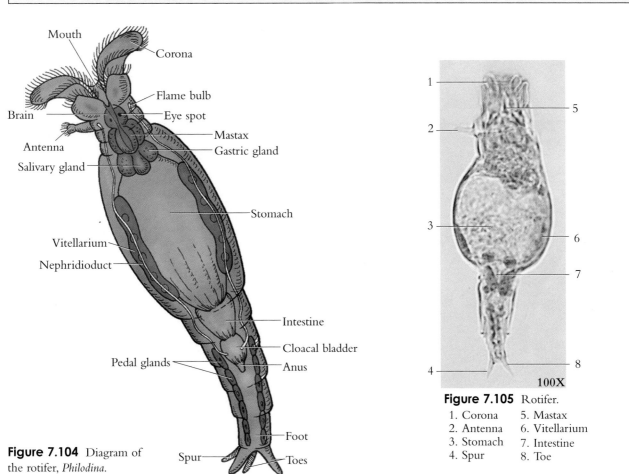

Mouth
Corona
Flame bulb
Brain
Eye spot
Antenna
Mastax
Salivary gland
Gastric gland
Stomach
Vitellarium
Nephridioduct
Intestine
Cloacal bladder
Pedal glands
Anus
Foot
Spur
Toes

Figure 7.104 Diagram of the rotifer, *Philodina.*

Figure 7.105 Rotifer.
1. Corona   5. Mastax
2. Antenna   6. Vitellarium
3. Stomach   7. Intestine
4. Spur   8. Toe

Phylum Arthropoda

Table 7.6 Representatives of the Phylum Arthropoda

Classes and Representative Kinds	Characteristics
Merostomata — horseshoecrab	Cephalothorax and abdomen; specialized front appendages into chelicerae; lack antennae and mandibles
Arachnida — spiders, mites, ticks, and scorpions	Cephalothorax and abdomen; four pairs of legs; book lungs or trchea; lack antennae and mandibles
Malacostraca — lobsters, crabs, and shrimp	Cephalothorax and abdomen; two pairs of antennae; pair of mandibles and two pairs of maxillae; biramous appendages; gills
Maxillopoda — copepods and barnacles	Cephalothorax and abdomen; freshwater and marine; up to six pairs of appendages
Insecta — beetles, butterflies, and ants	Head, thorax, and abdomen; three pairs of legs; well-developed mouth parts; usually two pair of wings; trachea
Chilopoda — centipedes	Head with segmented trunk; one pair of legs per segment; trachea; one pair of antennae
Diplopoda — millipedes	Head with segmented trunk; usually two pair of legs per segment; trachea

Figure 7.106 Trilobites are extinct arthropods from the Cambrian and Ordovician periods. (a) *Modicia typicalis*, and (b) *Dicranurus elegans*.

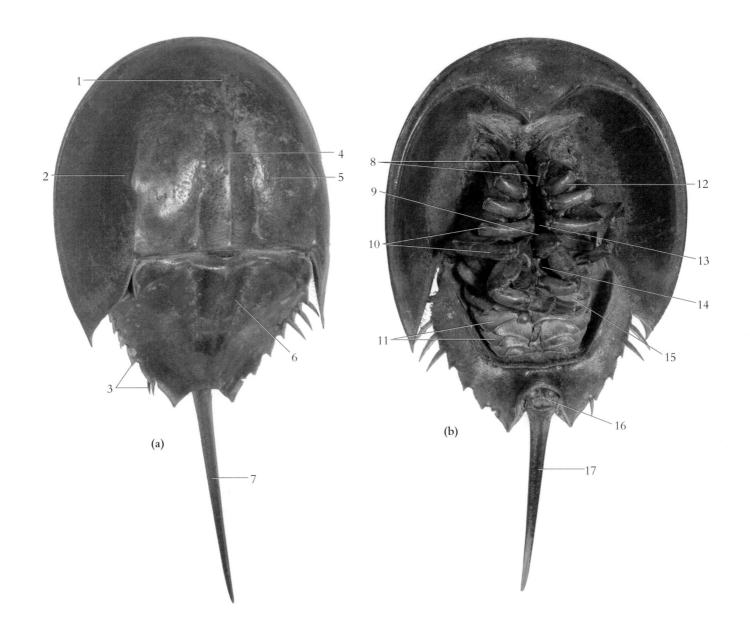

Figure 7.107 (a) Dorsal view and (b) a ventral view of the horseshoe crab, *Limulus*. This animal is commonly found in shallow waters along the Atlantic coast from Canada to Mexico.

1. Simple eye	6. Abdomen (opisthosoma)	11. Book gills	16. Anus
2. Compound eye	7. Telson	12. Pedipalp	17. Telson
3. Abdominal spines	8. Chelicerae	13. Mouth	
4. Anterior spine	9. Gnathobase	14. Chilaria	
5. Cephalothorax (prosoma)	10. Chelate legs	15. Genital operculum	

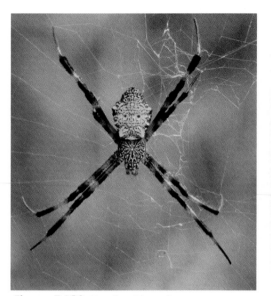

Figure 7.108 Beach spider , *Argiope appensa*, is an introduced species to Hawaii.

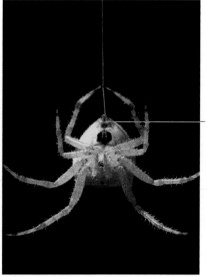

Figure 7.109 Garden spider in the process of spinning a web.
  1. Spinnerets

Figure 7.110 Ticks, within the family Ixodidae, are specialized parasitic arthropods. (a) A dorsal view and (b) a ventral view.

Eyes
Carapace
Chelicera
Fang
Pedipalp

Head, anterior view

Tibia
Patella
Tarsus
Femur
Maxilla
Trochanter

Female pedipalp

Claw
Tarsus
Metatarsus
Trochanter
Femur
Tibia
Patella

Walking leg

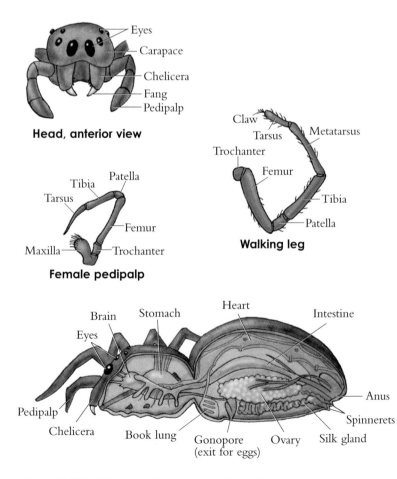

Brain
Stomach
Heart
Intestine
Eyes
Pedipalp
Chelicera
Book lung
Gonopore (exit for eggs)
Ovary
Silk gland
Spinnerets
Anus

Figure 7.111 Diagram of the anatomy of a spider.

Figure 7.112 Rose-haired tarantula, *Grammostola cola*.
  1. Opisthosoma   2. Pedipalp   3. Prosoma

Figure 7.113 Scorpion, *Pandinus.* Scorpions are most commonly found in tropical and subtropical regions, but there are also several species found in temperate zones.

1. Pedipalp
2. Cephalothorax
3. Walking legs
4. Preabdomen
5. Stinging apparatus
6. Postabdomen (tail)

Figure 7.114 Ticks attached and feeding on a savannah monitor, a large African lizard.

1. Ticks
2. Scales of monitor

Figure 7.115 Peppermint shrimp, *Lysmata wurdemanni.*

Figure 7.116 Ghost crab, *Ocypode ceratophthalmus.*

Figure 7.117 Water flea, *Daphnia,* is a common microscopic crustacean.

1. Heart
2. Midgut
3. Compound eye
4. Mouth
5. 2nd antenna
6. Setae
7. Brood chamber
8. Abdominal seta
9. Hindgut
10. Anus
11. Carapace

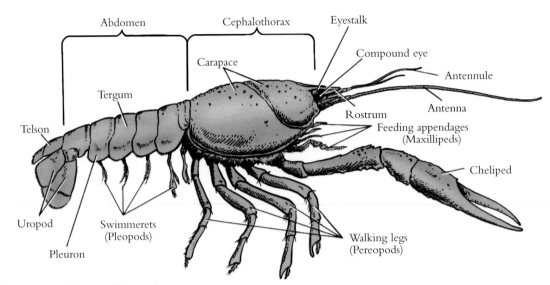

Figure 7.118 Diagram of the crayfish, *Cambarus*.

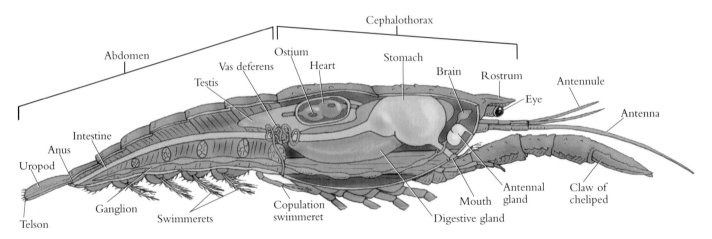

Figure 7.119 Anatomy of a crayfish. A sagittal section of an adult male.

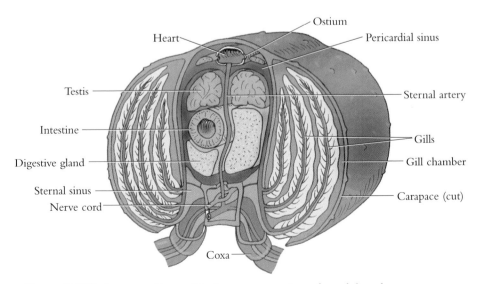

Figure 7.120 Anatomy of a crayfish. A transverse section of an adult male.

Figure 7.121 Dorsal view of the crayfish.

1. Cheliped
2. Walking legs
3. Carapace
4. Abdomen
5. Telson
6. Uropod
7. Antenna
8. Antennule
9. Rostrum
10. Eye
11. Cephalothorax
12. Tergum

Figure 7.122 Lateral view of the crayfish.

1. Carapace
2. Abdomen
3. Uropod
4. Swimmeret (pleopod)
5. Rostrum
6. Eye
7. Maxilliped
8. Cheliped
9. Walking legs

Figure 7.123 Ventral view of the oral region of the crayfish.

1. Third maxilliped
2. First maxilliped
3. Second maxilla
4. Green gland duct
5. Mandible

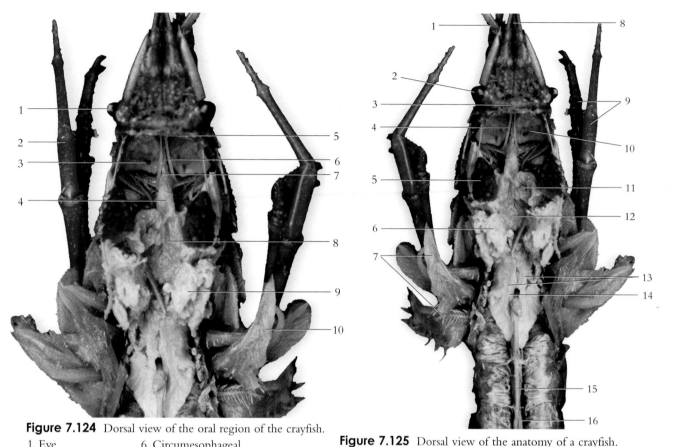

Figure 7.124 Dorsal view of the oral region of the crayfish.

1. Eye
2. Walking leg
3. Green gland
4. Cardiac chamber of stomach
5. Brain
6. Circumesophageal connection (of ventral nerve cord)
7. Esophagus
8. Region of gastric mill
9. Digestive gland
10. Gill

Figure 7.125 Dorsal view of the anatomy of a crayfish.

1. Antenna
2. Compound eye
3. Brain
4. Circumesophageal connection (of ventral nerve cord)
5. Mandibular muscle
6. Digestive gland
7. Gills
8. Antennules
9. Walking legs
10. Green gland
11. Esophagus
12. Pyloric stomach
13. Testis
14. Ductus deferens
15. Aorta
16. Intestine

(a)　(b)

Figure 7.126 Ventral views of (a) a female and (b) a male crayfish. The first pair of swimmerets are greatly enlarged in the male for the depositing of sperm in the female's seminal receptacle.

1. Third maxilliped
2. Walking legs
3. Disc covering oviduct
4. Seminal receptacle
5. Abdomen
6. Base of cheliped
7. Sperm ducts (genital pores)
8. Base of last walking leg
9. Copulatory swimmerets (pleopods)
10. Swimmerets (pleopods)

Field cricket, *Gryllus firmus*.

Dragonfly, *Anax*.

Seven-spot ladybird beetle, *Coccinella septempunctata*.

Paper wasp, *Polistes*.

Figure 7.127 Representative insects.

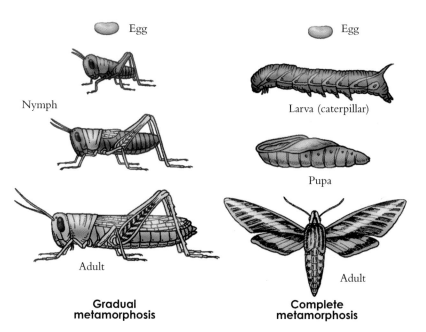

Egg

Nymph

Adult

Gradual metamorphosis

Egg

Larva (caterpillar)

Pupa

Adult

Complete metamorphosis

Figure 7.128 Insect development. In gradual (incomplete) metamorphosis the young resemble the adults but they are smaller and have different body proportions. In complete metamorphosis, the larvae look different than the adult and generally have different food requirements.

(a)

mm

(b)

(c)

Figure 7.129 Developmental stages of the common honeybee include (a) larval stage, (b) pupa, and (c) adult.

Figure 7.130 Developmental stages of the Monarch butterfly, *Danaus plexippus*, include (a) egg, (b) larval stage, (c) chrysalis, and (d) adult.

Figure 7.131 Common grey cricket molting. All arthropods must periodically shed their exoskeleton in order to grow. This process is called molting, or ecdysis.

40X

Figure 7.132 Honeybee stinger. The two darts contain barbs on the tips which point upward, making it difficult to remove a stinger from a wound.

  1. Sheath   2. Darts

40X

Figure 7.133 Housefly head, an example of a sponging type of mouthpart in insects. Notice the large lobes at the apex of the labium, which function in lapping up liquids.

  1. Compound eye   2. Labium

(a)   20X   (b)   75X

Figure 7.134 Wings of the honeybee, *Apis mellifera*. (a) Whole mount and (b) a close up.

  1. Cross veins   3. Hindwing   5. Transparent wing film
  2. Forewing   4. Cross veins   6. Hairs

(c)

(d)

(e)

(f)

(g)

(a)

(b)

20X

Figure 7.135 Common insect antennae. (a) Clavate - butterflies, (b) serrate - click beetles, (c) lamellate - scarab beetles, (d) aristate - house flies, (e) geniculate - weevils (f) moniliform - termites, and (g) plumose - moths.

1

2

3

4

200X

(a)

50X

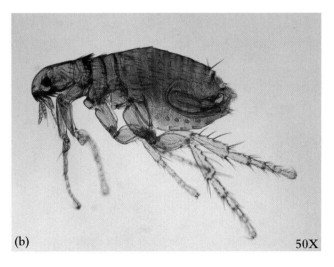

(b)

50X

Figure 7.136 Mouthparts of the flea, *Ctenocephalide*, which are specialized for parasitism. Notice the oral bristles beneath the mouth that aid the flea in penetrating between hairs to feed on the blood of mammals. (a) Female flea and (b) male flea.

1. Eye	3. Maxilla
2. Oral bristles	4. Maxillary palp

Figure 7.137 (a) Lateral view of the head of a butterfly. The most obvious structures on the head of a butterfly are compound eyes and the curled tongue for siphoning nectar from flowers. (b) A magnified view of the compound eye, and (c) a magnified view of the wing scales.

1. Compound eye   2. Tongue

Figure 7.138 Surface anatomy of a grasshopper, order Orthoptera.

1. Antenna	7. Labrum	13. Tergum
2. Compound eye	8. Labial palp	14. Spiracle
3. Ocelli	9. Femur	15. Cercus
4. Prothorax	10. Metathorax	16. Ovipositor
5. Mesothorax	11. Tibia	17. Tarsus
6. Tympanum	12. Forewing	18. Sternum

Figure 7.139 Preserved specimen of a grasshopper, order Orthoptera.

1. Mesothorax	7. Maxilla	13. Mesothorax
2. Vertex	8. Antenna	14. Spiracle
3. Compound eye	9. Claw	15. Abdomen
4. Vertex	10. Wing	16. Trochanter
5. Gena	11. Femur	17. Tarsus
6. Frons	12. Tibia	

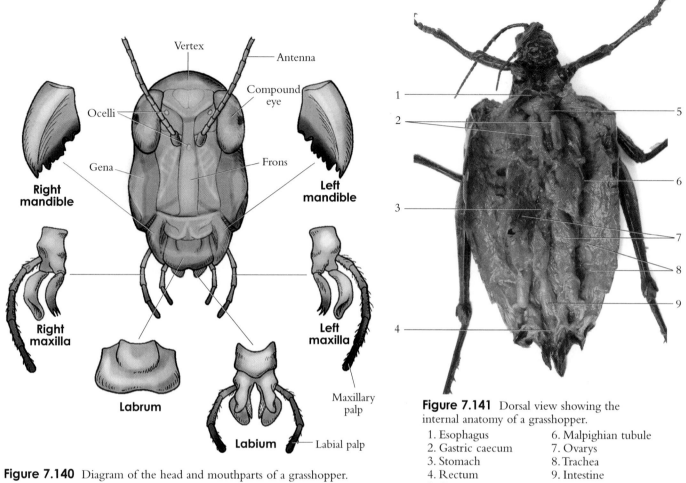

Figure 7.140 Diagram of the head and mouthparts of a grasshopper.

Figure 7.141 Dorsal view showing the internal anatomy of a grasshopper.

1. Esophagus
2. Gastric caecum
3. Stomach
4. Rectum
5. Crop
6. Malpighian tubule
7. Ovarys
8. Trachea
9. Intestine

Figure 7.142 Garden centipede, *Lithobius*, class chilopoda.

Figure 7.143 Giant african millipede, *Scaphiostreptus*, class diplopoda.

Phylum Echinodermata

Table 7.7 Representatives of the Phylum Echinodermata

Classes and Representative Kinds	Characteristics
Asteroidea — sea stars (star fish)	Pentaradial symmetry; appendages arranged around a central disk containing the mouth; tube feet with suckers
Echinoidea — sea urchins, and sand dollars	Disk-shaped with no arms; compact skeleton; movable spines; tube feet with suckers
Ophiuroidea — brittle stars	Pentaradial symmetry; appendages sharply marked off from central disk; tube feet without suckers
Holothuroidea — sea cucumbers	Cucumber-shaped with no arms; spines absent; tube feet with tentacles and suckers
Crinoidea — sea lilies and feather stars	Sessile during much of life cycle; calyx supported by elongated stalk in some

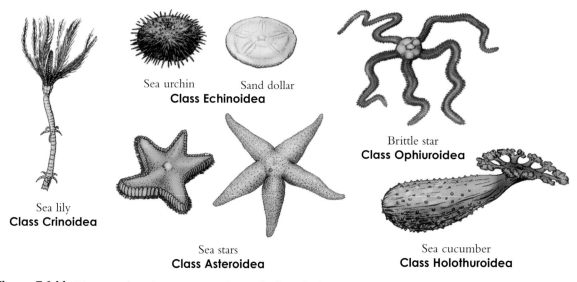

Sea urchin   Sand dollar
Class Echinoidea

Brittle star
Class Ophiuroidea

Sea lily
Class Crinoidea

Sea stars
Class Asteroidea

Sea cucumber
Class Holothuroidea

Figure 7.144 Diagram of specimens representing each class of echinoderms.

Figure 7.145 Sea stars (star fish), *Asterias*, grouped in a tide pool in southern California.

Figure 7.146 Green sea urchin, *Strongylocentrotus droebachiensis*.

Figure 7.147 California sea cucumber, *Parastichopus californicus*.

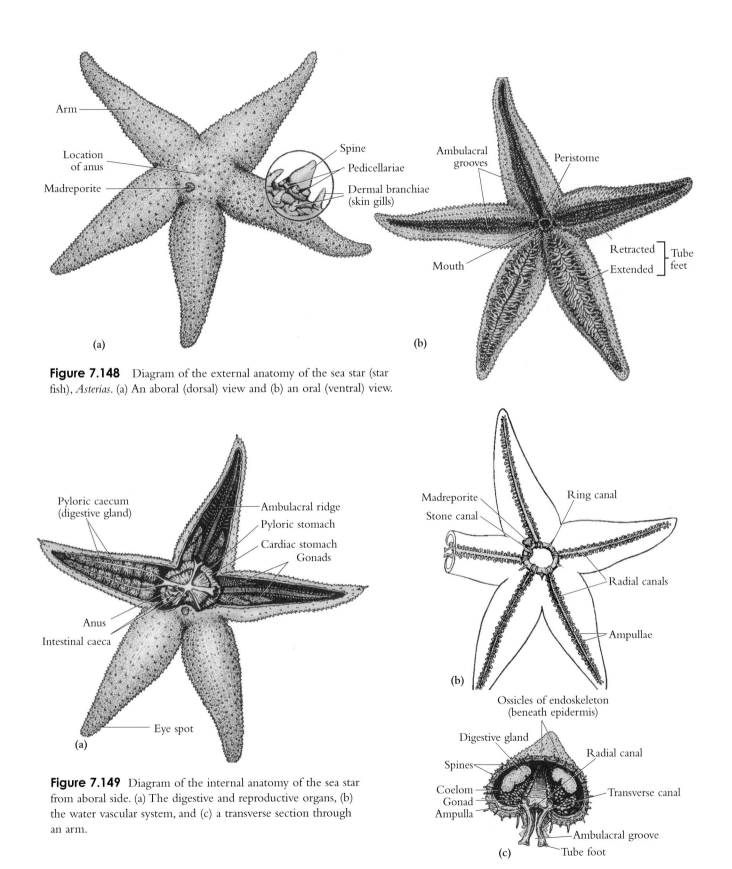

Figure 7.148 Diagram of the external anatomy of the sea star (star fish), *Asterias*. (a) An aboral (dorsal) view and (b) an oral (ventral) view.

Figure 7.149 Diagram of the internal anatomy of the sea star from aboral side. (a) The digestive and reproductive organs, (b) the water vascular system, and (c) a transverse section through an arm.

Figure 7.150 Aboral view of the internal anatomy of a sea star.
1. Ambulacral ridge
2. Gonad
3. Spines
4. Circular canal
5. Pyloric caecum (digestive gland)

Figure 7.151 Magnified aboral view of the internal anatomy of a sea star.
1. Polian vesicle
2. Ampullae
3. Stone canal
4. Ambulacral ridge
5. Madreporite
6. Pyloric duct
7. Pyloric caecum (digestive gland)
8. Gonad
9. Anus
10. Pyloric stomach
11. Spines

Figure 7.152 Oral view of a sea star.
1. Tube feet
2. Peristome
3. Mouth
4. Ambulacral groove
5. Oral spines

20X

Figure 7.153 Transverse section through the arm of a sea star.
1. Coelom
2. Tube foot
3. Epidermis
4. Sucker
5. Pyloric caecum
6. Radial canal
7. Gonad
8. Ambulacral groove

Figure 7.154
Oral view of the
sea urchin, *Arbacia*.
1. Mouth
2. Spines
3. Pedicellaria
4. Peristome

Figure 7.155
Aboral view of the
sea urchin.
1. Ossicles
2. Madreporite

Figure 7.156 Internal anatomy of a sea urchin.
1. Madreporite
2. Intestine
3. Aristotle's lantern
4. Mouth
5. Anus
6. Gonad
7. Stomach
8. Calcareous tooth

Tentacles
Aquapharyngeal
bulb
Ring canal
Polian
vesicle
Ampulla
Pharynx
Madreporite
Stomach
Intestine
Gonad
Tube
feet
Respiratory
tree
Cloaca
Anus

Figure 7.157 Sea cucumber,
Cucumaria.
1. Tentacles
2. Tube feet

Figure 7.158 Diagram of the internal
anatomy of a sea cucumber.

Figure 7.159 Internal anatomy
of a sea cucumber.
1. Tentacles
2. Longitudinal muscle
3. Gonad
4. Ampullae
5. Respiratory tree
6. Intestine
7. Tube feet
8. Anus

Phylum Chordata

Table 7.8 Representatives of the Phylum Chordata

Subphyla and Representative Kinds	Characteristics
Urochordata — tunicates	Marine, larvae are free-swimming and have notochord, gill slits, and dorsal hollow nerve cord; most adults are sessile (attached), filter-feeders, saclike animals
Cephalochordata — lancelets (*Amphioxus*)	Marine, segmented, elongated body with notochord extending the length of the body; cilia surrounding the mouth for obtaining food
Vertebrata — agnathans (lampreys and hagfishes), fishes (cartilaginous and bony), amphibians, reptiles, birds, mammals	Aquatic and terrestrial forms; distinct head and trunk supported by a series of cartilaginous or bony vertebrae in the adult; closed circulatory system and ventral heart; well-developed brain and sensory organs

Table 7.9 Representatives of the Subphylum Vertebrata

Taxa and Representative Kinds	Characteristics
Superclass Agnatha	Eel-like and aquatic; sucking mouth (some parasitic); lack jaws and paired appendages
Class Myxini — hagfishes	Terminal mouth with buccal funnel absent; nasal sac connected to pharynx; 4 pairs of tentacles; 5 to 10 pairs pharyngeal pouches
Class Cephalaspidomorphi — lampreys	Suctorial mouth with rasping teeth; nasal sac not connected to buccal cavity; 7 pairs of pharyngeal pouches
Superclass Gnathostomata	Jawed vertebrates; most with paired appendages
Class Chondrichthyes — sharks, rays, and skates	Cartilaginous skeleton; placoid scales; most have spiracle; spiral valve in digestive tract
Class Osteichthyes — bony fishes	Gills covered by bony operculum; most have swim bladder
Class Amphibia — salamanders, frogs, and toads	Larvae have gills and adults have lungs; scaleless skin (except apoda); an incomplete double circulation; three–chambered heart
Class Reptilia — turtles, snakes, and lizards	Amniotic egg; epidermal scales; three- or four-chambered heart; lungs
Class Aves — birds	Homeothermous (warm-blooded); feathers; toothless; air sacs; four-chambered heart with right aortic arch
Class Mammalia — mammals	Homeothermous; hair; mammary glands; most have seven cervical vertebrae; muscular diaphragm; three auditory ossicles; four–chambered heart with left aortic arch

Subphylum Urochordata

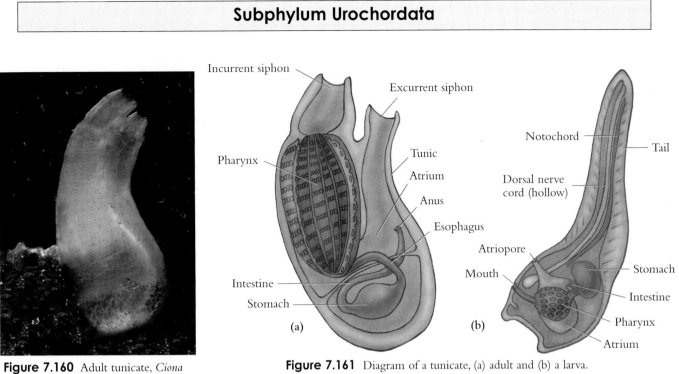

Figure 7.160 Adult tunicate, *Ciona intestinalis*.

Figure 7.161 Diagram of a tunicate, (a) adult and (b) a larva.

Subphylum Cephalochordata

Figure 7.162 Diagram of *Amphioxus*.

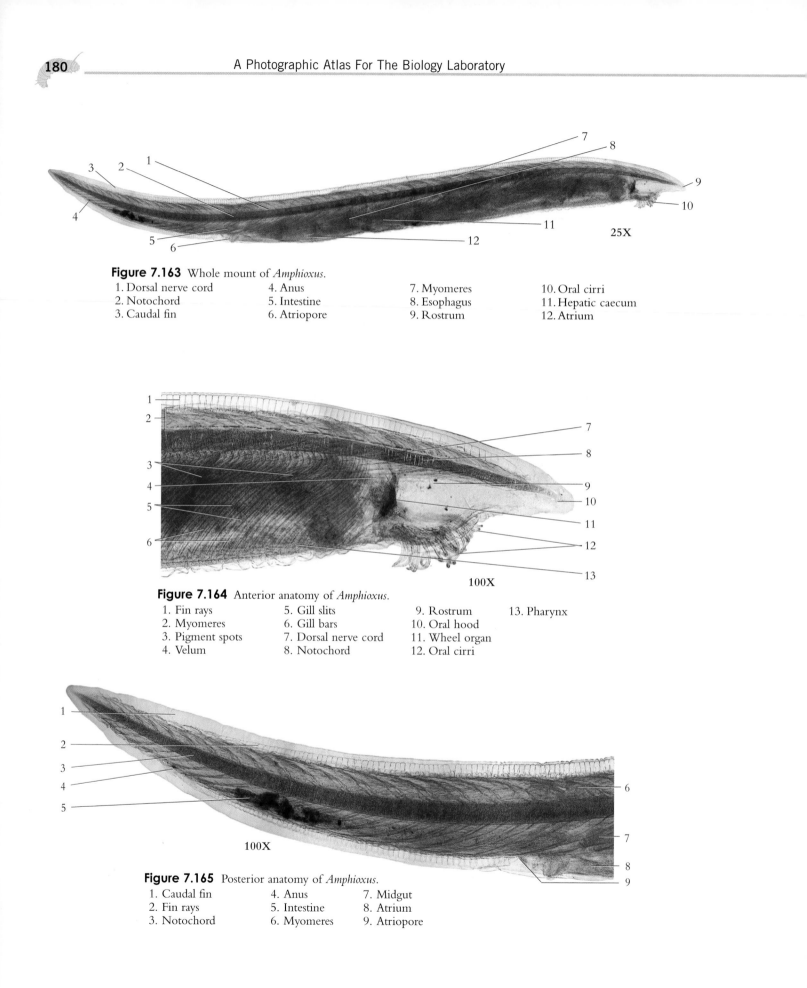

Figure 7.163 Whole mount of *Amphioxus*.

1. Dorsal nerve cord
2. Notochord
3. Caudal fin
4. Anus
5. Intestine
6. Atriopore
7. Myomeres
8. Esophagus
9. Rostrum
10. Oral cirri
11. Hepatic caecum
12. Atrium

25X

Figure 7.164 Anterior anatomy of *Amphioxus*.

1. Fin rays
2. Myomeres
3. Pigment spots
4. Velum
5. Gill slits
6. Gill bars
7. Dorsal nerve cord
8. Notochord
9. Rostrum
10. Oral hood
11. Wheel organ
12. Oral cirri
13. Pharynx

100X

Figure 7.165 Posterior anatomy of *Amphioxus*.

1. Caudal fin
2. Fin rays
3. Notochord
4. Anus
5. Intestine
6. Myomeres
7. Midgut
8. Atrium
9. Atriopore

100X

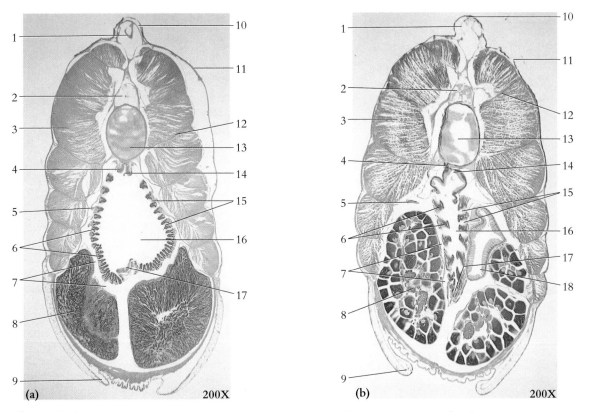

Figure 7.166 Transverse section through the pharyngeal region of (a) a male, and (b) a female *Amphioxus*.

1. Fin ray
2. Dorsal nerve cord
3. Myomere
4. Dorsal aorta
5. Nephridium
6. Gill bars
7. Atrium
8. Testis (male)
   Ovary (female)
9. Metapleural fold
10. Dorsal fin
11. Epidermis
12. Myoseptum
13. Notochord
14. Epibranchial groove
15. Gill slits
16. Pharynx
17. Endostyle (hypobranchial groove)
18. Hepatic caecum (liver)

Subphylum Vertebrata

Figure 7.167 External anatomy of a marine lamprey, *Petromyzon marinus*.

1. Head
2. Nostril
3. Pineal body
4. Caudal fin
5. Posterior dorsal fin
6. Trunk
7. Myomeres
8. Anterior dorsal fin

Figure 7.168
Anterior
anatomy of a marine
lamprey.
1. Eye
2. Buccal funnel
3. External gill slits

Figure 7.169 Oral
region of a marine
lamprey.
1. Buccal papillae
2. Horny teeth
3. Mouth

Figure 7.170
Cartilaginous skeleton
of a marine lamprey.
1. Buccal cavity
2. Cranium
3. Lingual cartilage
4. Branchial basket
5. Notochord

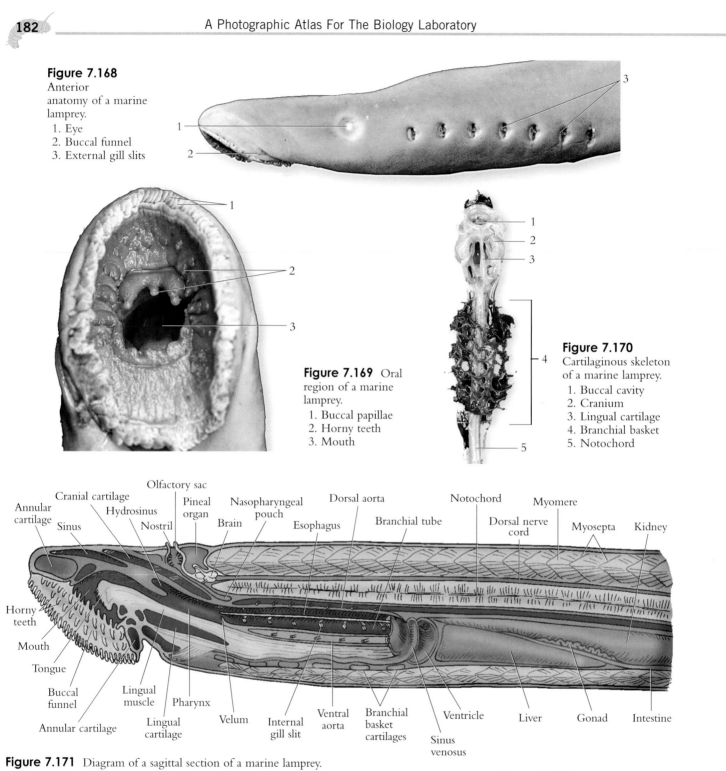

Figure 7.171 Diagram of a sagittal section of a marine lamprey.

Figure 7.172 Sagittal section
through the anterior region of
a lamprey.

1. Pineal organ	9. Esophagus
2. Nostril	10. Myomeres
3. Brain	11. Dorsal nerve
4. Annular	cord
cartilage	12. Notochord
5. Mouth	13. Dorsal aorta
6. Buccal muscle	14. Pericardial
7. Lingual	cavity
cartilage	15. Sinus venosus
8. Pharynx	16. Internal gill slits

Figure 7.173 Transverse section through the eyes of a lamprey.

1. Pineal organ	7. Cranial cartilage
2. Brain	8. Nasopharyngeal pouch
3. Lens of eye	9. Pharynx
4. Retina of eye	10. Pharyngeal gland
5. Lingual cartilage	
6. Myomere	

Figure 7.174 Transverse section through the branchial tube anterior to the fourth gill pouch of a lamprey. The ventral aorta is paired at this location.

1. Dorsal nerve cord	5. Anterior cardinal vein
2. Notochord	6. Esophagus
3. Branchial tube	7. Ventral aorta
4. Gill pouch	8. Lingual muscle

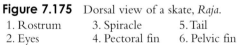

Figure 7.176 Detailed view of the head of a skate, *Raja*.
1. Eye   2. Spiracle   3. Rostrum

Figure 7.175 Dorsal view of a skate, *Raja*.

1. Rostrum	3. Spiracle	5. Tail
2. Eyes	4. Pectoral fin	6. Pelvic fin

Figure 7.177
Lateral view of the leopard shark, *Triakis semifasciata*.
1. Spiracle
2. Lateral line
3. Dorsal fins
4. Caudal fin (heterocercal tail)
5. Eye
6. Gill slits
7. Pectoral fin
8. Pelvic fin
9. Anal fin

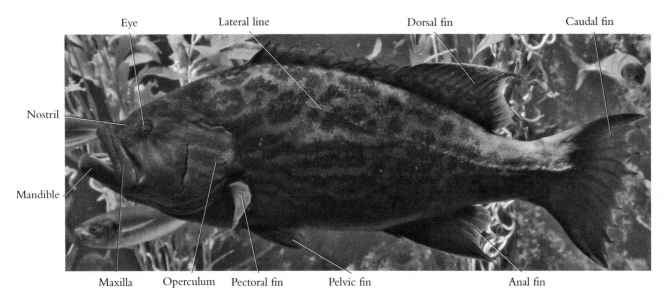

Eye   Lateral line   Dorsal fin   Caudal fin

Nostril

Mandible

Maxilla   Operculum   Pectoral fin   Pelvic fin   Anal fin

Figure 7.178 External structures of a grouper, *Mycteroperca bonaci*.

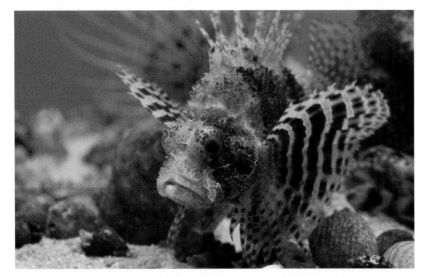

Figure 7.179 Lionfish, stonefish, and scorpionfish, within the family *Scorpaenidae*, have specialized spines in their dorsal fins for delivey of venom.

Figure 7.180 Tomato clownfish, *Amphiprion melanopus*, work as a pair to protect a group of eggs attached to rock surface.
1. Egg mass

Figure 7.181 Eastern newt, *Notophthalmus viridescens,* lives in humid sites, often beneath debris along stream banks.

(a)

Figure 7.182 Surface anatomy and body regions of the leopard frog, *Rana pipiens.*

1. Ankle	4. Eyes	7. Brachium
2. Knee	5. Nostril	8. Antebrachium
3. Foot	6. Tympanic membrane	9. Digits

Figure 7.183 Adult Indonesian giant tree frog, *Litoria infrafrenata.* (a) The frog is crouched on a person's fingers. (b) The adhesive toe discs can be seen in a ventral view.

(b)

Figure 7.184 Poison-dart frog, *Dendrobates,* secretes a toxic poison from the skin. South American indians have used this poison to coat darts.

Figure 7.185 Photograph showing hatching California king snakes, *Lampropeltis gentulus*. Most snakes are oviparous, meaning they lay eggs such as these. Some snakes, including all American pit vipers, are ovoviviparous, giving birth to well-developed young.

Figure 7.186 Aldabra giant tortoise, *Dipsochelys dussumieri*.

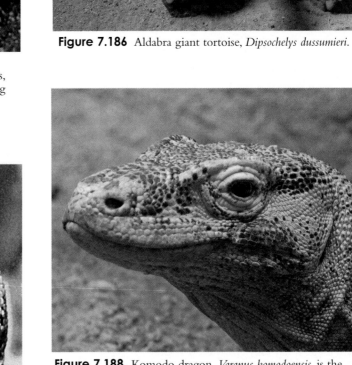

Figure 7.188 Komodo dragon, *Varanus komodoensis*, is the world's largest lizard species.

Figure 7.187 Veiled chameleon, *Chamaeleo calyptratus*. Chameleons are best known for their ability to change colors according to their surroundings.

Figure 7.189 Garter snake, *Thamnophis sirtalis*.

Figure 7.190 (a) Structure of a contour (pluma) feather. (b) Barbules and hooklets are shown in a photomicrograph.

1. Vane
2. Rachis
3. Calamus
4. Shaft
5. Hooklets
6. Barb
7. Barbule

Figure 7.191 American kestrel, *Falco sparverius*, is common throughout North America. It hunts small rodents and insects.

Figure 7.192 Robin, *Turdus migratorius*, is a member of the trush family. It is the state bird of Wisconsin.

Figure 7.193 Magellanic penguins, *Spheniscus magellanicus*, are the most common of the 17 species of penguins.

Figure 7.194 Gila woodpecker, *Melanerpes uropygialis*, "anting". A behavior where the woodpecker allows ants to crawl through its feathers and eat any parasites that the bird might have.

Figure 7.195 Malaysian fruit bat, *Pteropus hypomelanus*.

Figure 7.196 Capybara, *Hydrochaeris hydrochaeris*, is the world's largest rodent reaching a length of over 4 feet and weighing as much as 145 pounds.

Figure 7.197 Hawaiian Monk Seal, *Monachus schauinslandi*, is an endangered seal numbering less than 1,200.

Figure 7.198 Koala, *Phascolarctos cinereus*, is a marsupial carrying their young in a pouch.

Figure 7.199 Bottlenose dolphin, *Tursiops truncatus*, a highly social marine mammal.

Figure 7.200 Orangutan, *Pongo pygmaeus*, mean "person of the forest" and is found in Asia.

Chapter 8
Vertebrate Dissections

An understanding of the structure of a vertebrate organism is requisite to learning about physiological mechanisms and about how the animal functions in its environment. The selective pressures that determine evolutionary change frequently have an influence on anatomical structures. Studying dissected specimens, therefore, provides phylogenetic information about how groups of organisms are related.

Some biology laboratories have the resources to provide students with opportunities for doing selected vertebrate dissections. For these students, the photographs contained in this chapter will be a valuable source for identification of structures on your specimens as they are dissected and studied. If dissection specimens are not available, the excellent photographs of carefully dissected prepared specimens presented in this chapter will be an adequate substitute. Care has gone into the preparation of these specimens to depict and identify the principal body structures from representative specimens of each of the classes of vertebrates. Selected human cadaver dissections are shown in photographs contained in chapter 8. As the anatomy of vertebrate specimens is studied in this chapter, observe the photographs of human dissections in the previous chapter and note the similarities of body structure, particularly to those of another mammal.

Class Agnatha

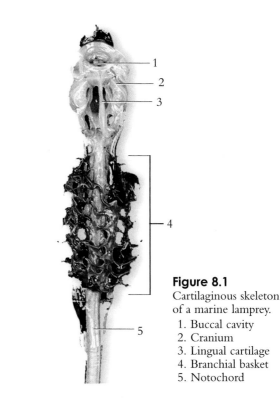

Figure 8.1
Cartilaginous skeleton of a marine lamprey.
1. Buccal cavity
2. Cranium
3. Lingual cartilage
4. Branchial basket
5. Notochord

Class Chondrichthyes

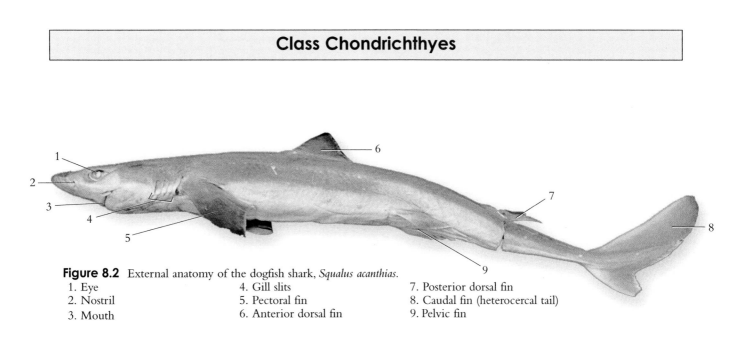

Figure 8.2 External anatomy of the dogfish shark, *Squalus acanthias.*

1. Eye
2. Nostril
3. Mouth
4. Gill slits
5. Pectoral fin
6. Anterior dorsal fin
7. Posterior dorsal fin
8. Caudal fin (heterocercal tail)
9. Pelvic fin

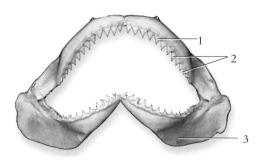

Figure 8.4 Shark jaws.
1. Palatopterygoquadrate   2. Placoid teeth
   cartilage   3. Meckel's cartilage

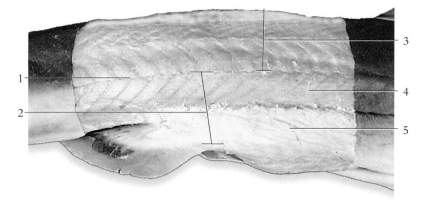

Figure 8.5 Lateral view of the axial musculature of the dogfish shark.
1. Transverse septum   4. Lateral bundle of myotomes
2. Hypaxial myotome portion   5. Ventral bundle of myotomes
3. Epaxial myotome portion

Figure 8.3 Ventral view of the
cartilaginous skeleton of a male
dogfish shark.
1. Palatopterygoquadrate
   cartilage (upper jaw)
2. Hypobranchial cartilage
3. Caudal fin
4. Caudal vertebrae
5. Pelvic fin
6. Posterior dorsal fin
7. Rostrum
8. Chondrocranium
9. Meckel's cartilage (lower jaw)
10. Visceral arches
11. Pectoral girdle
12. Pectoral fin
13. Trunk vertebrae
14. Anterior dorsal fin
15. Pelvic girdle
16. Clasper

Figure 8.6 Musculature of the jaw, gills, and pectoral fin of a dogfish shark.
1. 2nd dorsal constrictor   5. Facial nerve (hyomandibular branch)
2. Levator of pectoral fin   6. Mandibular adductor
3. 3rd through 6th ventral constrictors   7. 2nd ventral constrictor
4. Spiracular muscle

Figure 8.7 Ventral view of the hypobranchial musculature of the dogfish shark.

1. 1st ventral constrictor
2. Common coracoarcual
3. Linea alba
4. Depressor of pectoral fin
5. Mandibular adductor
6. 2nd ventral constrictor
7. 3rd through 6th ventral constrictors
8. Hypaxial muscle

Figure 8.8 Internal anatomy of a male dogfish shark.

1. Right lobe of liver
2. Pyloric sphincter valve
3. Stomach (pyloric region)
4. Spleen
5. Ileum
6. Testis
7. Esophagus
8. Stomach (cardiac region)
9. Kidney
10. Rectal gland
11. Cloaca
12. Clasper

Figure 8.9 Heart, gills, and associated vessels of a dogfish shark.

1. Mouth
2. Ventral aorta
3. Conus ateriosus
4. Gills
5. Ventricle
6. Pectoral girdle (cut)
7. Afferent branchial arteries
8. Gill cleft
9. Pericardial cavity
10. Sinus venosus
11. Transverse septum
12. Liver

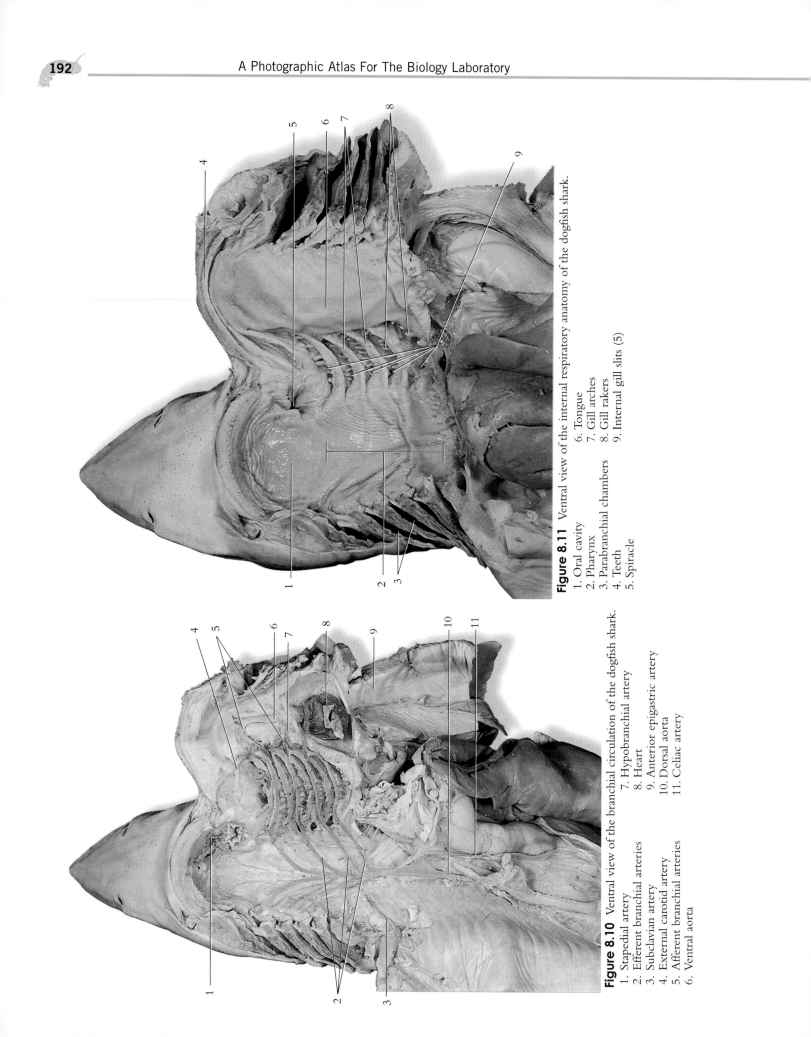

Figure 8.11 Ventral view of the internal respiratory anatomy of the dogfish shark.

1. Oral cavity
2. Pharynx
3. Parabranchial chambers
4. Teeth
5. Spiracle
6. Tongue
7. Gill arches
8. Gill rakers
9. Internal gill slits (5)

Figure 8.10 Ventral view of the branchial circulation of the dogfish shark.

1. Stapedial artery
2. Efferent branchial arteries
3. Subclavian artery
4. External carotid artery
5. Afferent branchial arteries
6. Ventral aorta
7. Hypobranchial artery
8. Heart
9. Anterior epigastric artery
10. Dorsal aorta
11. Celiac artery

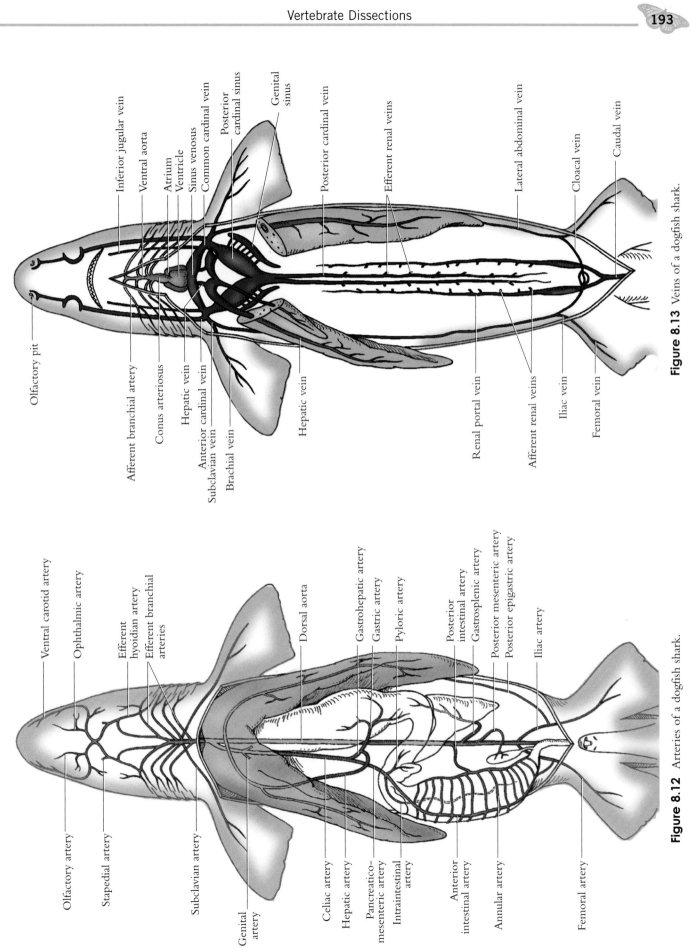

Olfactory pit

Afferent branchial artery

Conus arteriosus

Hepatic vein

Subclavian vein

Anterior cardinal vein

Brachial vein

Hepatic vein

Inferior jugular vein

Ventral aorta

Atrium

Ventricle

Sinus venosus

Common cardinal vein

Posterior cardinal sinus

Genital sinus

Posterior cardinal vein

Efferent renal veins

Lateral abdominal vein

Cloacal vein

Caudal vein

Renal portal vein

Afferent renal veins

Iliac vein

Femoral vein

Figure 8.13 Veins of a dogfish shark.

Ventral carotid artery

Ophthalmic artery

Efferent hyoidian artery

Efferent branchial arteries

Subclavian artery

Genital artery

Olfactory artery

Stapedial artery

Dorsal aorta

Gastrohepatic artery

Gastric artery

Pyloric artery

Posterior intestinal artery

Gastrosplenic artery

Posterior mesenteric artery

Posterior epigastric artery

Iliac artery

Celiac artery

Hepatic artery

Pancreatico-mesenteric artery

Intraintestinal artery

Anterior intestinal artery

Annular artery

Femoral artery

Figure 8.12 Arteries of a dogfish shark.

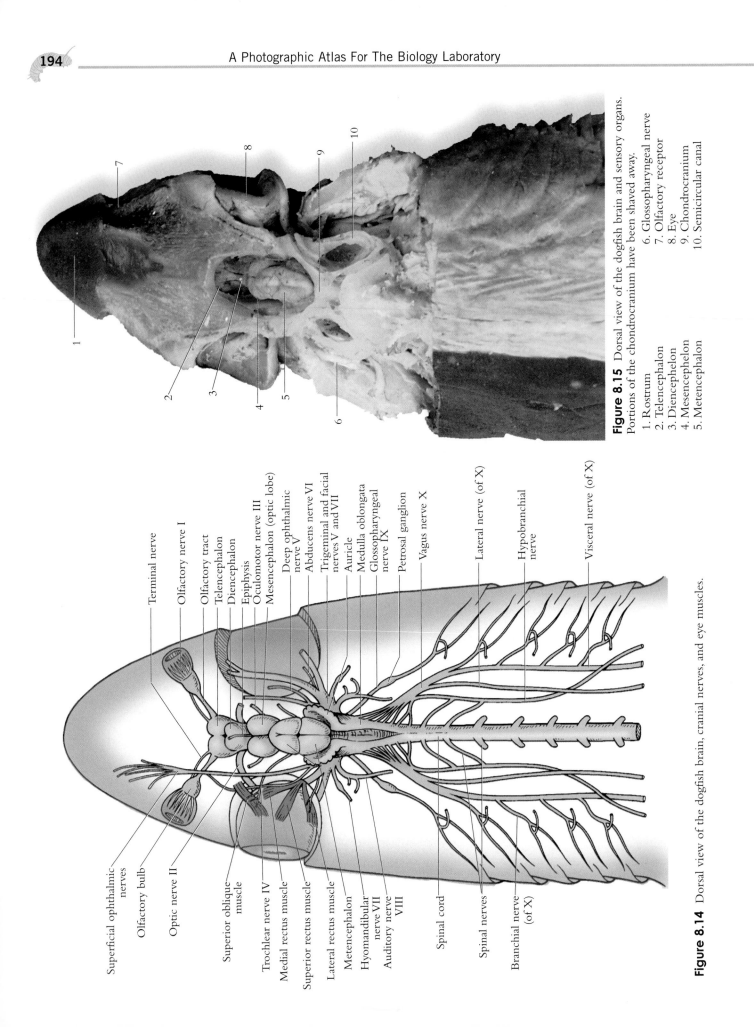

Figure 8.15 Dorsal view of the dogfish brain and sensory organs. Portions of the chondrocranium have been shaved away.

1. Rostrum
2. Telencephalon
3. Diencephalon
4. Mesencephalon
5. Metencephalon
6. Glossopharyngeal nerve
7. Olfactory receptor
8. Eye
9. Chondrocranium
10. Semicircular canal

Superficial ophthalmic nerves
Olfactory bulb
Optic nerve II
Superior oblique muscle
Trochlear nerve IV
Medial rectus muscle
Superior rectus muscle
Lateral rectus muscle
Metencephalon
Hyomandibular nerve VII
Auditory nerve VIII
Spinal cord
Spinal nerves
Branchial nerve (of X)

Terminal nerve
Olfactory nerve I
Olfactory tract
Telencephalon
Diencephalon
Epiphysis
Oculomotor nerve III
Mesencephalon (optic lobe)
Deep ophthalmic nerve V
Abducens nerve VI
Trigeminal and facial nerves V and VII
Auricle
Medulla oblongata
Glossopharyngeal nerve IX
Petrosal ganglion
Vagus nerve X
Lateral nerve (of X)
Hypobranchial nerve
Visceral nerve (of X)

Figure 8.14 Dorsal view of the dogfish brain, cranial nerves, and eye muscles.

Class Osteichthyes

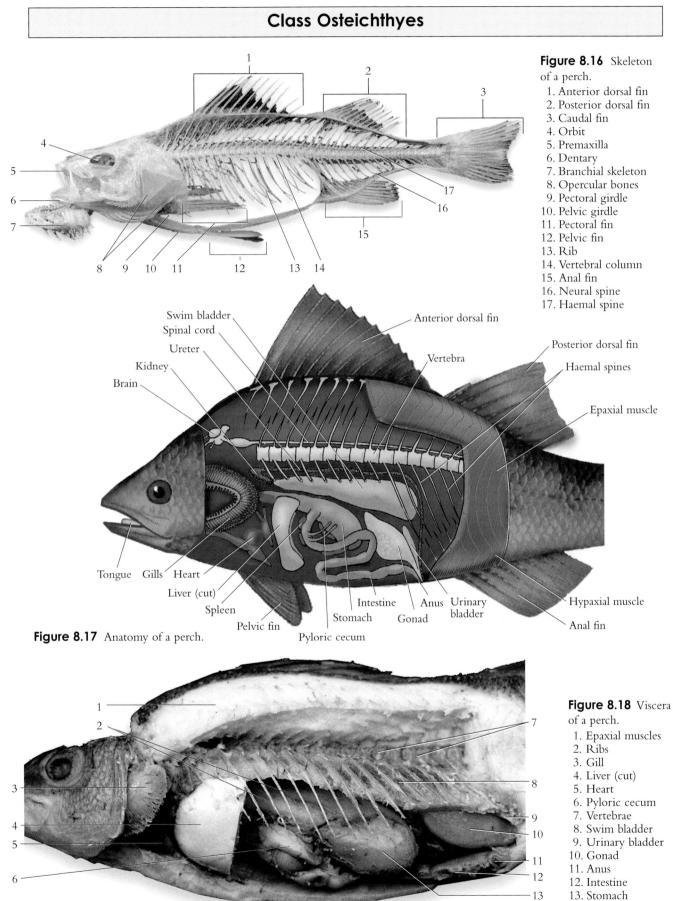

Figure 8.16 Skeleton of a perch.
1. Anterior dorsal fin
2. Posterior dorsal fin
3. Caudal fin
4. Orbit
5. Premaxilla
6. Dentary
7. Branchial skeleton
8. Opercular bones
9. Pectoral girdle
10. Pelvic girdle
11. Pectoral fin
12. Pelvic fin
13. Rib
14. Vertebral column
15. Anal fin
16. Neural spine
17. Haemal spine

Swim bladder
Spinal cord
Ureter
Kidney
Brain
Anterior dorsal fin
Vertebra
Posterior dorsal fin
Haemal spines
Epaxial muscle
Tongue   Gills   Heart
Liver (cut)
Spleen
Pelvic fin
Pyloric cecum
Stomach
Intestine
Gonad
Anus   Urinary bladder
Hypaxial muscle
Anal fin

Figure 8.17 Anatomy of a perch.

Figure 8.18 Viscera of a perch.
1. Epaxial muscles
2. Ribs
3. Gill
4. Liver (cut)
5. Heart
6. Pyloric cecum
7. Vertebrae
8. Swim bladder
9. Urinary bladder
10. Gonad
11. Anus
12. Intestine
13. Stomach

Class Amphibia

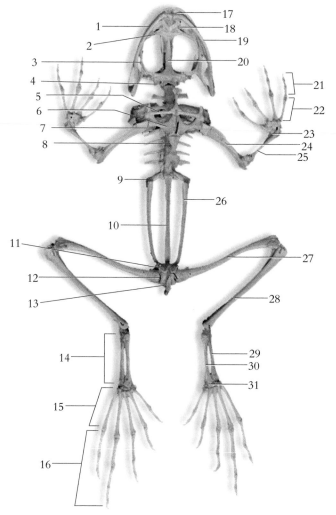

Figure 8.19 Dorsal view of the frog skeleton.

1. Squamosal bone
2. Quadratojugal bone
3. Phalanges of digits
4. Metacarpal bones
5. Carpal bones
6. Scapula
7. Vertebra
8. Transverse process of sacral (ninth) vertebra
9. Ilium
10. Acetabulum
11. Ischium
12. Tarsal bones
13. Metatarsal bones
14. Phalanges of digits
15. Nasal bone
16. Frontoparietal bone
17. Transverse process
18. Suprascapula
19. Humerus
20. Radioulna
21. Transverse process
22. Urostyle
23. Femur
24. Tibiofibula
25. Fibulare (calcaneum)
26. Tibiale (astragalus)
27. Distal tarsal bones

Figure 8.20 Ventral view of the frog skeleton.

1. Maxilla
2. Palatine
3. Pterygoid bone
4. Exoccipital bone
5. Clavicle
6. Coracoid
7. Glenoid fossa
8. Sternum
9. Transverse process of sacral (ninth) vertebra
10. Urostyle
11. Pubis
12. Acetabulum
13. Ischium
14. Tarsal bones
15. Metatarsal bones
16. Phalanges of digits
17. Premaxilla
18. Vomer
19. Dentary
20. Parasphenoid bone
21. Phalanges of digits
22. Metacarpal bones
23. Carpal bones
24. Humerus
25. Radioulna
26. Ilium
27. Femur
28. Tibiofibula
29. Fibulare (calcaneum)
30. Tibiale (astragalus)
31. Distal tarsal bones

Figure 8.22 Diagram of the dorsal frog musculature.

Figure 8.21 Dorsal view of the frog musulature (m.=muscle).

1. Deltoid m.
2. Anconeus m.
3. External abdominal oblique m.
4. Gluteus m.
5. Piriformis m.
6. Biceps femoris m.
7. Gracilis minor m.
8. Peroneus m.
9. Latissimus dorsi m.
10. Longissimus dorsi m.
11. Coccygeoiliacus m.
12. Cutaneus abdominis m.
13. Triceps femoris m.
14. Semimembranosus m.
15. Gastrocnemius m.

Figure 8.23 Dorsal view of the leg muscles of a frog (m.=muscle).

1. Gluteus m.
2. Cutaneus abdominis m.
3. Piriformis m.
4. Semimembranosus m.
5. Gracilis minor m.
6. Peroneus m.
7. Coccygeoiliacus m.
8. Triceps femoris m. (cut)
9. Iliacus internus m.
10. Biceps femoris m.
11. Adductor magnus m.
12. Semitendinosus m.
13. Gastrocnemius m.

Figure 8.24 A ventral view of the leg muscles of a frog (m.=muscle).

1. External abdominal oblique m.
2. Triceps femoris m.
3. Adductor longus m.
4. Adductor magnus m.
5. Semitendinosus m.
6. Semimembranosus m.
7. Gastrocnemius m.
8. Tibialis posterior m.
9. Rectus abdominis m.
10. Sartorius m.
11. Gracilis major m.
12. Gracilis minor m.
13. Extensor cruris m.
14. Tibialis anterior longus m.
15. Tibialis anterior brevis m.

Figure 8.25 Ventral view of the frog viscera.

1. External carotid artery
2. Truncus arteriosus
3. Right lobe of liver
4. Small intestine
5. Ovary
6. Duodenum
7. Ventral abdominal vein (cut)
8. Conus arteriosus
9. Heart
10. Left lobe of liver
11. Stomach
12. Large intestine

Figure 8.26 Deep view of the frog viscera.

1. Liver (reflected)
2. Gallbladder
3. Stomach
4. Small intestine
5. Ovary
6. Left lung
7. Oviduct
8. Spleen
9. Caudal vena cava
10. Large intestine

Figure 8.28 Ateries and veins of the frog trunk.

1. Systemic arch
2. Truncus arteriosus
3. Heart
4. Caudal vena cava
5. Right kidney
6. Left lung
7. Left kidney
8. Celiacomesenteric trunk
9. Urogenital arteries
10. Sciatic arteries

Figure 8.27 Deep view of the frog viscera.

1. Gallbladder
2. Stomach
3. Pancreas
4. Celiacomesenteric trunk
5. Spleen
6. Caudal vena cava
7. Large intestine
8. Ventral abdominal vein (cut)
9. Left lung
10. Oviduct
11. Ovary
12. Left kidney

Figure 8.30 Veins of a frog.

Figure 8.29 Arteries of a frog.

Class Reptilia

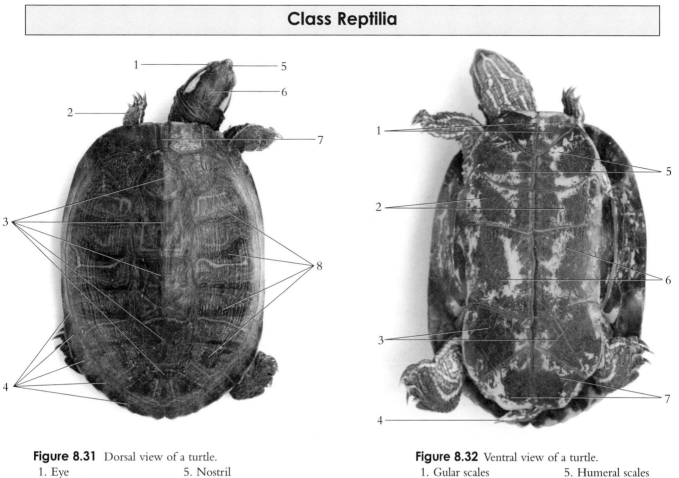

Figure 8.31 Dorsal view of a turtle.

1. Eye
2. Pentadactyl foot
3. Vertebral scales
4. Marginal scales
   (encircle the carapace)
5. Nostril
6. Head
7. Nuchal scale
8. Costal scales

Figure 8.32 Ventral view of a turtle.

1. Gular scales
2. Pectoral scales
3. Femoral scales
4. Tail
5. Humeral scales
6. Abdominal scales
7. Anal scales

Figure 8.33 Skull of a turtle.

1. Parietal bone
2. Supraoccipital bone
3. Postorbital bone
4. Jugal bone
5. Quadratojugal bone
6. Exoccipital bone
7. Quadrate bone
8. Supraangular bone
9. Articular bone
10. Angular bone
11. Frontal bone
12. Prefrontal bone
13. Palatine bone
14. Premaxilla
15. Maxilla
16. Beak
17. Dentary

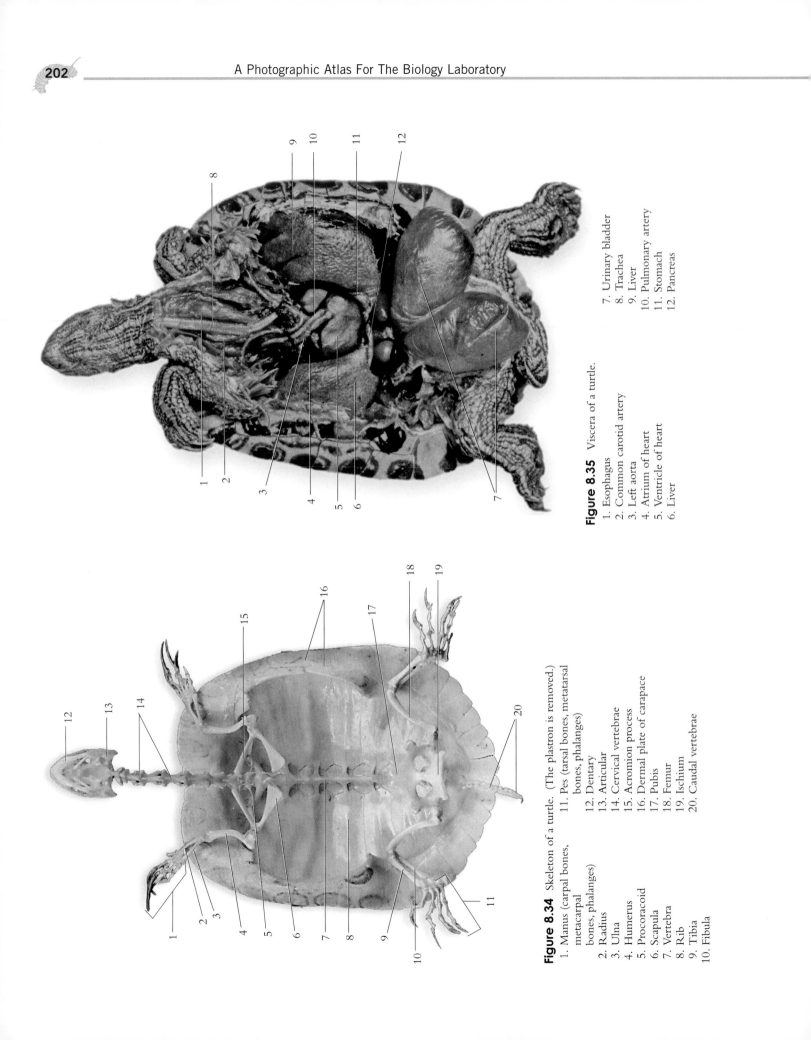

Figure 8.35 Viscera of a turtle.

1. Esophagus
2. Common carotid artery
3. Left aorta
4. Atrium of heart
5. Ventricle of heart
6. Liver
7. Urinary bladder
8. Trachea
9. Liver
10. Pulmonary artery
11. Stomach
12. Pancreas

Figure 8.34 Skeleton of a turtle. (The plastron is removed.)

1. Manus (carpal bones, metacarpal bones, phalanges)
2. Radius
3. Ulna
4. Humerus
5. Procoracoid
6. Scapula
7. Vertebra
8. Rib
9. Tibia
10. Fibula
11. Pes (tarsal bones, metatarsal bones, phalanges)
12. Dentary
13. Articular
14. Cervical vertebrae
15. Acromion process
16. Dermal plate of carapace
17. Pubis
18. Femur
19. Ischium
20. Caudal vertebrae

(a)   (b)

Figure 8.36 Comparison of the external anatomy of the head of (a) the savannah monitor lizard (*Varanus exanthematicus*) and (b) the green tree python (*Morelia viridis*). Lizards have eyelids and external ears, whereas, these structures are lacking in snakes. (Notice the heat pit receptors, which are characteristic of pythons and pit vipers and are adaptive for predation on warm-blooded vertebrates.)

1. Eyelids   2. External ear   3. Heat pits

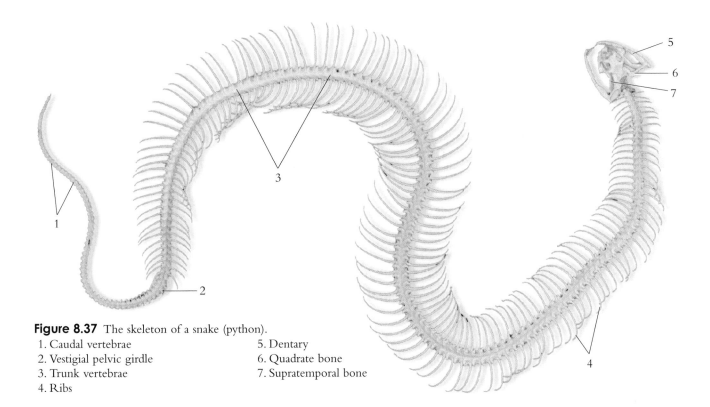

Figure 8.37 The skeleton of a snake (python).

1. Caudal vertebrae   5. Dentary
2. Vestigial pelvic girdle   6. Quadrate bone
3. Trunk vertebrae   7. Supratemporal bone
4. Ribs

Figure 8.38 Internal anatomy of a female rattlesnake, *Crotalus*. Note that the left lung of snakes is either rudimentary or absent.

1. Stomach
2. Pancreas
3. Trachea
4. Liver
5. Right lung
6. Heart

7. Thyroid gland
8. Anus
9. Intestine
10. Esophagus
11. Right ovary
12. Trachea

13. Left ovary
14. Oviducts
15. Rectum
16. Left kidney

Figure 8.39 Internal anatomy of a male snake. Note that the testes and kidneys are staggered.

1. Hemipenes
2. Anus
3. Ductus deferens
4. Right testis

5. Intestine
6. Left testis
7. Ductus deferens
8. Right kidney

9. Ureter
10. Left kidney

Class Aves

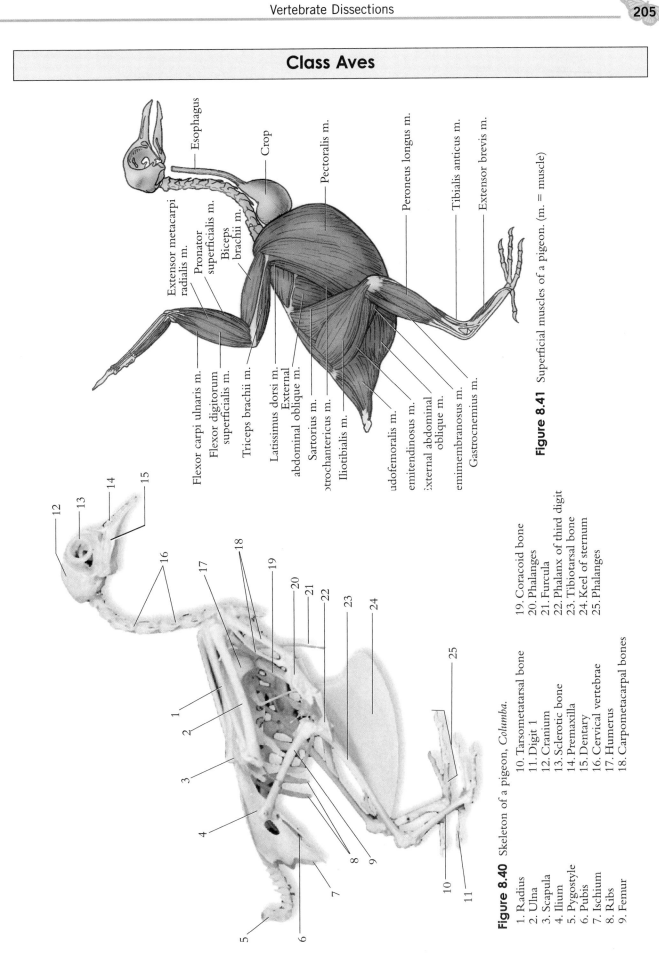

Figure 8.40 Skeleton of a pigeon, *Columba.*

1. Radius
2. Ulna
3. Scapula
4. Ilium
5. Pygostyle
6. Pubis
7. Ischium
8. Ribs
9. Femur

10. Tarsometatarsal bone
11. Digit 1
12. Cranium
13. Sclerotic bone
14. Premaxilla
15. Dentary
16. Cervical vertebrae
17. Humerus
18. Carpometacarpal bones

19. Coracoid bone
20. Phalanges
21. Furcula
22. Phalanx of third digit
23. Tibiotarsal bone
24. Keel of sternum
25. Phalanges

Esophagus
Crop
Pectoralis m.
Peroneus longus m.
Tibialis anticus m.
Extensor brevis m.

Extensor metacarpi radialis m.
Pronator superficialis m.
Biceps brachii m.

Flexor carpi ulnaris m.
Flexor digitorum superficialis m.
Triceps brachii m.
Latissimus dorsi m.
External abdominal oblique m.
Sartorius m.
Iliotrochantericus m.
Iliotibialis m.

Iliocaudofemoralis m.
Semitendinosus m.
External abdominal oblique m.
Semimembranosus m.
Gastrocnemius m.

Figure 8.41 Superficial muscles of a pigeon. (m. = muscle)

Figure 8.42 Ventral view of a pigeon heart and surrounding organs.

1. Crop
2. Common carotid artery
3. Esophagus
4. Right subclavian artery
5. Heart (within pericardium)
6. Right lung
7. Liver
8. Trachea
9. Leftt subclavian artery
10. Left lung
11. Greater omentum

Figure 8.43 Viscera of a pigeon with the heart sectioned.

1. Right atrium
2. Right lung
3. Right ventricle
4. Liver (cut)
5. Small intestine
6. Trachea
7. Aortic arch
8. Left atrium
9. Left ventricle
10. Gizzard

Class Mammalia

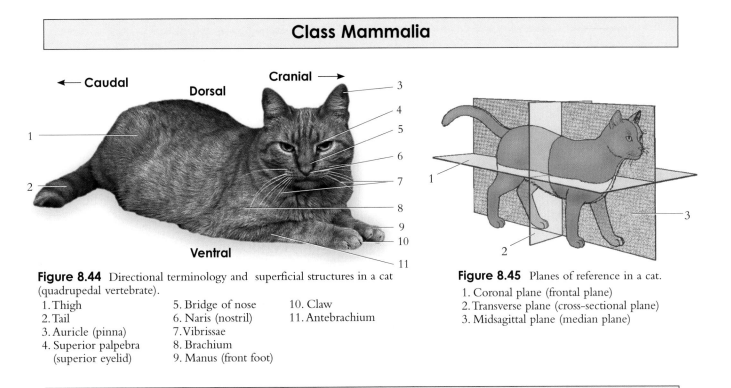

Figure 8.44 Directional terminology and superficial structures in a cat (quadrupedal vertebrate).

1. Thigh
2. Tail
3. Auricle (pinna)
4. Superior palpebra (superior eyelid)
5. Bridge of nose
6. Naris (nostril)
7. Vibrissae
8. Brachium
9. Manus (front foot)
10. Claw
11. Antebrachium

Figure 8.45 Planes of reference in a cat.

1. Coronal plane (frontal plane)
2. Transverse plane (cross-sectional plane)
3. Midsagittal plane (median plane)

Rat Dissection

Figure 8.46 Skeleton of a rat.

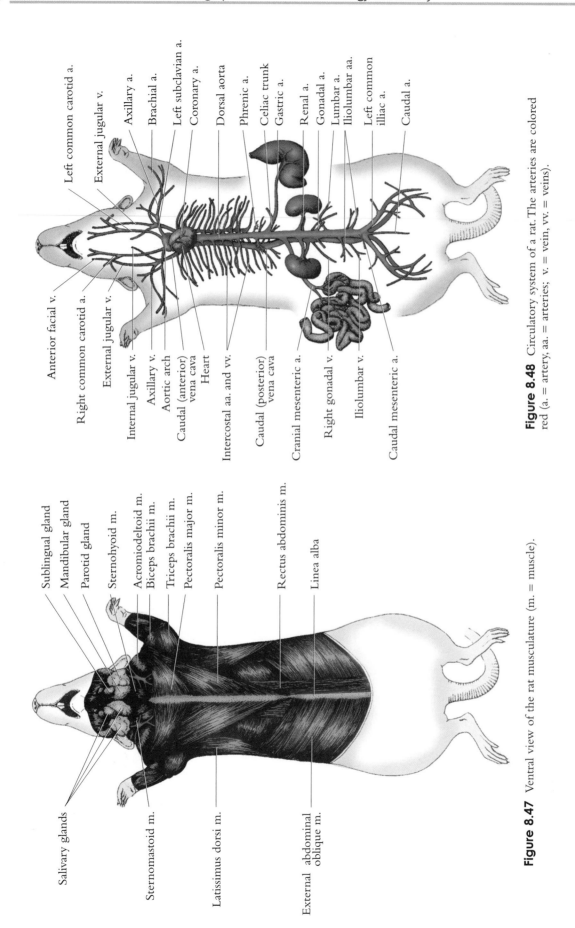

Left common carotid a.

External jugular v.

Axillary a.

Brachial a.

Left subclavian a.

Coronary a.

Dorsal aorta

Phrenic a.

Celiac trunk

Gastric a.

Renal a.

Gonadal a.

Lumbar a.

Iliolumbar aa.

Left common illiac a.

Caudal a.

Anterior facial v.

Right common carotid a.

External jugular v.

Internal jugular v.

Axillary v.

Aortic arch

Caudal (anterior) vena cava

Heart

Intercostal aa. and vv.

Caudal (posterior) vena cava

Cranial mesenteric a.

Right gonadal v.

Iliolumbar v.

Caudal mesenteric a.

Figure 8.48 Circulatory system of a rat. The arteries are colored red (a. = artery, aa. = arteries; v. = vein, vv. = veins).

Sublingual gland

Mandibular gland

Parotid gland

Sternohyoid m.

Acromiodeltoid m.

Biceps brachii m.

Triceps brachii m.

Pectoralis major m.

Pectoralis minor m.

Rectus abdominis m.

Linea alba

Salivary glands

Sternomastoid m.

Latissimus dorsi m.

External abdominal oblique m.

Figure 8.47 Ventral view of the rat musculature (m. = muscle).

Figure 8.49 Ventral view of the rat viscera.

1. Trachea
2. Right lung
3. Right uterine horn of pregnant female
4. Jejunum
5. Cecum
6. Esophagus
7. Heart
8. Diaphragm (cut)
9. Liver
10. Stomach
11. Spleen
12. Ileum
13. Left uterine horn of pregnant female

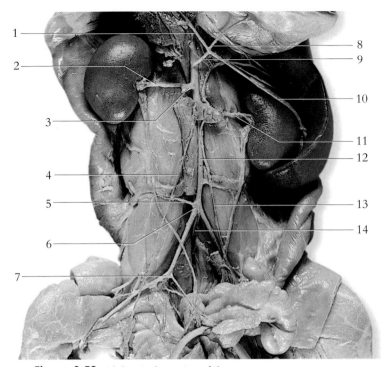

Figure 8.50 Abdominal arteries of the rat.

1. Hepatic a.
2. Right renal a.
3. Cranial mesentric a.
4. Right testicular a.
5. Right iliolumbar a.
6. Caudal mesenteric a. (cut)
7. Right common iliac a.
8. Gastric a.
9. Celiac trunk
10. Splenic a.
11. Left renal a.
12. Abdominal aorta
13. Left testicular a.
14. Middle sacral a.

Figure 8.51 Head and neck region of the rat.

1. Temporalis muscle
2. Extraorbital lacrimal gland
3. Extraorbital lacrimal duct
4. Facial nerve
5. Masseter muscle
6. Parotid duct
7. Parotid gland
8. Mandibular gland

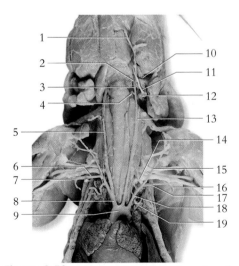

Figure 8.52 Arteries of the thoracic and neck regions of the rat.

1. Facial a.
2. Lingual a.
3. External carotid a.
4. Cranial thyroid a.
5. Common carotid a.
6. Axillary a.
7. Brachial a.
8. Brachiocephalic a.
9. Aortic arch
10. External maxillary a.
11. Internal carotid a.
12. Occipital a.
13. Common carotid a.
14. Vertebral a.
15. Cervical trunk
16. Lateral thoracic a.
17. Axillary a.
18. Subclavian a.
19. Internal thoracic a.

Figure 8.53 Reflected rat heart showing the major veins and arteries.

1. Right common carotid a.
2. Right cranial vena cava
3. Brachiocephalic trunk
4. Aortic arch
5. Pulmonary trunk
6. Left and right pulmonary a.a.
7. Left auricle
8. Left ventricle
9. Coronary vein
10. Left common carotid a.
11. Left subclavian a.
12. Left cranial vena cava
13. Intercostal a. and v.
14. Azygos v.
15. Coronary sinus
16. Aorta
17. Caudal vena cava

Figure 8.54 Veins of the thoracic and neck regions of the rat.

1. Cephalic v.
2. Cranial vena cava
3. Caudal vena cava
4. Linguofacial v.
5. Maxillary v.
6. External jugular v.
7. Internal jugular v.
8. Lateral thoracic v.

Figure 8.55 Abdominal viscera and vessels of the rat.

1. Duodenum
2. Biliary and duodenal parts of pancreas
3. Right renal v.
4. Right kidney
5. Liver (cut)
6. Stomach
7. Gastrosplenic part of pancreas
8. Spleen

Figure 8.56 Branches of the hepatic portal system.

1. Cranial pancreaticoduodenal v.
2. Hepatic portal v.
3. Cranial mesenteric v.
4. Intestinal branches
5. Gastric v.
6. Gastrosplenic v.
7. Splenic branches
8. Spleen

Figure 8.57 Urogenital system of the male rat.

1. Vesicular gland
2. Prostate (dorsolateral part)
3. Prostate (ventral part)
4. Urethra in the pelvic canal
5. Ductus (vas) deferens
6. Crus of penis (cut)
7. Head of epididymis
8. Testis
9. Tail of epididymis
10. Urinary bladder
11. Symphysis pubis (cut exposing pelvic canal)
12. Bulbourethral glands
13. Bulbocavernosus muscle
14. Penis

Figure 8.58 Urogenital system of the female rat.

1. Ovary
2. Uterine a. and v.
3. Uterine horn
4. Colon
5. Vesicular a. (umbilical a.)
6. Vagina
7. Preputial gland
8. Clitoris
9. Vaginal opening
10. Ovarian a. and v.
11. Ovary
12. Uterine a. and v.
13. Uterine horn
14. Uterine body
15. Urinary bladder
16. Urethra
17. Urethral opening
18. Anus

Fetal Pig Dissection

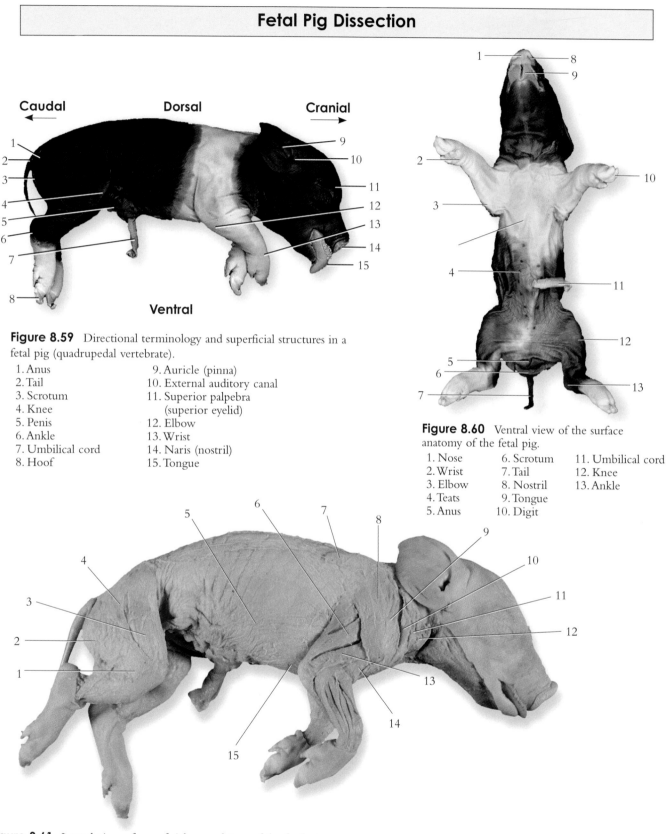

Caudal **Dorsal** **Cranial**

Ventral

Figure 8.59 Directional terminology and superficial structures in a fetal pig (quadrupedal vertebrate).

1. Anus
2. Tail
3. Scrotum
4. Knee
5. Penis
6. Ankle
7. Umbilical cord
8. Hoof
9. Auricle (pinna)
10. External auditory canal
11. Superior palpebra (superior eyelid)
12. Elbow
13. Wrist
14. Naris (nostril)
15. Tongue

Figure 8.60 Ventral view of the surface anatomy of the fetal pig.

1. Nose
2. Wrist
3. Elbow
4. Teats
5. Anus
6. Scrotum
7. Tail
8. Nostril
9. Tongue
10. Digit
11. Umbilical cord
12. Knee
13. Ankle

Figure 8.61 Lateral view of superficial musculature of the fetal pig.

1. Biceps femoris m.
2. Semitendinosus m.
3. Tensor fasciae latae m.
4. Gluteus medius m.
5. External abdominal oblique m.
6. Triceps brachii m. (long head)
7. Trapezius m.
8. Deltoid m.
9. Supraspinatus m.
10. Cleidooccipitalis m.
11. Cleidomastoid m.
12. Sternocephalicus m.
13. Triceps brachii m. (lateral head)
14. Brachialis m.
15. Pectoralis profundus m.

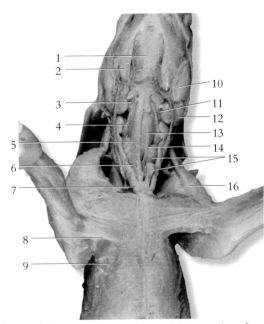

Figure 8.62 Ventral view of superficial muscles of neck and upper torso.

1. Mylohyoid m.
2. Digastric m.
3. Stylohyoid m.
4. Omohyoid m.
5. Sternohyoid m.
6. Thymus
7. Sternomastoid m.
8. Pectoralis superficialis m.
9. Pectoralis profundus m.
10. Masseter m.
11. Thyrohyoid m.
12. Mandibular gland
13. Larynx
14. Sternothyroid m.
15. Mandibular lymph nodes
16. Brachiocephalic m.

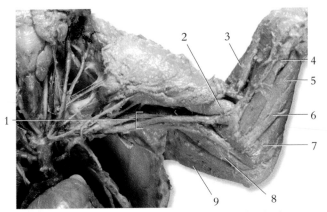

Figure 8.63 Superficial medial mucles of the forelimb.

1. Axillary a. and v., brachial plexus
2. Biceps brachii m.
3. Extensor carpi radialis m.
4. Flexor carpi radialis m.
5. Flexor digitorum profundus m.
6. Flexor digitorum superficialis m.
7. Flexor carpi ulnaris m.
8. Triceps brachii m. (lateral head)
9. Triceps brachii m. (long head)

Figure 8.64 Lateral view of the superficial thigh and leg.

1. Gluteus superficialis m.
2. Semitendinosus m.
3. Semimembranosus m.
4. Gastrocnemius m.
5. Extensor digitorum quarti and quinti mm.
6. Gluteus medius m.
7. Tensor fasciae latae m.
8. Biceps femoris m.
9. Peroneus longus m.
10. Peroneus tertius m.
11. Tibialis anterior m.

Figure 8.65 Medial muscles of thigh and leg.

1. External abdominal oblique m.
2. Psoas major m.
3. Iliacus m.
4. Tensor fasciae latae m.
5. Sartorius m.
6. Rectus femoris m.
7. Vastus medialis m.
8. Pectineus m.
9. Adductor m.
10. Aponeurosis of gracilis m. (cut)
11. Semimembranosus m.
12. Semitendinosus m.
13. Tibialis anterior m.
14. Linea alba
15. Rectus femoris m.
16. Vastus medialis m.
17. Sartorius m.
18. Gracilis m. (cut)
19. Gracilis m.
20. Semitendinosus m.

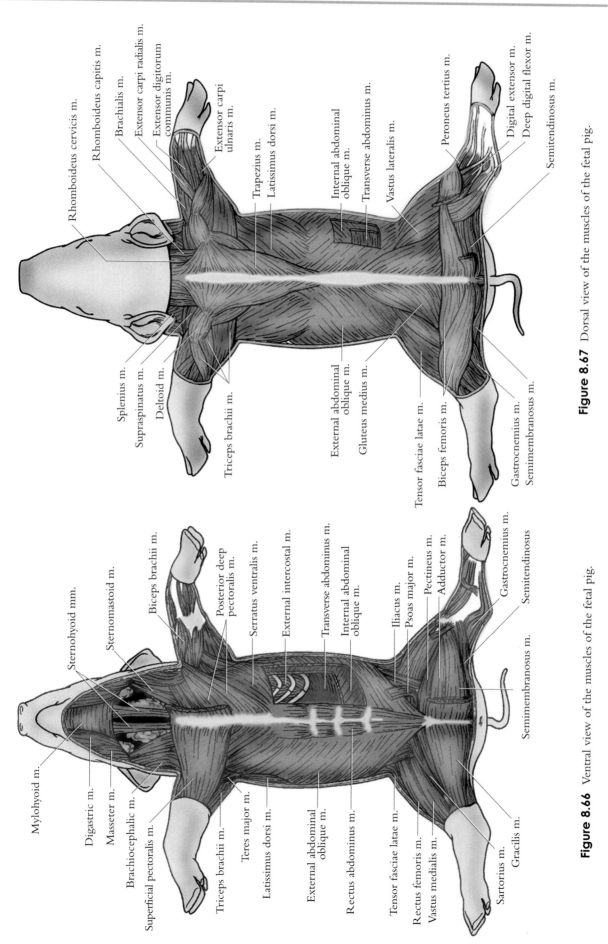

Figure 8.67 Dorsal view of the muscles of the fetal pig.

Figure 8.66 Ventral view of the muscles of the fetal pig.

Figure 8.70 Blood supply to the abdomen and lower extremities of the fetal pig.

1. Heart
2. Thoracic aorta
3. Small intestine
4. Colon
5. Ductus deferens
6. Kidney
7. Renal a.
8. Renal v.

Figure 8.69 Deep viscera and associated structures.

1. Liver (cut)
2. Stomach
3. Small intestine
4. Larynx
5. Heart
6. Lung
7. Spleen
8. Adrenal gland
9. Kidney

Figure 8.68 Arteries, veins and viscera of the neck and thoracic region of the fetal pig.

1. Larynx
2. Internal jugular v.
3. External jugular v.
4. Thyroid gland
5. Cranial (superior) vena cava
6. Right auricle
7. Coronary vessels
8. Right lung
9. Liver
10. Trachea
11. Left common carotid a.
12. Axillary a.
13. Left auricle
14. Left lung
15. Diaphragm
16. Small intestine

Figure 8.71 Urogenital system of the fetal pig.

1. Kidney
2. Caudal (inferior) vena cava
3. Ureter
4. Rectum (cut)
5. Partially dissected testis
6. Renal v.
7. Descending aorta
8. Ductus deferens
9. Urinary bladder
10. Umbilical a.
11. Epididymis

Figure 8.72 Urogenital system of the fetal pig.

1. Umbilical cord
2. Right kidney
3. Ureter
4. Umbilical a.
5. Urinary bladder
6. Penis
7. Vas (ductus) deferens
8. Spermatic cord
9. Right testis
10. Epididymis

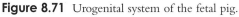

Figure 8.73 General structures of the fetal pig brain. Because the cerebrum is less defined in pigs, the regions are not known as lobes as they are in humans.

1. Occipital region of cerebrum
2. Cerebellum
3. Medulla oblongata
4. Spinal cord
5. External acoustic meatus
6. Longitudinal fissure
7. Parietal region of cerebrum
8. Frontal region of cerebrum
9. Temporal region of cerebrum
10. Eye

Cat Dissection

Figure 8.74 Cat skeleton.

1. Mandible	7. Metacarpal bones	13. Scapula	19. Ilium	25. Fibula
2. Hyoid bone	8. Phalanges	14. Sternum	20. Ischium	26. Tarsal bones
3. Humerus	9. Skull	15. Rib	21. Pubis	27. Metatarsal bones
4. Ulna	10. Atlas	16. Thoracic vertebra	22. Caudal vertebra	28. Phalanges
5. Radius	11. Axis	17. Lumbar vertebra	23. Femur	
6. Carpal bones	12. Cervical vertebra	18. Patella	24. Tibia	

Figure 8.75 Dorsal view of a cat skull.

1. Premaxilla
2. Nasal bone
3. Frontal bone
4. Sagittal suture
5. Coronal suture
6. Nuchal crest
7. Maxilla
8. Zygomatic (malar) bone
9. Orbit
10. Zygomatic arch
11. Temporal bone
12. Parietal bone
13. Interparietal bone

Figure 8.76 Lateral view of a cat skull.

1. Frontal bone
2. Parietal bone
3. Squamosal suture
4. Temporal bone
5. Nuchal crest
6. External acoustic meatus
7. Mastoid process
8. Tympanic bulla
9. Nasal bone
10. Premaxilla bone
11. Maxilla
12. Zygomatic (malar) bone
13. Coronoid process of mandible
14. Zygomatic arch
15. Mandible
16. Condylar process of mandible

Figure 8.78 Dorsal view of the cat neck and thorax.

1. Temporalis m.
2. Clavotrapezius m.
3. Acromiotrapezius m.
4. Latissimus dorsi m.
5. Supraspinatus m.
6. Rhomboideus m.
7. Serratus anterior m.

Figure 8.77 Dorsal view of the superficial muscles of the cat.

1. Lateral head of triceps brachii m.
2. Acromiotrapezius m.
3. Latissimus dorsi m.
4. Lumbodorsal fascia
5. Sacrospinalis m.
6. Gluteus medius m.
7. Caudal m.
8. Supraspinatus m.
9. Rhomboideus m.
10. Serratus anterior m.
11. Latissimus dorsi m.
12. Caudofemoralis m.

Figure 8.79 Anterior view of the cat brachium and antebrachium.

1. Extensor carpi radialis longus m.
2. Brachioradialis m.
3. Palmaris longus m. (cut)
4. Flexor carpi ulnaris m.
5. Pronator teres m.
6. Epitrochlearis
7. Masseter m.
8. Sternomastoid m.
9. Clavobrachialis m.
10. Pectoantebrachialis m.
11. Pectoralis major m.
12. Pectoralis minor m.

Figure 8.80 Ventral view of the cat neck and thorax.

1. Digastric m.
2. Mylohyoid m.
3. Sternomastoid m.
4. Clavotrapezius m.
5. Masseter m.
6. Clavobrachialis m.
7. Pectoantebrachialis m.
8. Pectoralis major m.
9. Pectoralis minor m.

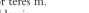

Figure 8.81 Anterior view of the cat trunk.

1. Pectoralis minor (cut)
2. Epitrochlearis m.
3. Subscapularis m.
4. Scalenus medius m.
5. Serratus anterior m.
6. Latissimus dorsi m. (cut)
7. External abdominal oblique m.
8. Sternomastoid m.
9. Scalenus anterior m.
10. Scalenus posterior m.
11. Epitrochlearis m.
12. Transverse costarum m.
13. Pectoralis minor m. (cut)
14. Rectus abdominis m.
15. Xiphihumeralis m. (cut)

Figure 8.82 Lateral view of the cat shoulder and brachium.

1. Acromiotrapezius m.
2. Levator scapulae ventralis m.
3. Spinodeltoid m.
4. Latissimus dorsi m.
5. Long head of triceps brachii m.
6. Clavobrachialis m.
7. Lateral head of triceps brachii m.
8. Clavotrapezius m.
9. Parotid gland
10. Acromiodeltoid m.
11. Brachioradialis m.

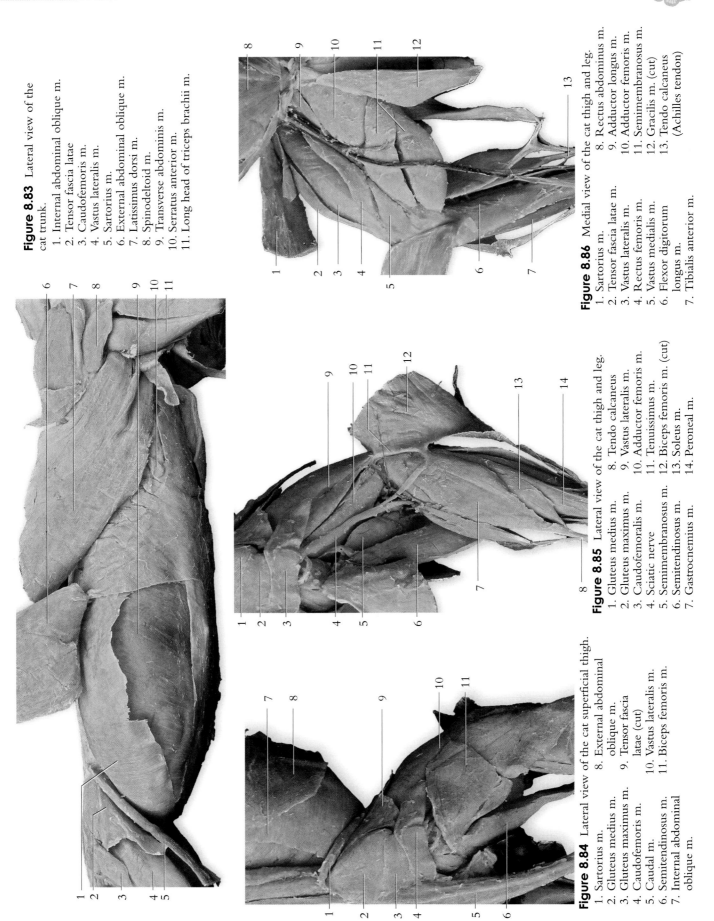

Figure 8.83 Lateral view of the cat trunk.
1. Internal abdominal oblique m.
2. Tensor fascia latae
3. Caudofemoris m.
4. Vastus lateralis m.
5. Sartorius m.
6. External abdominal oblique m.
7. Latissimus dorsi m.
8. Spinodeltoid m.
9. Transverse abdominis m.
10. Serratus anterior m.
11. Long head of triceps brachii m.

Figure 8.84 Lateral view of the cat superficial thigh.
1. Sartorius m.
2. Gluteus medius m.
3. Gluteus maximus m.
4. Caudofemoris m.
5. Caudal m.
6. Semitendinosus m.
7. Internal abdominal oblique m.
8. External abdominal oblique m.
9. Tensor fascia latae (cut)
10. Vastus lateralis m.
11. Biceps femoris m.

Figure 8.85 Lateral view of the cat thigh and leg.
1. Gluteus medius m.
2. Gluteus maximus m.
3. Caudofemoralis m.
4. Sciatic nerve
5. Semimembranosus m.
6. Semitendinosus m.
7. Gastrocnemius m.
8. Tendo calcaneus
9. Vastus lateralis m.
10. Adductor femoris m.
11. Tenuissimus m.
12. Biceps femoris m. (cut)
13. Soleus m.
14. Peroneal m.

Figure 8.86 Medial view of the cat thigh and leg.
1. Sartorius m.
2. Tensor fascia latae m.
3. Vastus lateralis m.
4. Rectus femoris m.
5. Vastus medialis m.
6. Flexor digitorum longus m.
7. Tibialis anterior m.
8. Rectus abdominus m.
9. Adductor longus m.
10. Adductor femoris m.
11. Semimembranosus m.
12. Gracilis m. (cut)
13. Tendo calcaneus (Achilles tendon)

Figure 8.88 Intact viscera of the cat.

1. Right brachiocephalic v.
2. Superior vena cava
3. Right lung
4. Greater omentum
5. Left brachiocephalic v.
6. Left lung
7. Heart
8. Liver
9. Stomach
10. Mesentery
11. Small intestine

Figure 8.87 Internal view of the cat heart.

1. Trachea
2. Right common carotid a.
3. Right subclavian v.
4. Right brachiocephalic v.
5. Cranial (superior) vena cava
6. Right atrium
7. Right ventricle
8. Left common carotid a.
9. Internal jugular v.
10. Brachiocephalic a.
11. Right common carotid a.
12. Aortic arch
13. Left ventricle

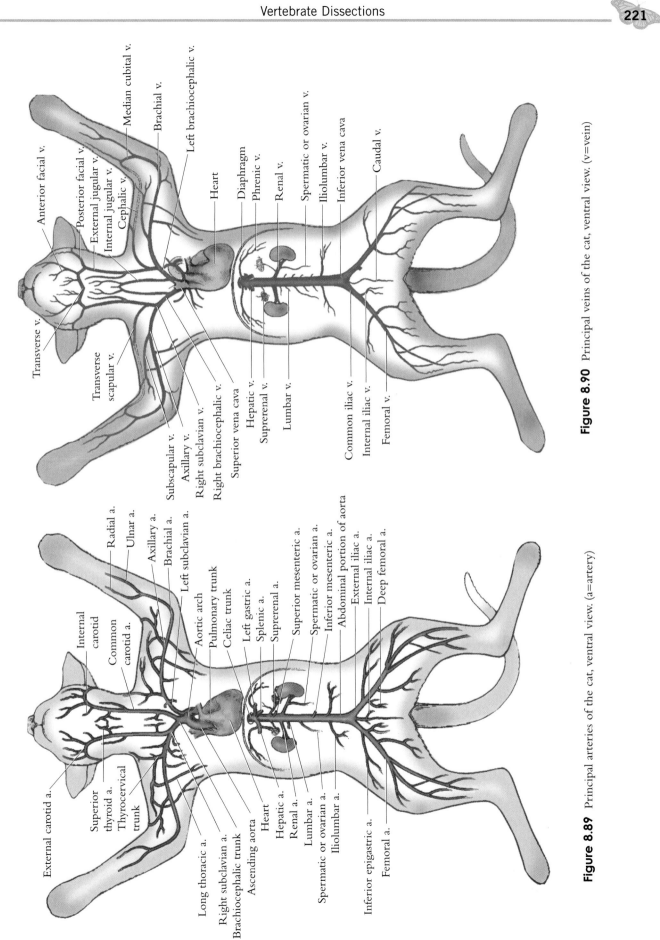

Figure 8.90 Principal veins of the cat, ventral view. (v=vein)

Figure 8.89 Principal arteries of the cat, ventral view. (a=artery)

Median cubital v.

Brachial v.

Left brachiocephalic v.

Anterior facial v.

Posterior facial v.

External jugular v.

Internal jugular v.

Cephalic v.

Heart

Diaphragm

Phrenic v.

Renal v.

Spermatic or ovarian v.

Iliolumbar v.

Inferior vena cava

Caudal v.

Transverse v.

Transverse scapular v.

Subscapular v.

Axillary v.

Right subclavian v.

Superior vena cava

Hepatic v.

Suprarenal v.

Lumbar v.

Common iliac v.

Internal iliac v.

Femoral v.

Radial a.

Ulnar a.

Axillary a.

Brachial a.

Left subclavian a.

Internal carotid

Common carotid a.

Aortic arch

Pulmonary trunk

Celiac trunk

Left gastric a.

Splenic a.

Suprarenal a.

Superior mesenteric a.

Spermatic or ovarian a.

Inferior mesenteric a.

Abdominal portion of aorta

External iliac a.

Internal iliac a.

Deep femoral a.

External carotid a.

Superior thyroid a.

Thyrocervical trunk

Long thoracic a.

Right subclavian a.

Brachiocephalic trunk

Ascending aorta

Heart

Hepatic a.

Renal a.

Lumbar a.

Spermatic or ovarian a.

Iliolumbar a.

Inferior epigastric a.

Femoral a.

Figure 8.91 Anterior view of the arteries and veins of the trunk of a cat.

1. Larynx
2. Trachea
3. Brachiocephalic trunk
4. Heart (cut)
5. Liver
6. Stomach
7. Superior mesenteric a.
8. Superior mesenteric v.
9. Urinary bladder
10. Left common carotid a.
11. Left axillary a.
12. Left subclavian a.
13. Intercostal a.a.
14. Suprarenal a.
15. Renal a.
16. Abdominal aorta
17. Left horn of uterus

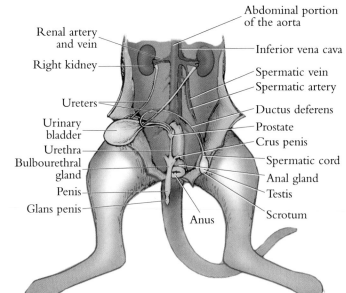

Figure 8.92 Diagram of the urogenital system of a male cat.

Renal artery and vein
Right kidney
Ureters
Urinary bladder
Urethra
Bulbourethral gland
Penis
Glans penis
Abdominal portion of the aorta
Inferior vena cava
Spermatic vein
Spermatic artery
Ductus deferens
Prostate
Crus penis
Spermatic cord
Anal gland
Testis
Scrotum
Anus

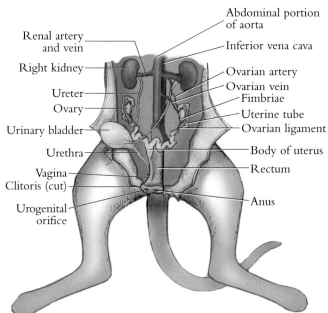

Figure 8.93 Diagram of the urogenital system of a female cat.

Renal artery and vein
Right kidney
Ureter
Ovary
Urinary bladder
Urethra
Vagina
Clitoris (cut)
Urogenital orifice
Abdominal portion of aorta
Inferior vena cava
Ovarian artery
Ovarian vein
Fimbriae
Uterine tube
Ovarian ligament
Body of uterus
Rectum
Anus

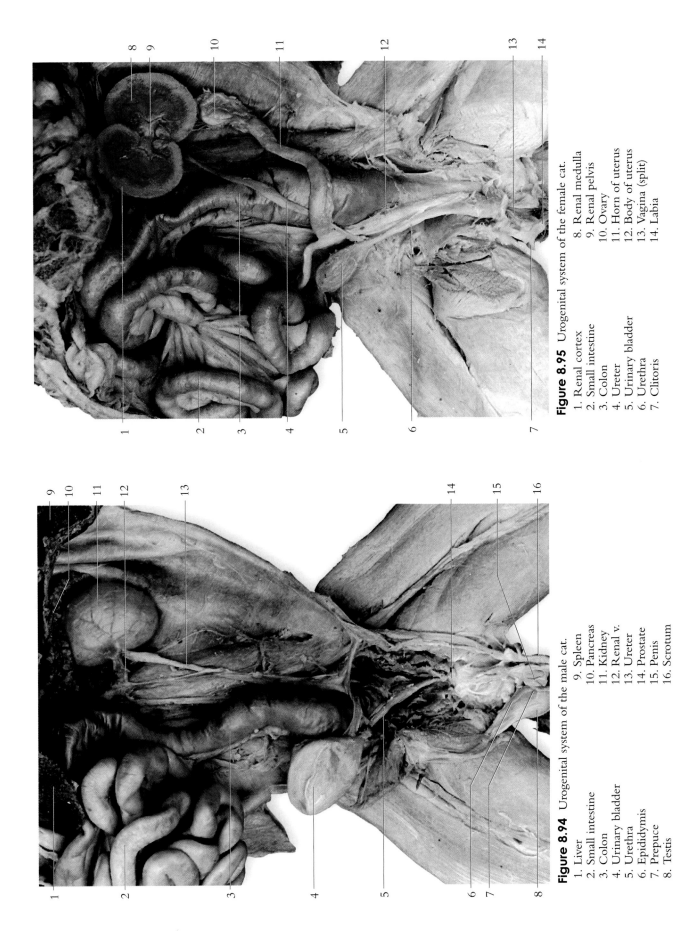

Figure 8.95 Urogenital system of the female cat.

1. Renal cortex	8. Renal medulla
2. Small intestine	9. Renal pelvis
3. Colon	10. Ovary
4. Ureter	11. Horn of uterus
5. Urinary bladder	12. Body of uterus
6. Urethra	13. Vagina (split)
7. Clitoris	14. Labia

Figure 8.94 Urogenital system of the male cat.

1. Liver	9. Spleen
2. Small intestine	10. Pancreas
3. Colon	11. Kidney
4. Urinary bladder	12. Renal v.
5. Urethra	13. Ureter
6. Epididymis	14. Prostate
7. Prepuce	15. Penis
8. Testis	16. Scrotum

Mammalian Heart Dissection

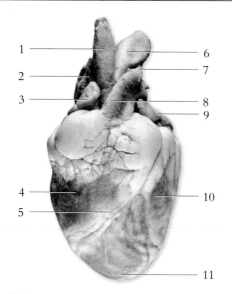

Figure 8.96 Ventral view of the mammalian (sheep) heart.
1. Brachiocephalic a.
2. Cranial vena cava
3. Right auricle of right atrium
4. Right ventricle
5. Interventicular groove
6. Ascending aorta
7. Ligamentum arteriosum
8. Pulmonary trunk
9. Left auricle of left atrium
10. Left ventricle
11. Apex of heart

Figure 8.97 Dorsal view of the mammalian (sheep) heart.
1. Aorta
2. Pulmonary a.
3. Pulmonary v.
4. Left auricle
5. Left atrium
6. Atrioventricular groove
7. Left ventricle
8. Brachiocephalic a.
9. Cranial vena cava
10. Right auricle
11. Right atrium
12. Pulmonary v.
13. Right ventricle
14. Interventricular groove

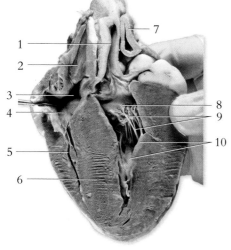

Figure 8.98 Coronal section of the mammalian (sheep) heart.
1. Aorta
2. Cranial vena cava
3. Right atrium
4. Right atrioventricular (tricuspid) valve
5. Right ventricle
6. Interventricalar septum
7. Pulmonary artery
8. Left atrioventricular (bicuspid) valve
9. Chordae tendineae
10. Papillary muscles

Figure 8.99 Coronal section of the mammalian (sheep) heart showing the valves.
1. Opening of the brachiocephalic a.
2. Pulmonary a.
3. Left atrioventricular (bicuspid) valve
4. Left ventricle
5. Opening of cranial vena cava
6. Opening of coronary sinus
7. Right atrium
8. Right atrioventricular (tricuspid) valve
9. Right ventricle
10. Interventricular septum

Figure 8.100 Coronal section of the mammalian (sheep) heart showing openings of coronary arteries.
1. Opening of brachiocephalic a.
2. Opening of left coronary a.
3. Opening of right coronary a.
4. Aortic valve
5. Coronary vessel

Because humans are vertebrate organisms, the study of human biology is appropriate in a general biology course. *Human anatomy* is the scientific discipline that investigates the structure of the body, and *human physiology* is the scientific discipline that investigates how body structures function. The purpose of this chapter is to present a visual overview of the principal anatomical structures of the human body.

Since both the *skeletal system* and the *muscular system* are concerned with body movement, they are frequently discussed together as the *skeletomusculature system*. In a functional sense, the flexible internal framework, or *bones* of the skeleton, support and provide movement at the *joints* where the muscles attached to the bones produce their actions as they are stimulated to contract.

The *nervous system* is anatomically divided into the *central nervous system* (CNS), which includes the *brain* and *spinal cord*, and the *peripheral nervous system* (PNS), which includes the *cranial nerves*, arising from the brain, and the *spinal nerves*, arising from the spinal cord. The *autonomic nervous system* (ANS) is a functional division of the nervous system devoted to regulation of involuntary activities of the body. The brain and spinal cord are the centers for integration and coordination of information. *Nerves*, composed of *neurons*, convey nerve impulses to and from the brain. *Sensory organs*, such as the eyes and ears, respond to impulses in the environment and convey sensations to the CNS. The nervous system functions with the *endocrine system* in coordinating body activities.

The *cardiovascular system* consists of the *heart, vessels* (both blood and lymphatic vessels), *blood*, and the tissues that produce the *blood*. The four-chambered human heart is enclosed with a *pericardial sac* within the thoracic cavity. *Arteries* and *arterioles* transport blood away from the heart, *capillaries* permeate the tissues and are the functional units for product exchange with the cells, and *venules* and *veins* transport blood toward the heart. *Lymphatic vessels* return interstitial fluid back to the circulatory system after first passing it through *lymph nodes* for cleansing. Blood cells are produced in the bone marrow and once old and worn, they are broken down in the liver.

The *respiratory system* consists of the *conducting division* that transports air to and from the *respiratory division* within the *lungs*. The *alveoli* of the lungs contact the capillaries of the cardiovascular system and are the sites for transport of respiratory gases into and out of the body.

The *digestive system* consists of a *gastrointestinal tract* (GI tract) and *accessory digestive organs*. Food traveling through the GI tract is processed such that it is suitable for absorption through the intestinal wall into the bloodstream. The *pancreas* and *liver* are the principal digestive organs. The pancreas produces hormones and enzymes. The liver processes nutrients, stores glucose as glycogen, and excretes bile.

Because of commonalty of prenatal development and dual functions of some of the organs, the *urinary system* and *reproductive system* may be considered together as the *urogenital system*. The urinary system, consisting of the *kidneys, ureters, urinary bladder*, and *urethra*, extracts and processes wastes from the blood in the form of urine. The male and female reproductive systems produce regulatory hormones and gametes (sperm and ova, respectively) within the gonads (testes and ovaries). Sexual reproduction is the mechanism for propagation of offspring that have traits from both parents. The process of prenatal development is made possible by the formation of *extraembryonic membranes* (placenta, umbilical cord, allantois, amnion, chorion, and yolk sac) within the uterus of the pregnant woman.

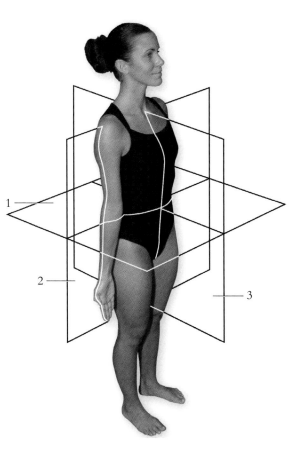

Figure 9.1 Planes of reference in a person while standing in anatomical position. The anatomical position provides a basis of reference for describing the relationship of one body part to another. In the anatomical position, the person is standing, the feet are parallel, the eyes are directed forward, and the arms are to the sides with the palms turned forward and the fingers are pointed straight down.

  1. Transverse plane
     (cross-sectional plane)
  2. Coronal plane
     (frontal plane)
  3. Sagittal plane

Figure 9.2 Major body parts and regions in humans (bipedal vertebrate).
(a) Anterior view and (b) a posterior view.

1. Upper extremity	9. Palmar region (palm)	17. Antebrachium (forearm)
2. Lower extremity	10. Patellar region (patella)	18. Gluteal region (buttock)
3. Head	11. Cervical region	19. Dorsum of hand
4. Neck, anterior aspect	12. Shoulder	20. Thigh
5. Thorax (chest)	13. Axilla (armpit)	21. Popliteal fossa
6. Abdomen	14. Brachium (upper arm)	22. Calf
7. Cubital fossa	15. Lumbar region	23. Plantar surface (sole)
8. Pubic region	16. Elbow	

Mediastinum

Pleural cavity
(surrounds lung)

Pericardial cavity
(surrounds heart)

Thoracic cavity

Diaphragm

Abdominal cavity
(contains abdominal
viscera)

Pelvic cavity
(contains internal
genitalia)

Abdominopelvic cavity

Figure 9.3 Anterior view of (coronal plane)
the body cavities of the trunk.

Figure 9.4 MR image of the trunk showing
the body cavities and their contents.

1. Thoracic cavity	5. Image of rib
2. Abdominopelvic cavity	6. Image of lumbar
3. Image of heart	vertebra
4. Image of diaphragm	7. Image of Ilium

Figure 9.5 Skin and certain epidermal structures.

1. Epidermis
2. Dermis
3. Hypodermis
4. Shaft of hair
5. Stratum corneum
6. Stratum basale
7. Sweat duct
8. Sensory receptor
9. Sweat duct
10. Sebaceous gland
11. Arrector pili muscle
12. Hair follicle
13. Apocrine sweat gland
14. Eccrine sweat gland
15. Bulb of hair
16. Adipose tissue
17. Cutaneous blood vessels

Figure 9.6 Gross structure of the skin and underlying fascia.

1. Epidermis
2. Dermis
3. Hypodermis
4. Fascia
5. Muscle

Figure 9.7 Epidermis and dermis.

1. Stratum corneum
2. Stratum lucidum
3. Stratum granulosum
4. Stratum spinosum
5. Stratum basale
6. Dermis

Figure 9.8 Electron micrograph of bone tissue.

1. Interstitial lamellae
2. Lamellae
3. Central canal (haversian canal)
4. Lacunae
5. Osteon (haversian system)

Figure 9.9 Transverse section of two osteons.

1. Lacunae
2. Central (haversian) canals
3. Lamellae

Figure 9.10 Anterior view of the skeleton.

1. Frontal bone	12. Pubis	23. Scapula
2. Zygomatic bone	13. Carpal bones	24. Manubrium
3. Mandible	14. Metacarpal bones	25. Costal cartilage
4. Cervical vertebra	15. Phalanges	26. Thoracic vertebra
5. Clavicle	16. Femur	27. Radius
6. Body of sternum	17. Patella	28. Ulna
7. Rib	18. Tarsal bones	29. Symphysis pubis
8. Humerus	19. Metatarsal bones	30. Fibula
9. Lumbar vertebra	20. Phalanges	31. Tibia
10. Ilium	21. Orbit	32. Calcaneus
11. Sacrum	22. Maxilla	

Figure 9.11 Posterior view of the skeleton.

1. Parietal bone	10. Tibia	18. Lumbar vertebra
2. Occipital bone	11. Fibula	19. Radius
3. Cervical vertebra	12. Metatarsal bones	20. Ulna
4. Scapula	13. Phalanges	21. Coccyx
5. Humerus	14. Mandible	22. Carpal bones
6. Ilium	15. Clavicle	23. Metacarpal bones
7. Sacrum	16. Thoracic	24. Phalanges
8. Ischium	vertebra	25. Tarsal bones
9. Femur	17. Rib	

Figure 9.12 Anterior view of the human skull.

1. Frontal bone	9. Supraorbital margin
2. Nasal bone	10. Sphenoid bone
3. Superior orbital fissure	11. Perpendicular plate of
4. Zygomatic bone	ethmoid bone
5. Vomer	12. Infraorbital foramen
6. Canine	13. Inferior nasal concha
7. Incisors	14. Maxilla
8. Mental foramen	15. Mandible

Figure 9.13 Lateral view of the human skull.

1. Coronal suture	11. Squamosal suture
2. Frontal bone	12. Temporal bone
3. Lacrimal bone	13. Lambdoidal suture
4. Nasal bone	14. External acoustic meatus
5. Zygomatic bone	15. Occipital bone
6. Maxilla	16. Condylar process of mandible
7. Premolars	17. Mandibular notch
8. Molars	18. Mastoid process of temporal bone
9. Mandible	19. Coronoid process of mandible
10. Parietal bone	20. Angle of mandible

Figure 9.14 Inferior view of the human skull.

1. Incisors	9. Foramen magnum	17. Mandibular fossa
2. Canine	10. Superior nuchal line	18. Styloid process of
3. Intermaxillary suture	11. Premolars	temporal bone
4. Maxilla	12. Molars	19. Mastoid process of
5. Palatine bone	13. Zygomatic bone	temporal bone
6. Foramen ovale	14. Sphenoid bone	20. Occipital condyle
7. Foramen lacerum	15. Zygomatic arch	21. Temporal bone
8. Carotid canal	16. Vomer	22. Occipital bone

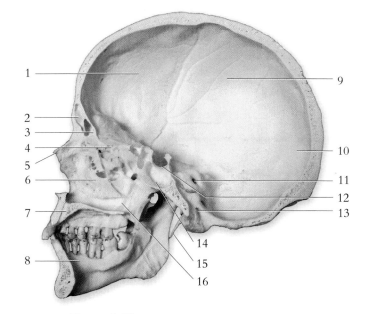

Figure 9.15 Sagittal view of the human skull.

1. Frontal bone	9. Parietal bone
2. Frontal sinus	10. Occipital bone
3. Crista galli of	11. Internal acoustic
ethmoid bone	meatus
4. Cribriform plate	12. Sella turcica
of ethmoid bone	13. Hypoglossal canal
5. Nasal bone	14. Sphenoidal sinus
6. Nasal concha	15. Styloid process of
7. Maxilla	temporal bone
8. Mandible	16. Vomer

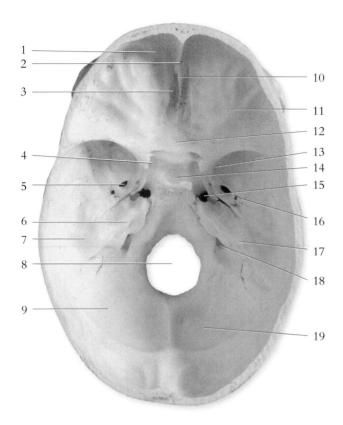

Figure 9.16 Superior view of the cranium.

1. Frontal bone
2. Foramen cecum
3. Cribriform plate of ethmoid bone
4. Optic canal
5. Foramen ovale
6. Petrous part of temporal bone
7. Temporal bone
8. Foramen magnum
9. Occipital bone
10. Crista galli of ethmoid bone
11. Anterior cranial fossa
12. Sphenoid bone
13. Foramen rotundum
14. Sella turcica of sphenoid bone
15. Foramen lacerum
16. Foramen spinosum
17. Internal acoustic meatus
18. Jugular foramen
19. Posterior cranial fossa

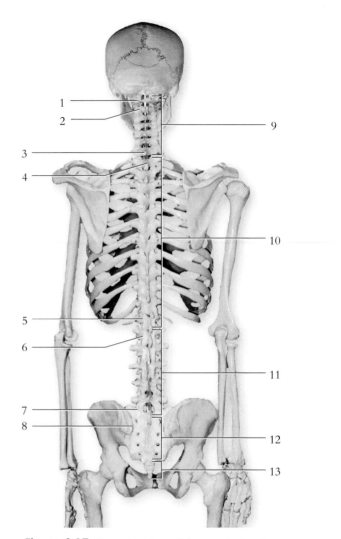

Figure 9.17 Posterior view of the vertebral column.

1. Atlas
2. Axis
3. Seventh cervical vertebra
4. First thoracic vertebra
5. Twelfth thoracic vertebra
6. First lumbar vertebra
7. Fifth lumbar vertebra
8. Sacroiliac joint
9. Cervical vertebrae
10. Thoracic vertebrae
11. Lumbar vertebrae
12. Sacrum
13. Coccyx

Figure 9.18 Anterior view of the rib cage.

1. True ribs (seven pairs)
2. False ribs (five pairs)
3. Jugular notch
4. Manubrium
5. Body of sternum
6. Xiphoid process
7. Costal cartilage
8. Floating ribs (inferior two pairs of false ribs)
9. Twelfth thoracic vertebra
10. Twelfth rib

Figure 9.19 Anterior view of the left scapula.
1. Superior border
2. Superior angle
3. Medial (vertebral) border
4. Inferior angle
5. Acromion
6. Coracoid process
7. Glenoid fossa
8. Infraglenoid tubercle
9. Subscapular fossa
10. Lateral (axillary) border

Figure 9.20 Posterior view of the left scapula.
1. Acromion
2. Glenoid fossa
3. Lateral (axillary) border
4. Superior angle
5. Supraspinous fossa
6. Spine
7. Infraspinous fossa
8. Medial (vertebral) border
9. Inferior angle

Figure 9.21 Right humerus. (a) Anterior view (b) Posterior view.
1. Greater tubercle
2. Intertubercular groove
3. Lesser tubercle
4. Deltoid tuberosity
5. Anterior body (shaft) of humerus
6. Lateral supracondylar ridge
7. Lateral epicondyle
8. Capitulum
9. Head of humerus
10. Surgical neck
11. Posterior body (shaft) of humerus
12. Olecranon fossa
13. Coronoid fossa
14. Medial epicondyle
15. Trochlea
16. Anatomical neck
17. Greater tubercle
18. Lateral epicondyle

Figure 9.22 Anterior view of the right ulna and radius.
1. Trochlear notch
2. Head of radius
3. Neck of radius
4. Radial tuberosity
5. Interosseous margin
6. Ulnar notch of radius
7. Styloid process of radius
8. Olecranon
9. Interosseous margin
10. Neck of ulna
11. Head of ulna

Figure 9.23 Posterior view of the right ulna and radius.
1. Olecranon
2. Radial notch of ulna
3. Interosseous margin
4. Head of ulna
5. Styloid process of ulna
6. Head of radius
7. Neck of radius
8. Interosseous margin
9. Styloid process of radius

Figure 9.24 Anterior view of the articulated pelvic girdle showing the two coxal bones, the sacrum, and the two femora.

1. Lumbar vertebra
2. Intervertebral disc
3. Ilium
4. Iliac fossa
5. Anterior superior iliac spine
6. Head of femur
7. Greater trochanter
8. Symphysis pubis
9. Crest of the ilium
10. Sacroiliac joint
11. Sacrum
12. Pelvic brim
13. Acetabulum
14. Pubic crest
15. Obturator foramen
16. Ischium
17. Pubic angle

Figure 9.25 Posterior view of the articulated pelvic girdle showing the two coxal bones, the sacrum, and the two femora.

1. Lumbar vertebra
2. Crest of ilium
3. Ilium
4. Sacrum
5. Greater sciatic notch
6. Coccyx
7. Head of femur
8. Greater trochanter
9. Intertrochanteric crest
10. Lesser trochanter
11. Sacroiliac joint
12. Acetabulum
13. Obturator foramen
14. Ischium
15. Pubis

Figure 9.26 Left femur. (a) An anterior view and (b) a posterior view.

1. Fovea capitis femoris
2. Head
3. Neck
4. Lesser trochanter
5. Medial epicondyle
6. Patellar surface
7. Greater trochanter
8. Intertrochanteric crest
9. Intertrochanteric line
10. Lateral epicondyle
11. Lateral condyle
12. Intercondylar fossa
13. Head
14. Fovea capitis femoris
15. Neck
16. Lesser trochanter
17. Linea aspera on shaft (body) of femur
18. Medial epicondyle
19. Medial condyle

Figure 9.27 Anterior view of the (a) left patella, tibia, and fibula. (b) A posterior view of the left tibia and fibula.

1. Base of patella
2. Apex of patella
3. Medial condyle
4. Tibial tuberosity
5. Anterior crest of tibia
6. Body (shaft) of tibia
7. Medial malleolus
8. Intercondylar tubercles
9. Lateral condyle
10. Tibial articular facet of fibula
11. Head of fibula
12. Neck of fibula
13. Body (shaft) of fibula
14. Lateral malleolus
15. Fibular articular facet of tibia
16. Fibular notch of tibia

Figure 9.29 Posterior view of human musculature (m=muscle).

Figure 9.28 Anterior view of human musculature (m=muscle).

Figure 9.30 Anterolateral view of the trunk.
1. Deltoid m.
2. Pectoralis major m.
3. Biceps brachii m. (long head)
4. Brachialis m.
5. Serratus anterior m.
6. Brachioradialis m.
7. External abdominal oblique m.
8. Umbilicus
9. Tendon of sternocleidomastoid m.
10. Sternum.
11. Xiphoid process
12. Tendinous inscriptions of rectus abdominis m.
13. Rectus abdominis m.

Figure 9.31 Posterolateral view of the trunk.
1. Trapezius m.
2. Triangle of ausculation
3. Latissimus dorsi mm.
4. Vertebral column (spinous processes)
5. Infraspinatus m.
6. Deltoid m.
7. Teres minor m.
8. Teres major m.
9. Serratus anterior mm.
10. Rib
11. External abdominal oblique m.
12. Iliac crest
13. Gluteus medius m.
14. Gluteus maximus m.

Figure 9.32 Superficial muscles of gluteal and thigh regions.
1. Gluteus maximus m.
2. Vastus lateralis m.
3. Biceps femoris m.
4. Semitendinosus m.
5. Semimembranosus m.
6. Gracilis m.

Figure 9.33 Deep structures of gluteal region.
1. Piriformis m.
2. Sciatic n.
3. Obturator internus m.
4. Quadratus femoris m.
5. Adductor minimus m.
6. Gluteus medius m.
7. Gluteus minimus m.
8. Superior gemellus m.
9. Inferior gemellus m.
10. Gluteus maximus m.

Figure 9.34 Deep posterior structures of thigh and popliteal regions.
1. Adductor magnus m.
2. Gracilis m.
3. Gastrocnemius m.
4. Gluteus maximus m.
5. Vastus lateralis m.
6. Biceps femoris m.
7. Semitendinosus m.
8. Semimembranosus m.

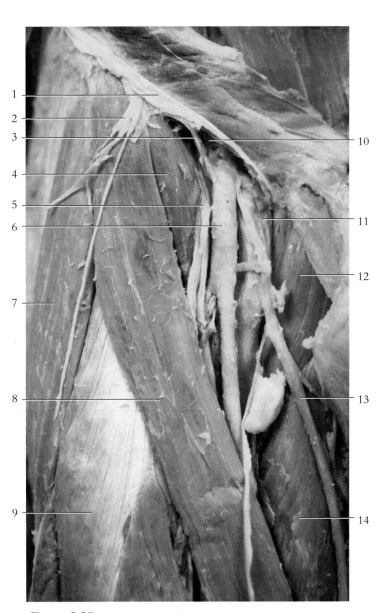

Figure 9.35 Anterior view of the right superior thigh.
1. Inguinal ligament
2. Lateral femoral cutaneous nerve
3. Superficial circumflex iliac artery
4. Iliacus m.
5. Femoral nerve
6. Femoral artery
7. Tensor fasciae latae m.
8. Sartorius m.
9. Rectus femoris m.
10. Femoral ring
11. Femoral vein
12. Pectineus m.
13. Great saphenous vein
14. Adductor longus m.

Figure 9.36 Medial brachium and superficial flexors of the right antebrachium.
1. Triceps brachii m. (lateral head)
2. Biceps brachii m. (short head)
3. Triceps brachii m. (medial head)
4. Flexor carpi radialis m.
5. Palmaris longus m.
6. Superficial digital flexor m.
7. Flexor carpi ulnaris m.

Figure 9.37 Anterior view of the superficial muscles of the right forearm.
1. Flexor carpi radialis m.
2. Palmaris longus m.
3. Superficial digital flexor m.
4. Flexor carpi ulnaris m.

Figure 9.38 Anterior view of the deep muscles of the right forearm.
1. Pronator teres m.
2. Flexor pollicis longus m.
3. Pronator quadratus m.
4. Median nerve
5. Deep digital flexor m.

Figure 9.39 Posterior view of the superficial muscles of the right forearm.
1. Triceps brachii m. (medial head)
2. Extensor carpi radialis longus m.
3. Extensor digitorum m.
4. Extensor carpi minimi m.
5. Extensor carpi ulnaris m.
6. Brachialis m.
7. Biceps brachii m. (long head)
8. Brachioradialis m.
9. Extensor carpi radialis brevis m.
10. Abductor pollicis longus m.
11. Extensor pollicis brevis m.
12. Radius
13. Extensor retinaculum
14. Tendon of extensor pollicis longus m.
15. Dorsal interosseous mm.

Figure 9.40 Lateral view of the brain.

1. Primary motor
   cerebral cortex
2. Gyri
3. Sulci
4. Frontal lobe of cerebrum
5. Lateral sulcus
6. Olfactory cerebral cortex
7. Temporal lobe of cerebrum

8. Central sulcus
9. Primary sensory
   cerebral cortex
10. Parietal lobe of cerebrum
11. Occipital lobe of cerebrum
12. Auditory cerebral cortex
13. Cerebellum
14. Medulla oblongata

Figure 9.41 Inferior view of the brain with the
eyes and part of the meninges still intact.

1. Eyeball
2. Muscles of the eye
3. Temporal lobe of cerebrum
4. Pituitary gland
5. Pons

6. Medulla oblongata
7. Cerebellum
8. Spinal cord
9. Dura mater

Figure 9.42 Sagittal view
of the brain.

1. Body of corpus callosum
2. Crus of fornix
3. Third ventricle
4. Posterior commissure
5. Splenium of corpus callosum
6. Pineal body
7. Inferior colliculus
8. Arbor vitae of cerebellum
9. Vermis of cerebellum
10. Choroid plexus of fourth
    ventricle
11. Tonsilla of cerebellum
12. Medulla oblongata
13. Septum pellucidum (cut)
14. Intraventricular foramen
15. Genu of corpus callosum
16. Anterior commissure
17. Hypothalmus
18. Optic chiasma
19. Oculomotor nerve
20. Cerebral peduncle
21. Midbrain
22. Pons
23. Mesencephalic
    (cerebral) aqueduct
24. Fourth ventricle
25. Pyramid

Figure 9.43 Purkinje neurons from the cerebellum.
1. Molecular layer of cerebellar cortex
2. Granular layer of cerebellar cortex
3. Dendrites of Purkinje cell
4. Purkinje cell body

Figure 9.44 Transverse section of the spinal cord.
1. Posterior (dorsal) root of spinal nerve
2. Posterior (dorsal) horn (gray matter)
3. Spinal cord tract (white matter)
4. Anterior (ventral) horn (gray matter)

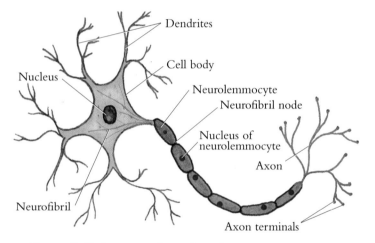

Figure 9.45 Structure of a myelinated neuron.

Figure 9.46 Photomicrograph of a neuron.
1. Cytoplasmic extensions   3. Cell body of neuron
2. Nucleus

Figure 9.47 Histology of a myelinated nerve.
1. Neurolemmal sheath   4. Neurofibril node
2. Axon   (node of Ranvier)
3. Myelin layer

Figure 9.48 Transverse section of a nerve.
1. Perineurium   3. Endoneurium
2. Epineurium   4. Bundle of axons

Figure 9.49 Neuromuscular junction.
1. Motor nerve   3. Skeletal muscle fiber
2. Motor end plates

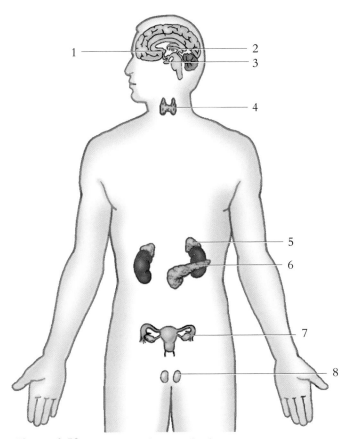

Figure 9.50 Principal endocrine glands.
1. Hypothalamus   5. Adrenal (suprarenal) gland
2. Pineal body   6. Pancreas
3. Pituitary gland   7. Ovary
4. Thyroid and parathyroid glands   8. Testis

Figure 9.51 Pituitary gland.
1. Pars intermedia (adenohypophysis)
2. Pars nervosa (neurohypophysis)
3. Pars distalis (adenohypophysis)

Figure 9.52 Thyroid gland.
1. Follicle cells
2. C cells
3. Colloid within follicle

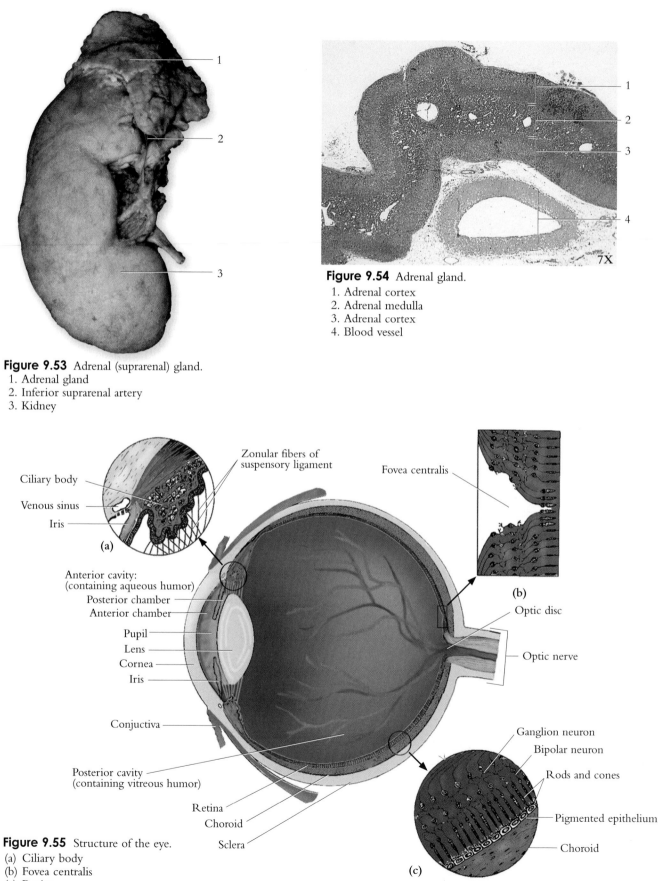

Figure 9.53 Adrenal (suprarenal) gland.
1. Adrenal gland
2. Inferior suprarenal artery
3. Kidney

Figure 9.54 Adrenal gland.
1. Adrenal cortex
2. Adrenal medulla
3. Adrenal cortex
4. Blood vessel

Ciliary body
Venous sinus
Iris

Zonular fibers of
suspensory ligament

(a)

Fovea centralis

(b)

Anterior cavity:
(containing aqueous humor)
Posterior chamber
Anterior chamber
Pupil
Lens
Cornea
Iris

Optic disc

Optic nerve

Conjuctiva

Posterior cavity
(containing vitreous humor)

Ganglion neuron
Bipolar neuron
Rods and cones

Pigmented epithelium

Choroid

Retina
Choroid
Sclera

Figure 9.55 Structure of the eye.
(a) Ciliary body
(b) Fovea centralis
(c) Retina

(c)

Figure 9.56 Anterior portion of the eye.
1. Conjunctivia
2. Iris
3. Cornea
4. Lens
5. Ciliary body

7X

Figure 9.57 Retina.
1. Retina
2. Rods and cones
3. Choroid
4. Sclera

250X

Figure 9.58 Structure of the ear.
1. Helix
2. Auricle
3. External auditory canal
4. Earlobe
5. Outer ear
6. Middle ear
7. Inner ear
8. Facial nerve
9. Vestibulocochlear nerve
10. Cochlea
11. Vestibular (oval) window
12. Auditory ossicles
13. Auditory tube
14. Tympanic membrane

Figure 9.59 Spiral organ (organ of Corti).
1. Vestibular membrane
2. Cochlear duct
3. Tectorial membrane
4. Hair cells
5. Basilar membrane

250X

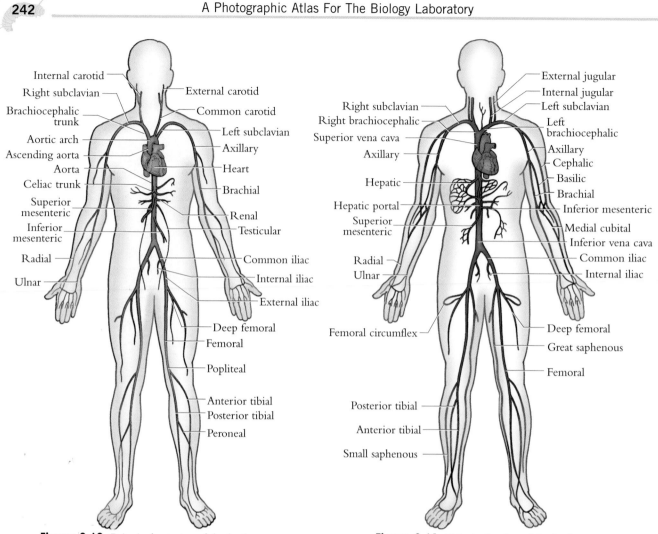

Internal carotid
Right subclavian
Brachiocephalic trunk
Aortic arch
Ascending aorta
Aorta
Celiac trunk
Superior mesenteric
Inferior mesenteric
Radial
Ulnar

External carotid
Common carotid
Left subclavian
Axillary
Heart
Brachial
Renal
Testicular
Common iliac
Internal iliac
External iliac
Deep femoral
Femoral
Popliteal
Anterior tibial
Posterior tibial
Peroneal

Figure 9.60 Principal arteries of the body.

Right subclavian
Right brachiocephalic
Superior vena cava
Axillary
Hepatic
Hepatic portal
Superior mesenteric
Radial
Ulnar

External jugular
Internal jugular
Left subclavian
Left brachiocephalic
Axillary
Cephalic
Basilic
Brachial
Inferior mesenteric
Medial cubital
Inferior vena cava
Common iliac
Internal iliac

Femoral circumflex
Deep femoral
Great saphenous
Femoral
Posterior tibial
Anterior tibial
Small saphenous

Figure 9.61 Principal veins of the body.

Figure 9.62 Position of the heart within the pericardium.

1. Mediastinum   4. Diaphragm
2. Right lung   5. Liver
3. Pericardium   6. Left lung

Figure 9.63 Anterior view of the heart and associated structures

1. Right vagus nerve
2. Right brachiocephalic vein
3. Superior vena cava
4. Right phrenic nerve
5. Ascending aorta
6. Pericardium (cut)
7. Right ventricle of heart

8. Brachiocephalic artery
9. Left brachiocephalic artery
10. Aortic arch
11. Left phrenic nerve
12. Left ventricle of heart
13. Apex of heart

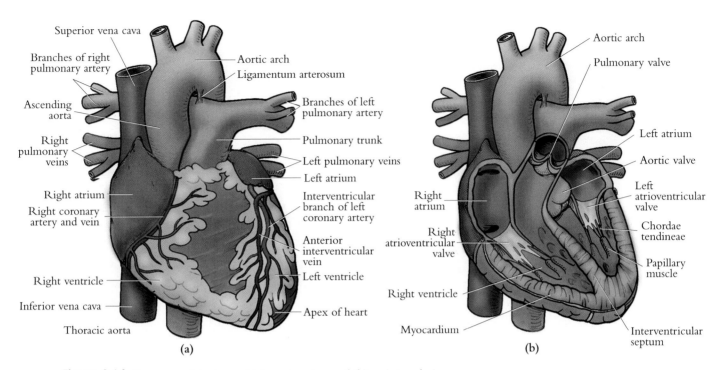

Figure 9.64 Structure of the heart. (a) Anterior view and (b) an internal view.

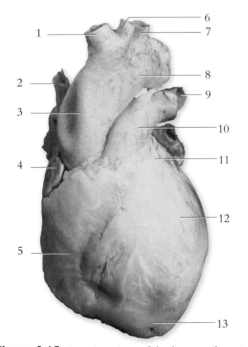

Figure 9.65 Anterior view of the heart and great vessels.

1. Brachiocephalic trunk   8. Aortic arch
2. Superior vena cava   9. Pulmonary artery
3. Ascending aorta   10. Pulmonary trunk
4. Right atrium   11. Left atrium
5. Right ventricle   12. Left ventricle
6. Left common carotid artery 13. Apex of heart
7. Left subclavian artery

Figure 9.66 Internal structure of the heart.

1. Right atrium   7. Aortic valve
2. Right atrioventricular valve   8. Left atrioventricular valve
3. Right ventricle   9. Myocardium
4. Interventricular septum   10. Papillary muscle
5. Trabeculae carneae   11. Left ventricle
6. Ascending aorta

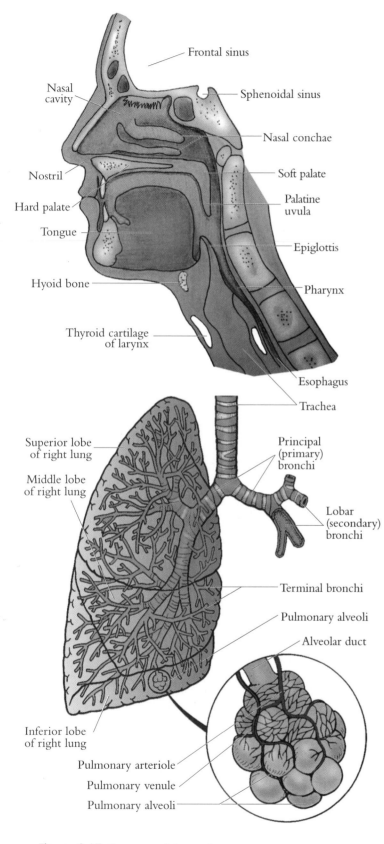

Figure 9.67 Structure of the respiratory system.

Figure 9.68 Anterior view of the larynx, trachea, and lungs.

1. Epiglottis
2. Thyroid cartilage
3. Cricoid cartilage
4. Thyroid gland
5. Right lung
6. Right principal (primary) bronchus
7. Pulmonary vessels
8. Trachea
9. Carnia
10. Left principal (primary) bronchus
11. Left lung

Figure 9.69 Tracheal wall.

1. Respiratory epithelium
2. Basement membrane
3. Duct of seromucous gland
4. Seromucous glands
5. Perichondrium
6. Hyaline cartilage

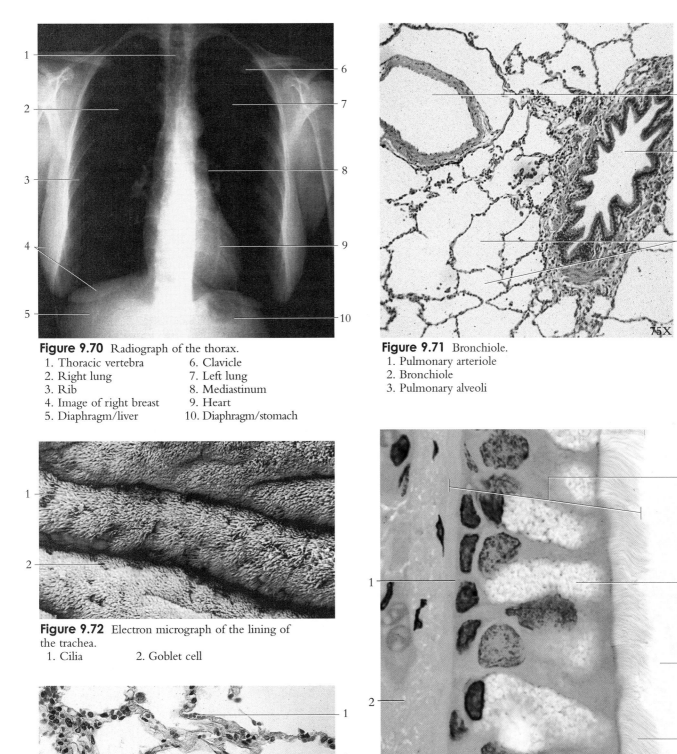

Figure 9.70 Radiograph of the thorax.
1. Thoracic vertebra
2. Right lung
3. Rib
4. Image of right breast
5. Diaphragm/liver
6. Clavicle
7. Left lung
8. Mediastinum
9. Heart
10. Diaphragm/stomach

Figure 9.71 Bronchiole.
1. Pulmonary arteriole
2. Bronchiole
3. Pulmonary alveoli

Figure 9.72 Electron micrograph of the lining of the trachea.
1. Cilia
2. Goblet cell

Figure 9.73 Pulmonary alveoli.
1. Capillary in alveolar wall
2. Macrophages
3. Type II pneumocytes

Figure 9.74 Bronchus.
1. Basement membrane
2. Lamina propria
3. Nucleus
4. Pseudostratified squamous epithelium
5. Goblet cell
6. Lumen of bronchus
7. Cilia

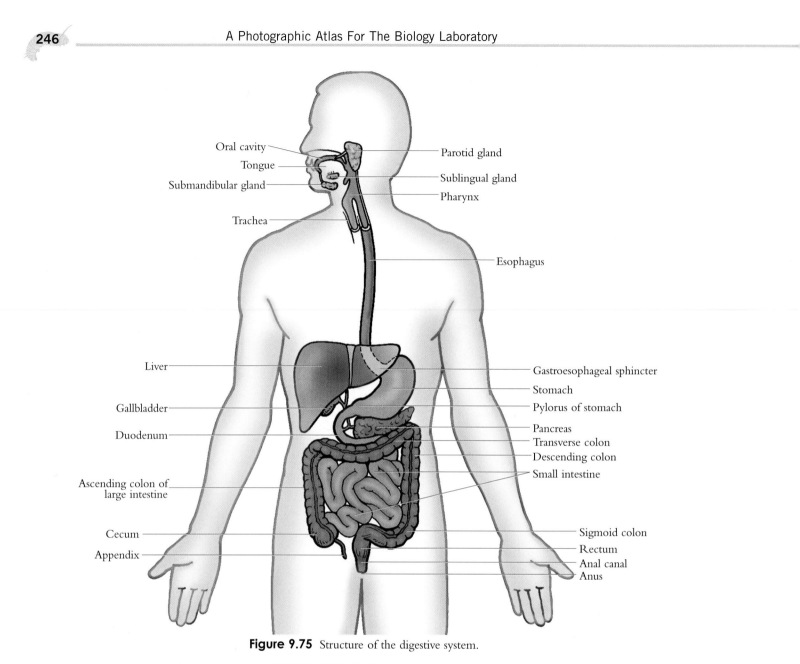

Oral cavity
Tongue
Submandibular gland
Trachea

Parotid gland
Sublingual gland
Pharynx

Esophagus

Liver
Gallbladder
Duodenum

Ascending colon of
large intestine

Cecum
Appendix

Gastroesophageal sphincter
Stomach
Pylorus of stomach
Pancreas
Transverse colon
Descending colon
Small intestine

Sigmoid colon
Rectum
Anal canal
Anus

Figure 9.75 Structure of the digestive system.

Figure 9.76 Developing tooth.

1. Ameloblasts   4. Odontoblasts
2. Enamel   5. Pulp
3. Dentin

Figure 9.77 Mature tooth.

1. Dentin (enamel has   3. Gingiva
   been dissolved away)   4. Alveolar bone
2. Pulp

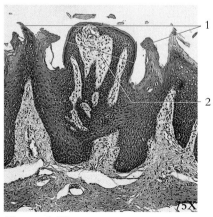

Figure 9.78 Filiform and
fungiform papillae.

1. Filiform papillae
2. Fungiform papilla

Figure 9.79 Wall of esophagus.
1. Inner circular layer (muscularis externa)
2. Outer longitudinal layer (muscularis externa)
3. Mucosa
4. Submucosa
5. Smooth muscle
6. Skeletal muscle

Figure 9.80 Transverse section of esophagus.
1. Mucosa
2. Submucosa
3. Muscularis
4. Lumen

Figure 9.81 Anterior aspect of the trunk.
1. Right lung
2. Falciform ligament
3. Right lobe of liver
4. Gallbladder
5. Body of stomach
6. Greater curvature of stomach
7. Left lung (reflected)
8. Diaphragm
9. Left lobe of liver
10. Lesser curvature of stomach
11. Transverse colon
12. Small intestine

Figure 9.82 Major regions and structures of the stomach.
1. Esophagus
2. Cardiac portion of stomach
3. Lesser curvature of stomach
4. Duodenum
5. Pylorus of stomach
6. Fundus of stomach
7. Body of stomach
8. Greater curvature of stomach

Figure 9.83 Wall of stomach.
1. Mucosa
2. Submucosa
3. Muscularis externa

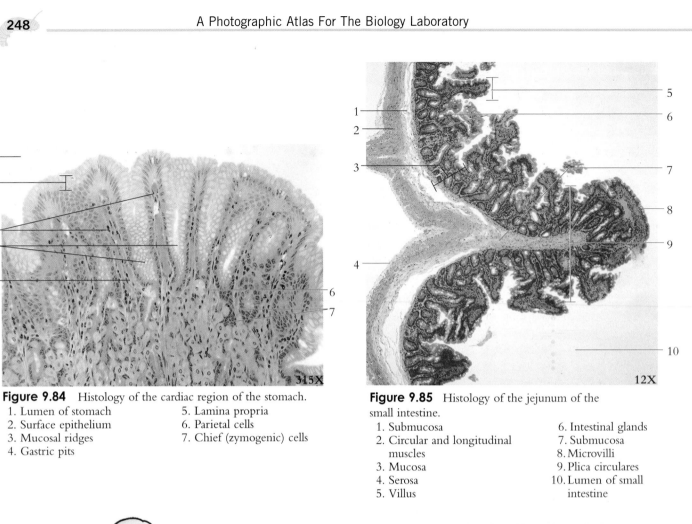

Figure 9.84 Histology of the cardiac region of the stomach.
1. Lumen of stomach
2. Surface epithelium
3. Mucosal ridges
4. Gastric pits
5. Lamina propria
6. Parietal cells
7. Chief (zymogenic) cells

315X

Figure 9.85 Histology of the jejunum of the small intestine.
1. Submucosa
2. Circular and longitudinal muscles
3. Mucosa
4. Serosa
5. Villus
6. Intestinal glands
7. Submucosa
8. Microvilli
9. Plica circulares
10. Lumen of small intestine

12X

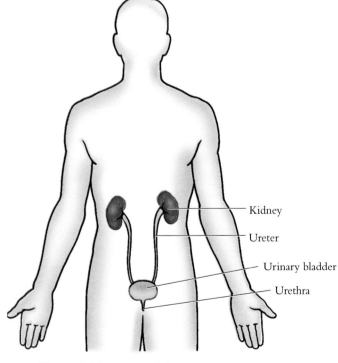

Kidney
Ureter
Urinary bladder
Urethra

Figure 9.86 Organs of the urinary system.

Figure 9.87 Kidney and ureter with overlying viscera removed.
1. Liver
2. Adrenal gland
3. Renal artery
4. Renal vein
5. Right kidney
6. Quadratus lumborum muscle
7. Gallbladder
8. Inferior vena cava
9. Ureter

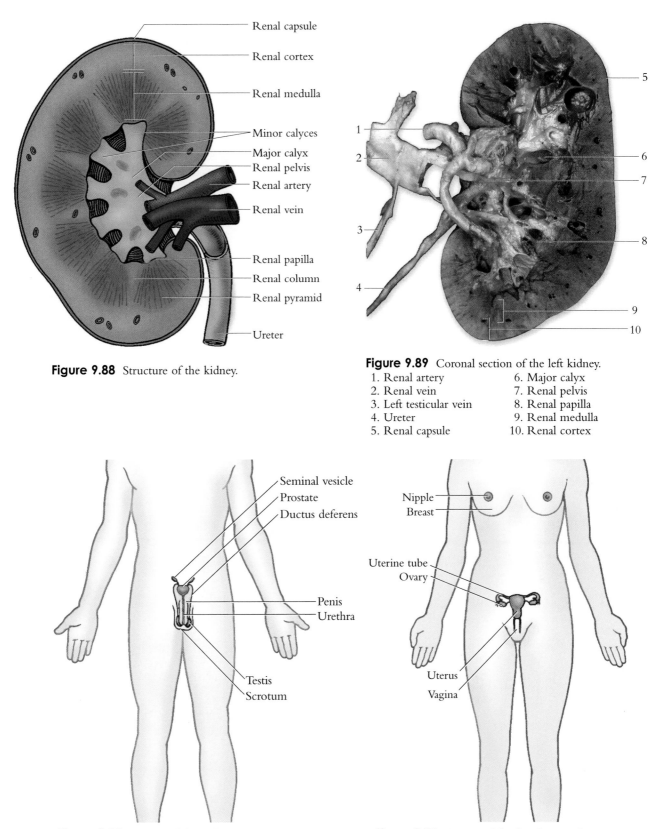

Figure 9.88 Structure of the kidney.

Renal capsule
Renal cortex
Renal medulla
Minor calyces
Major calyx
Renal pelvis
Renal artery
Renal vein
Renal papilla
Renal column
Renal pyramid
Ureter

Figure 9.89 Coronal section of the left kidney.

1. Renal artery   6. Major calyx
2. Renal vein   7. Renal pelvis
3. Left testicular vein 8. Renal papilla
4. Ureter   9. Renal medulla
5. Renal capsule   10. Renal cortex

Seminal vesicle
Prostate
Ductus deferens
Penis
Urethra
Testis
Scrotum

Figure 9.90 Organs of the male reproductive system.

Nipple
Breast
Uterine tube
Ovary
Uterus
Vagina

Figure 9.91 Organs of the female reproductive system.

Prostate

Bulb of penis

Ductus deferens

Epididymis:
Head
Body
Tail

Testis

Scrotum

Corpora cavernosa penis

Corpus spongiosum penis

Body (shaft) of penis

Corona glandis

Glans penis

Prepuce

External urethral opening

Figure 9.92 Structure of the male genitalia.

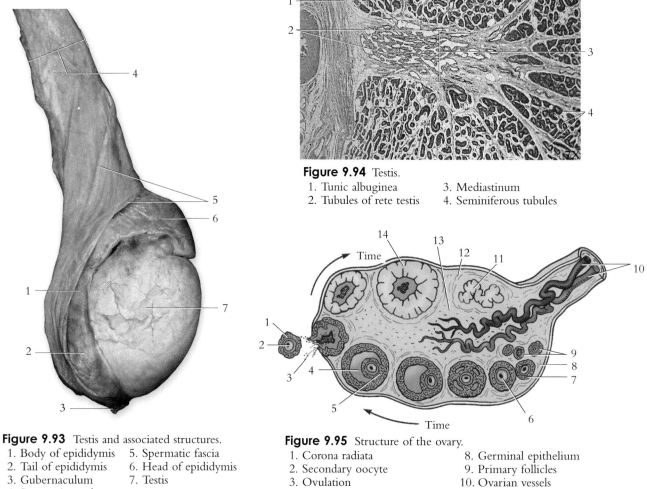

Figure 9.93 Testis and associated structures.
1. Body of epididymis
2. Tail of epididymis
3. Gubernaculum
4. Spermatic cord
5. Spermatic fascia
6. Head of epididymis
7. Testis

Figure 9.94 Testis.
1. Tunic albuginea
2. Tubules of rete testis
3. Mediastinum
4. Seminiferous tubules

Figure 9.95 Structure of the ovary.
1. Corona radiata
2. Secondary oocyte
3. Ovulation
4. Follicular fluid within antrum
5. Cumulus oophorus
6. Oocyte
7. Follicular cells
8. Germinal epithelium
9. Primary follicles
10. Ovarian vessels
11. Corpus albicans
12. Ovarian cortex
13. Ovarian medulla
14. Corpus luteum

Time

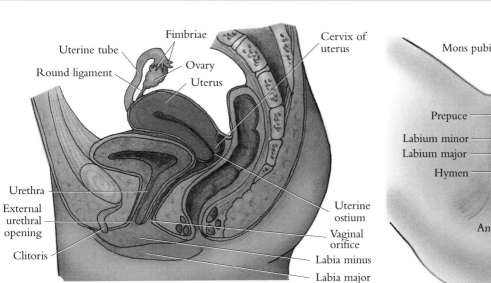

Figure 9.96 External genitalia and internal reproductive organs of the female reproductive system.

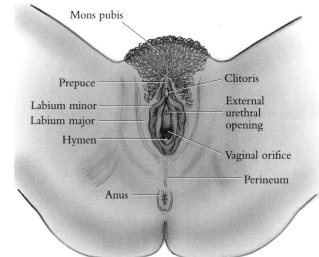

Figure 9.97 Female external genitalia.

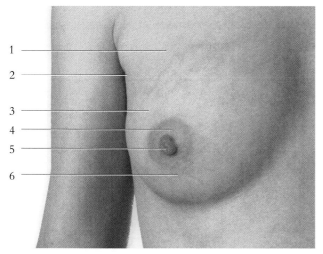

Figure 9.98 Surface anatomy of the female breast.
1. Pectoralis major muscle
2. Axilla
3. Lateral process of breast
4. Areola
5. Nipple
6. Breast (containing mammary glands)

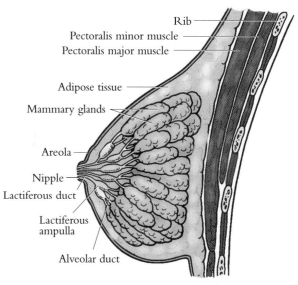

Figure 9.99 Mammary gland.

Figure 9.100 Mammary glands, (non–lactating glands).
1. Interlobular duct
2. Interlobular connective tissue
3. Lobule of glandular tissue

Figure 9.101 Mammary glands, (lactating glands).
1. Lobules of glandular tissue
2. Intralobular connective tissue
3. Adipose cells

Glossary of Terms

abdomen – the portion of the trunk of the mammalian body located between the diaphragm and the pelvis, that contains the abdominal cavity and its visceral organs; one of the three principal body regions (head, thorax, and abdomen) of many animals.

abduction – a movement away from the axis or midline of the body; opposite of adduction, a movement of a digit away from the axis of a limb.

abiotic – without living organisms; nonliving portions of the environment.

abscission – the shedding of leaves, flowers, fruits, or other plant parts, usually following the formation of an abscission zone.

absorption – movement of a substance into a cell or an organism, or through a surface within an organism.

acapnia – a decrease in normal amount of CO_2 in the blood.

accommodation – a change in the shape of the lens of the eye so that vision is more acute; the focusing for various distances.

acetone – an organic compound that may be present in the urine of diabetics; also called *ketone body*.

acetylcholine – a neurotransmitter chemical secreted at the terminal ends of many neurons, responsible for postsynaptic transmission; also called *ACh*.

acetylcholinesterase – an enzyme that breaks down acetylcholine; also called *AChE*.

Achilles tendon – see *tendo calcaneus*.

acid – a substance that releases hydrogen ions (H^+) in a solution.

acidosis – a disorder of body chemistry in which the alkaline substances of the blood are reduced in an amount below normal.

acoelomate – without a coelomic cavity; as in flatworms.

acoustic – referring to sound or the sense of hearing.

actin – a protein in muscle fibers that together with myosin is responsible for contraction.

action potential – the change in ionic charge propagated along the membrane of a neuron; the *nerve impulse*.

active transport – movement of a substance into or out of a cell from a lesser to a greater concentration, requiring a carrier molecule and expenditure of energy.

adaptation – structural, physiological, or behavioral traits of an organism that promote its survival and contributes to its ability to reproduce under environmental conditions.

adduction – a movement toward the axis or midline of the body; opposite of abduction, a movement of a digit toward the axis of a limb.

adenohypophysis – anterior pituitary.

adenoid – paired lymphoid structures in the naso-pharynx; also called *pharyngeal tonsils*.

adenosine triphosphate (ATP) – a chemical compound that provides energy for cellular use.

adhesion – an attraction between unlike substances.

adipose – fat, or fat-containing, such as adipose tissue.

adrenal glands – endocrine glands; one superior to each kidney; also called *suprarenal glands*.

adventitious root – Supportive root developing from the stem of a plant.

aerobic – requiring free O_2 for growth and metabolism as in the case of certain bacteria also called *aerobes*.

agglutination – clumping of cells; particular reference to red blood cells in an antigen-antibody reaction.

aggregate fruit – ripened ovaries from a single flower with several separate carpels.

aggression – provoking, domineering behavior.

alga (pl. algae) – any of a diverse group of aquatic photosynthesizing organisms that are either unicellular or multicellular; algae comprise the phytoplankton and seaweeds of the Earth.

alkaline – a substance having a pH greater than 7.0; *basic*.

allantois – an extraembryonic membranous sac that forms blood cells and gives rise to the fetal umbilical arteries and vein. It also contributes to the formation of the urinary bladder.

allele – an alternative form of a gene occurring at a given chromosome site, or *locus*.

all-or-none response – functioning completely when exposed to a stimulus of threshold strength; applies to action potentials through neurons and muscle fiber contraction.

alpha helix – right-handed spiral typical in proteins and DNA.

alternation of generations – two-phased life cycle characteristic of many plants in which sporophyte and gametophyte generations.

altruism – behavior benefiting other organisms without regard to its possible advantage or detrimental effect on the performer.

alveolus – An individual air capsule within the lung. Pulmonary alveoli are the basic functional units of respiration. Also, the socket that secures a tooth (dental alveolus).

amino acid – a unit of protein that contains an amino group (NH_2) and an acid group (COOH).

amnion – a membrane that surrounds the fetus to contain the amniotic fluid.

amniote – an animal that has an amnion during embryonic development; reptiles, birds, and mammals.

amoeba – protozoans that move by means of pseudo-podia.

amphiarthrosis – a slightly moveable joint in a functional classification of joints.

anaerobic respiration – metabolizing and growing in the absence of oxygen.

analogous – similar in function regardless of developmental origin; generally in reference to similar adaptations.

anatomical position – the position in human anatomy in which there is an erect body stance with the eyes directed forward, the arms at the sides, and the palms of the hands facing forward.

anatomy – the branch of science concerned with the structure of the body and the relationship of its organs.

angiosperm – flowering plant, having double fertilization resulting in development of specialized seeds within fruits.

annual – a flowering plant that completes its entire life cycle in a single year or growing season.

annual ring – yearly growth demarcation in woody plants formed by buildup of secondary xylem.

annulus – a ringlike segment, such as body rings on leeches.

antebrachium – the forearm.

antenna – a sensory appendage on many species of invertebrate animals.

anterior (ventral) – toward the front; the opposite of *posterior (dorsal)*.

anther – the position of a plant stamen in which pollen is produced.

antheridium – male reproductive organ in certain nonseed plants and algae where motile sperm are produced.

anticodon – three ("a triplet") nucleotides sequence in transfer RNA that pairs with a complementary codon (triplet) in messenger RNA.

antigen – a foreign material, usually a protein, that triggers the immune system to produce antibodies.

anus – the terminal end of the GI tract, opening of the anal canal.

aorta – the major systemic vessel of the arterial portion of the circulatory system, emerging from the left ventricle.

apical meristem – embryonic plant tissue in the tip of a root, bud, or shoot where continual cell divisions cause growth in length.

apocrine gland – a type of sweat gland that functions in evaporative cooling.

apopyle – opening of the radial canal into the spongocoel of sponges.

appeasement – submission behavior, usually soliciting an end of aggression.

appendix – a short pouch that attaches to the cecum.

aqueous humor – the watery fluid that fills the anterior and posterior chambers of the eye.

arachnoid – the weblike middle covering (meninx) of the central nervous system.

arbor vitae – the branching arrangement of white matter within the cerebellum.

archaebacteria – organisms within the kingdom Monera that represents an early group of simple life forms.

archegonium – female reproductive organ in certain nonseed plants; a gametangium where eggs are produced.

archenteron – the principal cavity of an embryo during the gastrula stage. Lined with endoderm, the archenteron develops into the digestive tract.

areola – the pigmented ring around the nipple.

artery – a blood vessel that carries blood away from the heart.

articular cartilage – a hyaline cartilaginous covering over the articulating surface of bones of synovial joints.

ascending colon – the portion of the large intestine between the cecum and the hepatic (right colic) flexure.

asexual – lacking distinct sexual organs and lacking the ability to produce gametes.

aster – minute rays of microtubules at the ends of the spindle apparatus in animal cells during cell division.

asymmetry – not symetrical.

atom – the smallest unit of an element that can exist and still have the properties of the element; collectively, atoms form molecules in a compound.

atomic number – the weight of the atom of a particular element.

atomic weight – the number of protons together with the number of neutrons within the nucleus of an atom.

ATP (adensoine triphosphate) – a compound of adenine, ribose, and three phosphates; it is the energy source for most cellular processes.

atrium – either of two superior chambers of the heart that receive venous blood.

atrophy – a wasting away or decrease in size of a cell or organ.

auditory tube – a narrow canal that connects the middle ear chamber to the pharynx; also called the *eustachian canal*.

autonomic – self-governing; pertaining to the division of the nervous system which controls involuntary activities.

autosome – a chromosome other than a sex chromosome.

autotroph – an organism capable of synthesizing its own organic molecules (food) from inorganic molecules.

axilla – the depressed hollow under the arm; the armpit.

axillary bud – a group of meristematic cells at the junction of a leaf and stem which develops branches or flowers; also called *lateral bud*.

axon – The elongated process of a neuron (nerve cell) that transmits an impulse away from the cell body.

bacillus (pl. bacilli) – a rod-shaped bacterium.

bacteria – prokaryotes within the kingdom Monera, lacking the organelles of eukaryotic cells.

bark – outer tissue layers of a tree consisting of cork, cork cambium, cortex, and phloem.

basal – at or near the base or point of attachment, as of a plant shoot.

base – a substance that contributes or liberates hydroxide ions in a solution.

basement membrane – a thin sheet of extracellular substance to which the basal surfaces of membranous epithelial cells are attached.

basidia – club shaped reproductive structures of club fungi that produce basidiospores during sexual reproduction.

basophil – a granular leukocyte that readily stains with basophilic dye.

belly – the thickest circumference of a skeletal muscle.

benign – nonmalignant; a confined tumor.

berry – a simple fleshy fruit.

biennial – a plant that lives through two growing seasons; generally, these plants often have vegetative growth during the first season, and flower and set seed during the second season.

bilateral symmetry – the morphologic condition of having similar right and left halves.

binary fission – a process of sexual reproduction that does not involve a mitotic spindle.

binomial nomenclature – assignment of two names to an organism, the first of which is the genus and the second the species; together constituting the scientific name.

biome – a major climax community characterized by a particular group of plants and animals.

biosphere – the portion of the earth's atmosphere and surface where living organisms exist.

biotic – pertaining to aspects of life, especially to characteristics of ecosystems.

bisexual flower – a flower that contains both male and female sexual structures.

blade – the broad expanded portion of a leaf.

blastocoel – the cavity of a blastocyst.

blastula – an early stage of prenatal development between the morula and embryonic stages.

blood – the fluid connective tissue that circulates through the cardiovascular system to transport substances throughout the body.

bolus – a moistened mass of food that is swallowed from the oral cavity into the pharynx.

bone – an organ composed of solid, rigid connective tissue, forming a component of the skeletal system.

Bowman's capsule – see *glomerular capsule*.

brain – the enlarged superior portion of the central nervous system, located in the cranial cavity of the skull.

brain stem – the portion of the brain consisting of the medulla oblongata, pons, and midbrain.

bronchial tree – the bronchi and their branching bronchioles.

bronchiole – a small division of a bronchus within the lung.

bronchus – a branch of the trachea that leads to a lung.

buccal cavity – the mouth, or oral cavity.

budding – a type of asexual reproduction in which outgrowths from the parent plant pinch off to live independently or may remain attached to form colonies.

buffer – a compound or substance that prevents large changes in the pH of a solution.

bulb – a thickened underground stem often enclosed by enlarged, fleshy leaves containing stored food.

bursa – a saclike structure filled with synovial fluid, which occurs around joints.

buttock – the rump or fleshy mass on the posterior aspect of the lower trunk, formed primarily by the gluteal muscles.

calorie – the heat required to raise one kilogram of water one degree centigrade.

calyx – a cup-shaped portion of the renal pelvis that encircles renal papillae; the collective term for the sepals of a flower.

cambium – the layer of meristematic tissue in roots and stems of many vascular plants that continues to produce tissue.

cancellous bone – spongy bone; bone tissue with a latticelike structure.

capillary – a microscopic blood vessel that connects an arteriole and a venule; the functional unit of the circulatory system.

carapace – protective covering over the dorsal part of the body of certain crustaceans and turtles.

carcinogenic – stimulating or causing the growth of a malignant tumor, or cancer.

carnivore – any animal that feeds upon another; especially, flesh-eating mammal.

carpus – the proximal portion of the hand that contains the carpal bones.

carrying capacity – the maximum number of organisms of a species that can be maintained indefinitely in an ecosystem.

cartilage – a type of connective tissue with a solid elastic matrix.

catalyst – a chemical, such as an enzyme, that accelerates the rate of a reaction of a chemical process but is not used up in the process.

caudal – referring to a position more toward the tail.

cecum – the pouchlike portion of the large intestine to which the ileum of the small intestine is attached.

cell – the structural and functional unit of an organism; the smallest structure capable of performing all the functions necessary for life.

cell wall – a rigid protective structure of a plant cell surrounding the cell (plasma) membrane; often composed of cellulose fibers embedded in a polysaccharide/protein matrix.

cellular respiration – the reactions of glycolysis, Krebs cycle, and electron transport system that provide cellular energy and accompanying reactions to produce ATP.

cellulose – a polysaccharide produced as fibers that forms a major part of the rigid cell wall around a plant cell.

central nervous system (CNS) – the brain and the spinal cord.

centromere – a portion of the chromosome to which a spindle fiber attaches during mitosis or meiosis.

centrosome – a dense body near the nucleus of a cell that contains a pair of centrioles.

cephalothorax – fusion of the head and thoracic regions, characteristics of certain arthropods.

cercaria – larva of trematodes (flukes).

cerebellum – the portion of the brain concerned with the coordination of movements and equilibrium.

cerebrospinal fluid (CSF) – a fluid that buoys and cushions the central nervous system.

cerebrum – the largest portion of the brain, composed of the right and left hemispheres.

cervical – pertaining to the neck or a necklike portion of an organ.

chelipeds – front pair of pincerlike legs in most decapod crustaceans, adapted for seizing and crushing.

chitin – strong, flexible polysaccharide forming the exoskeleton of arthropods.

chlorophyll – green pigment in photosynthesizing organisms that absorbs energy from the sun.

chloroplast – a membrane-enclosed organelle that contains chlorophyll and is the site of photosynthesis.

choanae – the two posterior openings from the nasal cavity into the nasopharynx.

cholesterol – a lipid used in the synthesis of steroid hormones.

chondrocyte – a cartilage cell.

chorion – An extraembryonic membrane that participates in the formation of the placenta.

choroid – the vascular, pigmented middle layer of the wall of the eye.

chromatin – threadlike network of DNA and proteins within the nucleus.

chromosome – structure in the nucleus that contains the genes for genetic expression.

chyme – The mass of partially digested food that passes from the stomach into the duodenum of the small intestine.

cilia – microscopic, hairlike processes that move in a wavelike manner on the exposed surfaces of certain epithelial cells.

ciliary body – a portion of the choroid layer of the eye that secretes aqueous humor and contains the ciliary muscle.

ciliates – protozoans that move by means of cilia.

circadian rhythm – a daily physiological or behavioral event, occurring on an approximate 24 hour cycle.

circumduction – a conelike movement of a body part, such that the distal end moves in a circle while the proximal portion remains relatively stable.

clitoris – A small, erectile structure in the vulva of the female.

cochlea – the spiral potion of the inner ear that contains the spiral organ (organ of corti).

climax community – the final stable stage in succession.

clone – asexually produced organisms having a consistent genetic constitution.

cnidarian – small aquatic organisms having radial symmetry and stinging cells with nematocysts.

cocoon – protective, or resting, stage of development in certain invertebrate animals.

codon – a "triplet" of three nucleotides in RNA that directs the placement of an amino acid into a polypeptide chain.

coelom – body cavity of higher animals, containing visceral organs.

collar cells – flagella-supporting cells in the inner layer of the wall of sponges.

colon – the first portion of the large intestine.

common bile duct – a tube that is formed by the union of the hepatic duct and cystic duct, transports bile to the duodenum.

compact bone – tightly packed bone that is superficial to spongy bone; also called *dense bone*.

competition – interaction between individuals of the same or different species for a mutually necessary resource.

complete flower – a flower that has four whorls of floral components including sepals, petals, stamens, and carpels.

compound eye – arthropod eye consisting of multiple lenses.

compound leaf – a leaf blade divided into distinct leaflets.

condyle – a rounded process at the end of a long bone that forms an articulation.

conidia – spores produced by fungi during asexual reproduction.

conifer – a cone-bearing woody seed plant, such as pine, fir, and spruce.

conjugation – sexual union in which the nuclear material of one cell enters another.

connective tissue – one of the four basic tissue types within an animal's body. It is a binding and supportive tissue with abundant matrix.

consumer – an organism that derives nutrients by feeding upon another.

control – a sample in an experiment that undergoes all the steps in the experiment except the one being investigated.

convergent evolution – the evolution of similar structures in different groups of organisms exposed to similar environments.

coral – a cnidarian that has a calcium carbonate skeleton whose remains contribute to form reefs.

cork – the protective outer layer of bark of many trees, composed of dead cells that may be sloughed off.

cornea – the transparent convex, anterior portion of the outer layer of the vertebrate eye.

cortex – the outer layer of an organ such as the convoluted cerebrum, adrenal gland, or kidney.

costal cartilage – the cartilage that connects the ribs to the sternum.

cranial – pertaining to the cranium.

cranial nerve – one of twelve pairs of nerves that arise from the inferior surface of the brain.

cranium – the bones of the skull that enclose the brain and support the organs of sight, hearing, and balance.

crossing over – the exchange of corresponding chromatid segments of genetic material of homologous chromosomes during synapsis of meiosis I.

cuticle – waxlike covering on the epidermis of nonwoody plants to prevent water loss.

cyanobacteria – photosynthetic prokaryotes that have chlorophyll and release oxygen.

cytokinesis – division of the cellular cytoplasm.

cytology – the science dealing with the study of cells.

cytoplasm – the protoplasm of a cell located outside of the nucleus.

cytoskeleton – protein filaments throughout the cytoplasm of certain cells that help maintain the cell shape.

deciduous – plants that seasonally sheds their leaves.

dendrite – a nerve cell process that transmits impulses toward a neuron cell body.

denitrifying bacteria – single-cellular organisms of the kindom of Monera that convert nitrate to atmospheric nitrogen.

dentin – the principal substance of a tooth, covered by enamel over the crown and by cementum on the root.

dermis – the second, or deep, layer of skin beneath the epidermis.

descending colon – the segment of the large intestine that descends on the left side from the level of the spleen to the level of the left iliac crest.

detritus – non-living organic matter important in the nutrient cycle in soil formation.

diaphragm – a flat dome of skeletal muscle and connective tissue that separates the thoracic and abdominal cavities, in mammals.

diaphysis – the body, or of a long bone.

diastole – the portion of the cardiac cycle during which the ventricular heart chamber wall is relaxed.

diarthrosis – a freely movable joint in a functional classification of joints.

diatoms – aquatic unicellular algae characterized by a cell wall composed of two silica impregnated valves.

dicot – a kind of angiosperm characterized by the presence of two cotyledons in the seed; also called *dicotyledon*.

diffusion – movement of molecules from an area of greater concentration to an area of lesser concentration.

dihybrid cross – a breeding experiment in which parental varieties differing in two traits are mated.

dimorphism – two distinct forms within a species, with regards to size, color, organ structure, and so on.

diphyodent – two sets of teeth, deciduous and permanent.

diploid – having two copies of each different chromosome, pairs of homologous chromosomes (2N).

distal – away from the midline or origin; the opposite of *proximal*.

division – a major taxonomic grouping of plants that includes classes sharing certain features with close biological relationships.

dominant – a hereditary characteristic that expresses itself even when the genotype is heterozygous.

dormancy – a period of suspended activity and growth.

dorsal – pertaining to the back or posterior portion of a body part; the opposite of *ventral*.

double helix – a double spiral used to describe the three-dimensional shape of DNA.

ductus deferens – a tube that carries spermatozoa from the epididymis to the ejaculatory duct – also called the *vas deferens* or *seminal duct*.

duodenum – the first portion of the small intestine.

dura mater – the outermost meninx covering the central nervous system.

eccrine gland – a sweat gland that functions in body cooling.

ecology – the study of the relationship of organisms and the physical environment and their interactions.

ecosystem – a biological community and its associated abiotic environment.

ectoderm – the outermost of the three primary embryonic germ layers.

edema – an excessive retention of fluid in the body tissues.

effector – an organ such as a gland or muscle that responds to motor stimulation.

efferent – conveying away from the center of an organ or structure.

ejaculation – the discharge of semen from the male urethra during climax.

electrocardiogram – a recording of the electrical activity that accompanies the cardiac cycle; also called *ECG* or *EKG*.

electroencephalogram – a recording of the brain wave pattern; also called *EEG*.

electromyogram – a recording of the activity of a muscle during contraction; also called *EMG*.

electrolyte – a solution that conducts electricity by means of charged ions.

electron – the unit of negative electricity.

element – a structure comprised of only one type of atom (i.e., carbon, hydrogen, oxygen).

embryo – a plant or an animal at an early stage of development..

emulsification – the process of dispersing one liquid in another.

enamel – the outer, dense substance covering the crown of a tooth.

endocardium – the fibrous lining of the heart chambers and valves.

endochondral bone – bones that form as hyaline cartilage models first and then are ossified.

endocrine gland – a hormone-producing gland that secretes directly into the blood or body fluids.

endoderm – the innermost of the three primary germ layers of an embryo.

endodermis – a plant tissue composed of a single layer of cells that surrounds and regulates the passage of materials into the vascular cylinder of roots.

endometrium – the inner lining of the uterus.

endoskeleton – hardened, supportive internal tissue of echinoderms and vertebrates.

endosperm – a plant tissue of angiosperm seeds that stores nutrients; the endosperm of an angiosperm is *3n* in chromosome number.

endothelium – the layer of epithelial tissue that forms the thin inner lining of blood vessels and heart chambers.

enzyme – a protein catalyst that activates a specific reaction.

eosinophil – a type of white blood cell that becomes stained by acidic eosin dye; constitutes about 2%–4% of the human white blood cells.

epicardium – the thin, outer layer of the heart; also called the *visceral pericardium*.

epicotyl – plant embryo that contributes to stem development.

epidermis – the outermost layer of the skin, composed of stratified squamous epithelium.

epididymis – a coiled tube located along the posterior border of the testis; stores spermatozoa and discharges them during ejaculation.

epidural space – a space between the spinal dura mater and the bone of the vertebral canal.

epiglottis – a cartilaginous leaflike structure positioned on top of the larynx that covers the glottis during swallowing.

epinephrine – a hormone secreted from the adrenal medulla resulting in actions similar to those from sympathetic nervous system stimulation; also called *adrenaline*.

epiphyseal plate – a cartilaginous layer located between the epiphysis and diaphysis of a long bone, which functions in longitudinal bone growth.

epiphysis – the end segment of a long bone, distinct in early life but later becoming part of the larger bone.

epiphyte – nonparasitic plant , such as orchid and Spanish moss, that grows on the surface of other plants.

epithelial tissue – one of the four basic tissue types; the type of tissue that covers or lines all exposed body surfaces.

erection – a response within an organ, such as the penis, when it becomes turgid and erect as opposed to being flacid.

erythrocyte – a red blood cell.

esophagus – a tubular organ of the GI tract that leads from the pharynx to the stomach.

estrogen – female sex hormone secreted from the ovarian (Graafian) follicle.

estuary – a zone of mixing between fresh water and seawater.

eukaryotic – possessing the membranous organelles characteristic of complex cells.

eustachian canal – see *auditory tube*.

evolution – genetic and phenotypic changes occuring in populations of organisms through time, generally resulting in increased adaptation for continued survival.

excretion – discharging waste material.

exocrine gland – a gland that secretes its product to an epithelial surface, directly or through ducts.

exoskeleton – an outer, hardened supporting structure secreted by ectoderm or epidermis.

expiration – the process of expelling air from the lungs through breathing out; also called *exhalation*.

extension – a movement that increases the angle between two bones of a joint.

external ear – the outer portion of the ear, consisting of the auricle (pinna), external auditory canal, and tympanum.

extracellular – outside a cell or cells.

extraembryonic membranes – membranes that are not a part of the embryo but are essential for the health and development of the organism.

extrinsic – pertaining to an outside or external origin.

facet – a small, smooth surface of a bone where articulation occurs.

facilitated transport – transfer of a particle into or out of a cell along a concentration gradient by a process requiring a carrier.

fallopian tube – see *uterine tube*.

fascia – a tough sheet of fibrous connective tissue binding the skin to underlying muscles or supporting and separating muscle.

fasciculus – a bundle of muscle or nerve fibers.

feces – waste material expelled from the GI tract during defecation, composed of food residue, bacteria, and secretions; also called *stool*.

fertilization – the fusion of two haploid gamete nuclei to form a diploid zygote nucleus.

fetus – the unborn offspring during the last stage of prenatal development.

fibrous root – an intertwining mass of roots of about equal size.

filament – a long chain of cells.

filter feeder – an animal that obtains food by straining it from the water.

filtration – the passage of a liquid through a filter or a membrane.

fimbriae – fringelike extensions from the borders of the open end of the uterine tube.

fissure – a groove or narrow cleft that separates two parts of an organ.

flagella – long slender locomotor processes characteristic of flagellate protozoans, certain bacteria, and sperm.

flexion – a movement that decreases the angle between two bones of a joint; opposite of extension.

flora – a general term for the plant life of a region or area.

flower – the blossom of an angiosperm that contains the reproductive organs.

fluke – a parasitic flatworm within the class Trematoda.

follicle – the portion of the ovary that produces the egg and the female sex hormone, estrogen; the depression that supports and develops a feather or hair.

fontanel – a membranous-covered region on the skull of a fetus or baby where ossification has not yet occurred; also called a *soft spot*.

food web – the food links between population in a community.

foot – the terminal portion of the lower extremity, consisting of the tarsus, metatarsus, and digits.

foramen – an opening in a bone for the passage of a blood vessel or a nerve.

foramen ovale – the opening through the interatrial septum of the fetal heart.

fossa – a depressed area, usually on a bone.

fossil – any preserved remains or impressions of an organism.

fourth ventricle – a cavity within the brain containing cerebrospinal fluid.

fovea centralis – a depression on the macula lutea of the eye where only cones are located, which is the area of keenest vision.

frond – the leaf of a fern containing many leaflets.

fruit – a mature ovary enclosing a seed or seeds.

gallbladder – a pouchlike organ, attached to the inferior side of the liver, which stores and concentrates bile.

gamete – a haploid sex cell, sperm or egg.

gametophyte – the haploid, gamete-producing generation in the life cycle of a plant.

gamma globulins – protein substances that act as antibodies often found in immune serums.

ganglion – an aggregation of nerve cell bodies outside the central nervous system.

gastrointestinal tract – the tubular portion of the digestive system that includes the stomach and the small and large intestines; also called the *GI tract*.

gene – part of the DNA molecule located in a definite position on a certain chromosome and coding for a specific product.

gene pool – the total of all the genes of the individuals in a population.

genetic drift – evolution by chance process.

genetics – the study of heredity.

genotype – the genetic makeup of an organism.

genus – the taxonomic category above species and below family.

geotropism – plant growth oriented with respect to gravity; stems grow upward, roots grow downward.

germ cells – gametes or the cells that give rise to gametes or other cells.

germination – the process by which a spore or seed ends dormancy and resumes normal metabolism, development, and growth.

gill – a gas exchange organ characteristic of fishes and other aquatic or semiaquatic animals.

gingiva – the fleshy covering over the mandible and maxilla through which the teeth protrude within the mouth; also called the *gum*.

girdling – removal of a strip of bark from around a tree down to the wood layer.

gland – an organ that produces a specific substance or secretion.

glans penis – the enlarged, distal end of the penis.

glomerular capsule – the double-walled proximal portion of a renal tubule that encloses the glomerulus of a *nephron;* also called *Bowman's capsule.*

glomerulus – a coiled tuft of capillaries that is surrounded by the glomerular capsule and filters urine from the blood.

glottis – a slitlike opening into the larynx, positioned between the true vocal folds.

glycogen – the principal storage carbohydrate in animals. It is stored primarily in the liver and is made available as glucose when needed by the body cells.

goblet cell – a unicellular gland within columnar epithelia that secretes mucus.

gonad – a reproductive organ, testis or ovary, that produces gametes and sex hormones.

granum – a "stack" of membrane flattened disks within the chloroplast that contain chlorphyll.

gray matter – the portion of the central nervous system that is composed of nonmyelinated nervous tissue.

grazer – animal that feeds on low growing vegetation, such as grasses.

growth ring – a growth layer of secondary xylem (wood) or secondary phloem in gymnospems or angiosperms.

guard cell – an epidermal cell to the side of a leaf stoma that helps to control the stoma size.

gut – pertaining to the intestine; generally a developmental term.

gymnosperm – a vascular seed-producing plant.

gyrus – a convoluted elevation or ridge.

habitat – the ecological abode of a plant or animal species.

hair – an epidermal structure consisting of keratinized dead cells that have been pushed up from a dividing basal layer.

hair cells – specialized receptor nerve endings for responding to sensations, such as in the spiral orgen of the inner ear.

hair follicle – a tubular depression in the skin in which a hair develops.

hand – the terminal portion of the upper extremity, consisting of the carpus, metacarpus, and digits.

haploid – having one copy of each different chromosome.

hard palate – the bony partition between the oral and nasal cavities, formed by the maxillae and palatine bones.

haversian system – see *osteon.*

heart – a muscular, pumping organ positioned in the thoracic cavity.

hematocrit – the volume percentage of red blood cells in whole blood.

hemoglobin – the pigment of red blood cells that transports O_2 and CO_2.

hemopoiesis – production of red blood cells.

hepatic portal circulation – the return of venous blood from the digestive organs and spleen through a capillary network within the liver before draining into the heart.

herbaceous – a nonwoody plant.

herbaceous stem – stem of a nonwoody plant.

herbivore – an organism that feeds exclusively on plants.

heredity – the transmission of certain characteristics, or traits, from parents to offspring, via the genes.

heterodont – having teeth differentiated into incisors, canines, premolars, and molars for specific functions.

heterotroph – an organism that utilizes preformed food.

heterozygous – having two different alleles (i.e., *Bb*) for a given trait.

hiatus – an opening or fissure.

hilum – a concave or depressed area where vessels or nerves enter or exit an organ.

histology – microscopic anatomy of the structure and function of tissues.

holdfast – basal extension of a multicellular alga that attaches it to a solid object.

homeostasis – a consistency and uniformity of the internal body environment which maintains normal body function.

homologous – similar in developmental origin and sharing a common ancestry.

homothallic – species in which individuals produce both male and female reproductive structures and are self-fertile.

hormone – a chemical substance that is produced in an endocrine gland and secreted into the bloodstream to cause an effect in a specific target organ.

host – an organism on or in which another organism lives.

ileum – the terminal portion of the small intestine between the jejunum and cecum.

imprinting – a type of learned behavior during a limited critical period.

indigenous – organisms that are native to a particular region; not introduced.

inguinal – pertaining to the groin region.

insertion – the more movable attachment of a muscle, usually more distal in location.

inspiration – the act of breathing air into the pulmonary alveoli of the lungs; also called *inhalation.*

instar – stage of insect or other arthropod development between molts.

integument – pertaining to the skin.

internal ear – the innermost portion or chamber of the ear, containing the cochlea and the vestibular organs.

internode – region between stem nodes.

interstitial – pertaining to spaces or structures between the functioning active tissue of any organ.

intracellular – within the cell itself.

intervertebral disc – a pad of fibrocartilage between the bodies of adjacent vertebrae.

intestinal gland – a simple tubular digestive gland that opens onto the surface of the intestinal mucosa and secretes digestive enzymes; also called *crypt of Lieberkühn.*

intrinsic – situated or pertaining to internal origin.

invertebrate – an animal that lacks a vertebral column.

iris – the pigmented vascular tunic portion of the eye that surounds the pupil and regulates its diameter.

islets of Langerhans – see *pancreatic islets.*

isotope – a chemical element that has the same atomic number as another but a different atomic weight.

jejunum – the middle portion of the small intestine, located between the duodenum and the ileum.

joint capsule – a fibrous tissue cuff surrounding a movable joint.

jugular – pertaining to the veins of the neck which drain the areas supplied by the carotid arteries.

karyotype – the arrangement of chromosomes that is characteristic of the species or of a certain individual.

keratin – an insoluble protein present in the epidermis and in epidermal derivatives such as scales, feathers, hair, and nails.

kidney – one of the paired organs of the urinary system that contains nephrons and filters wastes from the blood in the formation of the urine.

kingdom – a taxonomic category grouping related divisions (plants) or phyla (animals).

labia major – a portion of the external genitalia of a female, consisting of two longitudinal folds of skin extending downward and backward from the mons pubis.

labia minora – two small folds of skin, devoid of hair and sweat glands, lying between the labia majora of the external genitalia of a female.

lacrimal gland – a tear-secreting gland, located on the superior lateral portion of the eyeball underneath the upper eyelid.

lacteal – a small lymphatic duct within a villus of the small intestine.

lacuna – a hollow chamber that houses an osteocyte in mature bone tissue or a chondrocyte in cartilage tissue.

lamella – a concentric ring of matrix surrounding the central canal in an osteon of mature bone tissue.

large intestine – the last major portion of the GI tract, consisting of the cecum, colon, rectum, and anal canal.

larva – an immature, developmental stage that is quite different from the adult.

larynx – the structure located between the pharynx and trachea that houses the vocal cords; commonly called the *voice box*.

lateral root – a secondary root that arises by branching from an older root.

leaf veins – plant structures that contain the vascular tissues in a leaf.

legume – a member of the pea, or bean, family.

lens – a transparent refractive structure of the eye, derived from ectoderm and positioned posterior to the pupil and iris.

lenticel – spongy area in the bark of a stem or root that permits interchange of gases between internal tissues and the atmosphere.

leukocyte – a white blood cell; also spelled *leucocyte*.

lichen – alga or bacteria and fungi coexisting in a mutualistic relationship.

ligament – a fibrous band of connective tissue that binds bone to bone to strengthen and provide support to the joint; also may support viscera.

limbic system – a portion of the brain concerned with emotions and autonomic activity.

locus – the specific location or site of a gene within the chromosome.

lumbar – pertaining to the region of the loins.

lumen – the space within a tubular structure through which a substance passes.

lung – one of the two major organs of respiration within the thoracic cavity.

lymph – a clear fluid that flows through lymphatic vessels.

lymph node – a small, oval mass located along the course of lymph vessels.

lymphocyte – a type of white blood cell characterized by a granular cytoplasm.

macula lutea – a depression in the retina that contains the fovea centralis, the area of keenest vision.

malnutrition – any abnormal assimilation of food; receiving insufficient nutrients.

mammary gland – the gland of the mammalian female breast responsible for lactation and nourishment of the young.

mantle – fleshy fold of the body wall of a mollusk, typically involved in shell formation.

marine – pertaining to the sea or ocean.

marrow – the soft vascular tissue that occupies the inner cavity of certain bones and produces blood cells.

matrix – the intercellular substance of a tissue.

mediastinum – the partition in the center of the thorax between the two pleural cavities.

medulla – the center portion of an organ.

medulla oblongata – a portion of the brain stem between the pons and the spinal cord.

medullary cavity – the hollow center of the diaphysis of a long bone, occupied by red bone marrow.

megaspore – a plant spore that will germinate to become a female gametophyte.

meiosis – cell division by which gametes, or haploid sex cells, are formed.

melanocyte – a pigment-producing cell in the deepest epidermal layer of the skin.

membranous bone – bone that forms from membranous connective tissue rather than from cartilage.

menarche – the first menstrual discharge.

meninges – a group of three fibrous membranes that cover the central nervous system.

meniscus – wedge-shaped cartilage in certain synovial joints.

menopause – the cessation of menstrual periods in the human female.

menses – the monthly flow of blood from the human female genital tract.

menstrual cycle – the rhythmic female reproductive cycle, characterized by changes in hormone levels and physical changes in the uterine lining.

menstruation – the discharge of blood and tissue from the uterus at the end of the menstrual cycle.

meristem tissue – undifferentiated plant tissue that is capable of dividing and producing new cells.

mesentery – a fold of peritoneal membrane that attaches an abdominal organ to the abdominal wall.

mesoderm – the middle one of the three primary germ layers.

mesophyll – the middle tissue layer of a leaf containing cells that are active in photosynthesis.

mesothelium – a simple squamous epithelial tissue that lines body cavities and covers visceral organs; also called *serosa*.

metabolism – the chemical changes that occur within a cell.

metacarpus – the region of the hand between the wrist and the phalanges, including the five bones that compose the palm of the hand.

metamorphosis – change in morphologic form, such as when an insect larva develops into the adult or as a tadpole develops into an adult frog.

metatarsus – the region of the foot between the ankle and the phalanges, comprised of five bones.

microbiology – the science dealing with microscopic organisms, including bacteria, fungi, protozoa, and viruses.

microspore – a spore in seed plants that develops into a pollen grain, the male gametophyte.

microvilli – microscopic, hairlike projections of cell membranes on certain epithelial cells.

midbrain – the portion of the brain between the pons and the forebrain.

middle ear – the middle of the three ear chambers, containing the three auditory ossicles.

migration – movement of organisms from one geographical site to another.

mimicry – a protective resemblance of an organism to another.

mitosis – the process of cell division, in which the two daughter cells are identical and contain the same number of chromosomes.

mitral valve – the left atrioventricular heart valve; also called the *bicuspid valve*.

mixed nerve – a nerve containing both motor and sensory nerve fibers.

molecule – a minute mass of matter, composed of a combination of atoms that form a given chemical substance or compound.

molting – periodic shedding of an epidermal derived structure.

monocot – a type of angiosperm in which the seed has only a single cotyledon; also called *monocotyledon*.

motor neuron – a nerve cell that conducts action potential away from the central nervous system and innervates effector organs (muscles and glands); also called *efferent neuron*.

motor unit – a single motor neuron and the muscle fibers it innervates.

mucosa – a mucous membrane that lines cavities and tracts opening to the exterior.

muscle – an organ adapted to contract; three types of muscle tissue are cardiac, smooth, and skeletal.

mutation – a variation in an inheritable characteristic, a permanent transmissible change in which the offspring differ from the parents.

mutualism – a beneficial relationship between two organisms of different species.

myelin – a lipoprotein material that forms a sheathlike covering around nerve fibers.

myocardium – the cardiac muscle layer of the heart.

myofibril – a bundle of contractile fibers within muscle cells.

myoneural junction – the site of contact between an axon of a motor neuron and a muscle fiber.

myosin – a thick filament protein that together with actin causes muscle contraction.

nail – a hardenend, keratinized plate that develops from the epidermis and forms a protective covering on the surfaces of the digits.

nares – the opening into into the nasal cavity; also called *nostrisl*.

nasal cavity – a mucosa-lined space above the oral cavity, which is divided by a nasal septum and is the first chamber of the respiratory system.

nasal septum – a bony and cartilaginous partition that separates the nasal cavity into two portions.

natural selection – the evolutionary mechanism by which better adapted organisms are favored to reproduce and pass on their genes to the next generation.

nephron – the functional unit of the kidney, consisting of a glomerulus, glomerular capsule, convoluted tubules, and the nephron loop.

nerve – a bundle of nerve fibers outside the central nervous system.

neurofibril node – a gap in the myelin sheath of a nerve fiber; also called the *node of Ranvier*.

neuroglia – specialized supportive cells of the central nervous system.

neurolemmocyte – a specialized neuroglial cell that surrounds an axon fiber of a peripheral nerve and forms the neurilemmal sheath; also called the *Schwann cell*.

neuron – the structural and functional unit of the nervous system, composed of a cell body, dendrites, and an axon; also called a *nerve cell*.

neutron – a subatomic particle in the nucleus of an atom that has a weight of one atomic mass unit and carries no charge.

neutrophil – a type of phagocytic white blood cell.

niche – the position and functional role of an organism in its ecosystem.

nipple – a dark pigmented, rounded projection at the tip of the breast.

nitrogen fixation – a process carried out by certain organisms, such as by soil bacteria, whereby free atmospheric nitrogen is converted into ammonia or nitrate compounds.

node – location on a stem where a leaf is attached.

node of Ranvier – see *neurofibril node*.

notochord – a flexible rod of tissue that extends the length of the back of an embryo.

nucleic acid – an organic molecule composed of joined nucleotides, such as RNA and DNA.

nucleus – a spheroid body within a eukaryotic cell that contains the chromosomes of the cell.

nut – a hardened and dry single-seeded fruit.

olfactory – pertaining to the sense of smell.

oocyte – a developing egg cell.

oogenesis – the process of female gamete formation.

oogonium – a unicellular female reproductive organ of various protists that contains a single or several eggs.

optic – pertaining to the eye and the sense of vision.

optic chiasma – an X-shaped structure on the inferior aspect of the brain where there is a partial crossing over of fibers in the optic nerves.

optic disc – a small region of the retina where the fibers of the ganglion neurons exit from the eyeball to form the optic nerve; also called the *blind spot*.

oral – pertaining to the mouth; also called *buccal*.

organ – a structure consisting of two or more tissues, which performs a specific function.

organelle – a minute structure of the eukaryotic cell that performs a specific function.

organism – an individual living creature.

orifice – an opening into a body cavity or tube.

origin – the place of muscle attachment onto the more stationary point or proximal bone; opposite the insertion.

osmosis – the diffusion of water, from a solution of lesser concentration to one of greater concentration through a semipermeable membrane.

ossicle – one of the three bones of the middle ear.

osteocyte – a mature bone cell.

osteon – a group of osteocytes and concentric lamellae surrounding a central canal within bone tissue; also called a *haversian system.*

oval window – see *vestibular window*

ovarian follicle – a developing ovum and its surrounding epithelial cells.

ovary – the female gonad in which ova and certain sexual hormones are produced.

oviduct – the tube that transports ova from the ovary to the uterus; also called the *uterine tube* or *fallopian tube.*

ovipositor – a structure at the posterior end of the abdomen in many female insects for laying eggs.

ovulation – the rupture of an ovarian follicle with the release of an ovum.

ovule – the female reproductive organ in a seed plant that contains megasporangium where meiosis occurs and the female gametophyte is produced.

ovum – a secondary oocyte after ovulation but before fertilization.

palisade layer – the upper layer of the mesophyll of a leaf that carries out photosynthesis.

pancreas – organ in the abdominal cavity that secretes gastric juices into the GI tract and insulin and glucagon into the blood.

pancreatic islets – a cluster of cells within the pancreas that forms the endocrine portion of the pancreas; also called *islets of Langerhans.*

papillae – small nipplelike projections.

paranasal sinus – a mucous-lined air chamber that communicates with the nasal cavity.

parasite – an organism that resides in or on another from which it derives sustenance.

parasympathetic – pertaining to the division of the autonomic nervous system concerned with activities that are antagonistic to the sympathetic division of the autonomic nervous system.

parathyroids – small endocrine glands that are embedded on the posterior surface of the thyroid glands and are concerned with calcium metabolism.

parenchyma – the principal structural cells of plants

parietal – pertaining to a wall of an organ or cavity.

parotid gland – one of the paired salivary glands on the sides of the face over the masseter muscle.

parturition – the process of childbirth.

pathogen – any disease-producing organism.

pectin – an organic compound in the intercellular layer and primary wall of plant cell walls; the basis of fruit jellies.

pedicel – the stalk of a flower in an inflorescence.

pectoral girdle – the portion of the skeleton that supports the upper extremities.

pelvic – pertaining to the pelvis.

pelvic girdle – the portion of the skeleton to which the lower extremities are attached.

penis – the external male genital organ, through which urine passes during urination and which transports semen to the female during coitus.

perennial – a plant that lives throughout several to many growing seasons.

pericardium – a protective serous membrane that surrounds the heart.

pericarp – the fruit wall that forms from the wall of a mature ovary.

perineum – the floor of the pelvis.

periosteum – a fibrous connective tissue covering the surface of bone.

peripheral nervous system – the nerves and ganglia of the nervous system that lie outside of the brain and spinal cord.

peristalsis – rhythmic contractions of smooth muscle in the walls of various tubular organs, which move the contents along.

peritoneum – the serous membrane that lines the abdominal cavity and covers the abdominal viscera.

petal – the leaf of a flower, which is generally colored.

petiole – structure of a leaf that connects the blade to the stem.

phagocyte – any cell that engulfs other cells, including bacteria, or small foreign particles.

phalanx – a bone of the finger or toe.

pharynx – the region of the GI tract and respiratory system located at the back of the oral and nasal cavities and extending to the larynx anteriorly and the esophagus posteriorly; also called the *throat.*

phenotype – the appearance of an organism caused by the genotype and environmental influences.

pheromone – a chemical secreted by one organism that influences the behavior of another.

phloem – vascular tissue in plants that transports nutrients.

photoperiodism – the response of an organism to periods of light and dark.

photosynthesis – the process of using the energy of the sun to make carbohydrate from carbon dioxide and water.

phototropism – plant growth or movement in response to a directional light source.

physiology – the science that deals with the study of body functions.

phytoplankton – microscopic, free-floating, photosynthetic organisms that are the major primary producers in fresh-water and marine ecosystems.

pia mater – the innermost meninx that is in direct contact with the brain and spinal cord.

pineal gland – a small cone-shaped gland located in the roof of the third ventricle of the brain.

pistil – a reproductive structure of a flower comprised of the stigma, style, and ovary.

pith – a centrally located tissue within a dicot stem.

pituitary gland – a small, pea-shaped endocrine gland situated on the inferior surface of the brain that secretes a number of hormones; also called the *hypophysis*

placenta – the organ of metabolic exchange between the mother and the fetus.

plankton – aquatic, free-floating microscopic organisms.

plasma – the fluid, extracellular portion of circulating blood.

plastid – an organelle of a plant that assists chloroplasts in photosynthesis

platelets – fragments of specific bone marrow cells that function in blood coagulation; also called *thrombocytes.*

pleural membranes – serous membranes that surround the lungs and line the thoracic cavity.

plexus – a network of enterlaced nerves or vessels.

pollen grain – male gametophyte generation of seed plants.

pollination – the delivery by wind, water, or animals of pollen to the ovule of a seed plant leading to fertilization.

polypeptide – a molecule of many amino acids linked by peptide bonds.

pons – the portion of the brain stem just above the medulla oblongata and anterior to the cerebellum.

population – all the organisms of the same species in a particular location.

posterior (*dorsal*) – toward the back.

predation – the consumption of one organism of another.

pregnancy – a condition where a female has a developing offspring in the uterus.

prenatal – the period of offspring development during pregnancy; before birth.

prey – organisms that are food for a predator.

producer – organisms within an ecosystem that synthesizes organic compounds from inorganic constituents.

prokaryote – organism, such as a bacterium, that lacks the specialized organelles characteristic of complex cells.

proprioceptor – a sensory nerve ending that responds to changes in tension in a muscle or tendon.

prostate – a walnut-shaped gland surrounding the male urethra just below the urinary bladder that secretes an additive to seminal fluid during ejaculation.

protein – a macromolecule composed of one or several polypeptides.

prothallus – a heart-shaped structure that is the gametophyte generation of a fern.

proton – a subatomic particle of the atom nucleus that has a weight of one atomic mass unit and carries a positive charge; also a *hydrogen ion.*

proximal – closer to the midline of the body or origin of an appendage; opposite of distal.

puberty – the period of human development in which the reproductive organs become functional.

pulmonary – pertaining to the lungs.

pupil – the opening through the iris that permits light to pass through the lens and enter the posterior cavity

radial symmetry – symmetry around a central axis so that any half of an organism is identical to the other.

receptacle – the tip of the axis of a flower stalk that bears the floral organs.

receptor – a sense organ or a specialized end of a sensory neuron that receives stimuli from the environment.

rectum – the terminal portion of the GI tract, between the sigmoid colon and the anal canal.

reflex arc – the basic conduction pathway through the nervous system, consisting of a sensory neuron, interneuron (association), and a motor neuron.

regeneration – regrowth of tissue or the formation of a complete organism from a portion.

renal – pertaining to the kidney.

renal corpuscle – the portion of the nephron consisting of the glomerulus and a glomerular capsule.

renal pelvis – the inner cavity of the kidney formed by the expanded ureter and into which the calyces open.

renewable resource – a commodity that is not used up because it is continually produced in the environment.

replication – the process of producing a duplicate; a copying or duplication, such as DNA replication.

respiration – the exchange of gases between the external environment and the cells of an organism; the metabolic activity of cells resulting in the production of ATP.

retina – the inner layer of the eye that contains the rods and cones.

rhizome – an underground stem in some plants that stores photosynthetic products and gives rise to above-ground stems and leaves.

rod – a photoreceptor in the retina of the eye that is specialized for colorless, dim light vision.

root – the anchoring subterranean portion of a plant that permits absorption and conduction of water and minerals.

root cap – end mass of parenchyma cells that protects the apical meristem of a root.

root hair – unicellular epidermal projection from the root of a plant, which functions in absorption.

rugae – the folds or ridges of the mucosa of an organ.

sagittal – a vertical plane through the body that divides it into right and left portions.

salinity – saltiness in water or soil; a measure of the concentration of dissolved salts.

salivary gland – an accessory digestive gland that secretes saliva into the oral cavity.

sarcolemma – the cell membrane of a muscle fiber.

sarcomere – the portion of a skeletal muscle fiber between the two adjacent Z lines that is considered the functional unit of a myofibril.

savanna – open grassland with scattered trees.

Schwann cell – see *neurolemmocyte.*

sclera – the outer white layer of connective tissue that forms the protective covering of the eye.

sclerenchyma – supporting tissue in plants composed of hollow cells with thickened walls.

scolex – head region of a tapeworm.

scrotum – a pouch of skin that contains the testes and their accessory organs.

sebaceous gland – an exocrine gland of the skin that secretes *sebum,* an oily protective product.

secondary growth – plant growth in girth from secondary or lateral meristems.

seed – a plant embryo with a food reserve that is enclosed in a protective seed coat; seeds develop from matured ovules.

semen – the secretion of the reproductive organs of the male, consisting of spermatozoa and additives.

semilunar valve – crescent-shaped heart valves, positioned at the entrances to the aorta and the pulmonary trunk.

sensory neuron – a nerve cell that conducts an impulse from a receptor organ to the central nervous system; also called *afferent neuron*.

sepal – outermost whorl of flower structures beneath the petals; collectively called the *calyx*.

serous membrane – an epithelial and connective tissue membrane that lines body cavities and covers viscera; also called *serosa*.

sesamoid bone – a membranous bone formed in a tendon in response to joint stress.

sessile – organisms that lack locomotion and remain stationary, such as sponges and plants.

shoot – portion of a vascular plant that includes a stem with its branches and leaves.

sinoatrial node – a mass of cardiac tissue in the wall of the right atrium that initiates the cardiac cycle; the SA node; also called the *pacemaker*.

sinus – a cavity or hollow space within a body organ such as a bone.

skeletal muscle – a type of muscle tissue that is multinucleated, occurs in bundles, has crossbands of proteins, and contracts either in a voluntary or involuntary fashion.

small intestine – the portion of the GI tract between the stomach and the cecum, functions in absorption of food nutrients.

smooth muscle – a type of muscle tissue that is nonstriated, composed of fusiform, single-nucleated fibers, and contracts in an involuntary, rhythmic fashion within the walls of visceral organs.

solute – a substance dissolved in a solvent to form a solution.

solvent – a fluid such as water that dissolves solutes.

somatic – pertaining to the nonvisceral parts of the body.

somatic cells – all the cells of the body of an organism except the germ cells.

sorus – a cluster of sporangia on the underside of fern pinnae.

species – a group of morphologically similar (common gene pool) organisms that are capable of interbreeding and producing fertile offspring and reproductively isolated.

spermatic cord – the structure of the male reproductive system composed of the ductus deferens, spermatic vessels, nerve, cremasteric muscle, and connective tissue.

spermatogenesis – the production of male sex gametes, or spermatozoa.

spermatozoon – a sperm cell, or gamete.

sphincter – a circular muscle that constricts a body opening or the lumen of a tubular structure.

spinal cord – the portion of the central nervous system that extends from the brain stem through the vertebral canal.

spinal nerve – one of the thirty-one pairs of nerves that arise from the spinal cord.

spiracle – a respiratory opening in certain animals such as arthropods and sharks.

spirillum (pl. spirilla) – a spiral-shaped bacterium.

spleen – a large, blood-filled organ located in the upper left of the abdomen and attached by the mesenteries to the stomach.

spongy bone – a type of bone that contains many porous spaces; also called *cancellous bone*.

sporangium – any structure within which spores are produced.

spore – a reproductive cell capable of developing into an adult organism without fusion with another cell.

sporophyll – an organ within which spores are produced.

stamen – a reproductive structure of a flower, comprised of a filament and an anther, where pollen grains are produced.

starch – carbohydrate molecule synthesized from photosynthetic products; common food storage substance in many plants.

stigma – the upper portion of the pistil of a flower.

stele – the vascular tissue and pith or ground tissue at the central core of a root or stem.

stoma – an opening in a plant leaf through which gas exchange takes place.

stomach – a pouchlike digestive organ between the esophagus and the duodenum.

style – the long slender portion of the pistil of a flower.

submucosa – a layer of supportive connective tissue that underlies a mucous membrane.

succession – the sequence of ecological stages by which a particular biotic community gradually changes until there is a community of climax vegetation.

sucrose – a disaccharide (double sugar) consisting of a linked glucose and fructose molecule; the principal transport sugar in plants.

surfactant – a substance produced by the lungs that decreases the surface tension within the pulmonary alveoli.

suture – a type of immovable joint articulating between bones of the skull.

symbiosis – a close association between two organisms where one or both species derive benefit.

sympathetic – pertaining to that part of the autonomic nervous system concerned with activites antagonistic to the parasympathetic.

synapse – a minute space between the axon terminal of a presynaptic neuron and a dendrite of a postsynaptic neuron.

syngamy – union of gametes in sexual reproduction; fertilization.

synovial cavity – a space between the two bones of a synovial joint, filled with synovial fluid.

system – a group of body organs that function together.

systole – the muscular contraction of the ventricles of the heart during the cardiac cycle.

systolic pressure – arterial blood pressure during the ventricular systolic phase of the cardiac cycle.

taproot – a plant root system in which a single root is thick and straight.

target organ – the specific body organ that a particular hormone affects.

tarsus – pertaining to the ankle; the proximal portion of the foot that contains the tarsal bones.

taxonomy – the science of describing, classifying, and naming organisms.

tendo calcaneous – the tendon that attaches the calf muscles to the calcaneous bone.

tendon – a band of dense regular connective tissue that attaches muscle to bone.

testis – the primary reproductive organ of a male, which produces spermatozoa and male sex hormones.

tetrapod – a four-appendaged vertebrate, such as amphibian, reptile, bird, or mammal.

thoracic – pertaining to the chest region.

thorax – the chest.

thymus gland – a bi-lobed lymphoid organ positioned in the upper mediastinum, posterior to the sternum and between the lungs.

tissue – an aggregation of similar cells and their binding substances, joined to perform a specific function.

tongue – a protrusible muscular organ on the floor of the oral cavity.

toxin – a poisonous compound.

trachea – a tubule in the respiratory system of some invertebrates; the airway leading from the larynx to the bronchi in the respiratory system of vertebrates; also called the *windpipe*.

tract – a bundle of nerve fibers within the central nervous system.

trait – a distinguishing feature studied in heredity.

transpiration – the evaporation of water from a leaf, which pulls water from the roots through the stem of a leaf.

tricuspid valve – the heart valve between the right atrium and the right ventricle; also called *right atrioventricular valve*.

turgor pressure – osmotic pressure that provides rigidity to a cell.

tympanic membrane – the membranous eardrum positioned between the outer and middle ear; also called the *tympanum*, or the *ear drum*.

umbilical cord – a cordlike structure containing the umbilical arteries and vein, which connects the fetus with the placenta.

umbilicus – the site where the umbilical cord was attached to the fetus; also called the *navel*.

ureter – a tube that transports urine from the kidney to the urinary bladder.

urethra – a tube that transports urine from the urinary bladder to the outside of the body.

urinary bladder – a distensible sac in the pelvic cavity which stores urine.

uterine tube – the tube through which the ovum is transported to the uterus and where fertilization takes place; also called the *oviduct* or *fallopian tube*.

uterus – a hollow, muscular organ in which a fetus develops. It is located within the female pelvis between the urinary bladder and the rectum.

uvula – a fleshy, pendulous portion of the soft palate that blocks the nasopharynx during swallowing.

vacuole – a fluid-filled organelle.

vagina – a tubular organ that leads from the uterus to the vestibule of the female reproductive tract and receives the male penis during coitus.

vascular tissue – plant tissue composed of xylem and phloem, functioning in transport of water, nutrients, and photosynthetic products throughout the plant.

vegetative – plant parts not specialized for reproduction; asexual reproduction.

vein – a blood vessel that conveys blood toward the heart.

ventral (anterior) – toward the front surface of the body.

vertebrate – an animal that possesses a vertebral column.

vestibular folds – the supporting folds of tissue for the vocal folds within the larynx; also called *vocal cords*.

vestibular window – a membrane-covered opening in the bony wall between the middle and inner ear, into which the footplate of the stapes fits; also called *oval window*.

viscera – the organs within the abdominal or thoracic cavities.

vitreous humor – the transparent gell that occupies the space between the lens and retina of the eye.

vocal folds – folds of the mucous membrane in the larynx that produce sound as they are pulled taut and vibrated; also called *vocal cords*.

vulva – the external genitalia of the female that surround the opening of the vagina; also called the *pudendum*.

wood – interior tissue of a tree composed of secondary xylem.

zoospore – a flagellated or ciliated spore produced asexually by some protists

zygote – a fertilized egg cell formed by the union of a sperm and an ovum.

Index